PRODUCTION
PLANNING
AND
CONTROL

PRODUCTION PLANNING AND CONTROL:

TEXT AND READINGS

ROBERT H. BOCK

**School of Business Administration
Northwestern University**

WILLIAM K. HOLSTEIN

**Graduate School of
Business Administration
Harvard University**

CHARLES E. MERRILL BOOKS, INC.
COLUMBUS, OHIO

130907

Library of Congress Catalog Card Number: 63–7389

First Printing .... April, 1963
Second Printing .... May, 1964

PRINTED IN THE UNITED STATES OF AMERICA

Preface

Production management is concerned with the function of producing goods or services in large-scale industrial activity. It is the counterpart of marketing management, which is concerned with the function of selling the goods or services. In terms of business organization, the chief executive charged with fulfilling the production function is usually called the production manager, or manufacturing manager in the particular case of manufacturing operations. This book is about the functions of the production manager.

We are further concerned with the analytical underpinnings of production management. The treatment, although oriented toward these management science aspects, is not about analysis as such. That is, we prefer to treat operating problems in an analytical framework rather than analytical problems with operating examples. We are thus centered on the functional decisions of the production manager and have therefore utilized only those analytical tools which have been sufficiently proven in application.

Mathematics is employed—its use could hardly be avoided in an analytical presentation. Since we employ only proven analytical tools such as linear programming and simulation, however, the amount and level of mathematics is limited. In two areas where the reader's mathematics might not suffice—linear programming and calculus—appendices are provided to build on the usual background of algebra and trigonometry. This foundation is ample for the subject matter, and the book is entirely self-contained as far as mathematics is concerned.

To analyze the production management function, we have selected a blend of readings and text. The readings are utilized because in many rapidly developing analytical areas, an expert can say far better, and with greater authority, what we could only attempt to rephrase. The readings also result in the inclusion of more updated material, an example of which is the treatment of PERT and heuristics in production planning.

The textual material is designed to complement the readings by introducing and tying together the three major parts and surveying the conventional approaches to the general area. The reader is thereby provided with a survey of traditional methods and their deficiencies before he begins his examination of the analytical treatment.

v

In addition to the introductory material, editorial notes are provided wherever the readings discuss a narrow aspect of the problem in question. Thus the editorial notes broaden the readings and prevent them from leaving the reader with a limited perspective. Finally, the appendices provide the necessary mathematical base, so that the readings are comprehensible to the reader with a minimal mathematics background. We feel that this arrangement combines the strength of readings (currentness and expertness) with the advantages of text (continuity and completeness).

We believe that the direction suggested by *Production Planning and Control: Text and Readings*—the analytical approach to production management—offers one of the really challenging concepts in business management.

We wish to express our thanks to the publishers and authors whose works we have drawn upon, and who have cooperated with us in the selection of illustrations for this book.

Evanston, Illinois
Lafayette, Indiana

Contents

PRODUCTION
PLANNING
AND
CONTROL

PART I

Planning and Controlling Production Levels

Chapter 1

INTRODUCTION TO PART I

The material in this section focuses on the management functions involved in the production process—planning, scheduling, and control.

Production planning and production scheduling are often considered as two names for the same activity. This idea is erroneous, but understandable, since in many ways the two functions are quite similar. Both production planning and scheduling set the levels at which the production process will operate in the future; and both assign responsibilities for accomplishing the production job. The major differences between planning and scheduling lie in the time span covered by production plans and the amount of detail in the plan.

Production planning involves setting production levels for *several* periods in the future and assigning *general* responsibility to provide data for making decisions on the size and composition of the labor force, capital equipment and plant additions, and planned inventory levels. The ability to meet demand levels generated by possible alternative sales programs is also a function of production planning.

At this point the phrase "setting production levels for several periods in the future" may need some clarification. Production plans are used for many different purposes. One example is the use of a production plan to help determine the amount of new capital equipment to be purchased in the future. In this instance a plan covering the next five, eight, or even ten years would be required and would indicate the production job to be done and the capital equipment necessary to accomplish this job.

At the same time that a production plan covering the next several years is necessary, another plan covering a much shorter time period might also be called for. This plan might cover only the next few months and might be used to set aggregate production rates to meet forecasted demand and planned future inventory levels.

3

Thus, at any given time a company may require several production plans, each covering a different time period and each used for a different purpose.

Production scheduling typically covers a much shorter time period than production planning. Production schedules determine how production required in the next several days or weeks will be assigned to specific departments, processes, machines, and operators in order to meet real deadlines imposed by the sales department and desired inventory levels.

Whereas most production planning is concerned only with aggregate productive facilities such as "the packaging department," a production schedule must stipulate orders in more detail, using such units as "packaging line #1" or "Warner and Swasey Lathe #6." In addition, in the strictest definition of the term, a production schedule should stipulate whether Tillie or Mary pushes the appropriate buttons on the appropriate machine. In actual practice, this decision is usually left to the foreman to make on the spot.

Production control involves the constant re-adjustment of plans and schedules in the light of collected operating facts. Any production plan, and most production schedules, are based on some forecast of future demand, and the only certain element in any forecast is error. As new forecasts are made to account for recent sales and inventory positions, and apparent changes in future trends, production plans and schedules must be up-dated.

Production control is somewhat analogous to maintaining the proper idling speed on an automobile engine. The car owner is faced with two related decisions—how often to adjust the idling speed of his automobile, and, once he has decided to make an adjustment, how great an adjustment to make. A sports car enthusiast who tinkers with his car every Saturday morning need make only very minor adjustments on his carburetor since the car has had only one week to get out of adjustment. A more typical driver would readjust the carburetor only once a year, but at that time would make a fairly sizable adjustment.

And so it goes with production control. A company can constantly revise and up-date forecasts and make numerous adjustments in production plans, or it can make more sizable adjustments at less frequent intervals.

It may also be advisable for a company to take little or no action even in the light of significant differences between actual and forecasted demands. This would be the case when the variation between actual and forecasted demand could be attributed purely to random factors and not to any trend or long-term deviation from forecasted figures. A strategy like this one would be justifiable if the cost of changing the production level was large relative to the cost of carrying the extra inventory to protect against deviation from forecasts.

With these broad definitions and differences in mind, we are now in a position to look at some of the tools which have been developed to cope with problems in planning, scheduling, and control.

CONVENTIONAL METHODS

Schematic drawings and graphs have proved very useful in the areas of production planning and scheduling. A simple graph can, for example, bring into focus the differences between alternate production plans for meeting forecasted demand requirements. To illustrate one technique, assume that a company faces the following demand forecast for the coming year:

Month	Forecasted Demand (Units)	Cumulative Demand (Units)	Production Days in Month	Cumulative Production Days
January	1,000	1,000	22	22
February	1,000	2,000	20	42
March	1,500	3,500	22	64
April	2,500	6,000	21	85
May	4,000	10,000	23	108
June	4,000	14,000	21	129
July	5,500	19,500	22	151
August	7,500	27,000	23	174
September	10,500	37,500	20	194
October	11,000	48,500	23	217
November	9,000	57,500	22	239
December	2,000	59,500	21	260

By plotting the forecasted production requirements (assuming that we want to meet expected demand), the extreme seasonal variation becomes very apparent (Figure 1).

Two alternative production plans might be considered for meeting these production requirements. Plan I could stipulate a constant or uniform production rate to be used without variation throughout the year. Plan II could follow demand exactly, changing the production rate whenever demand changes. The difference between these extreme plans is indicated by plotting the cumulative production requirements versus time, where time now represents production days rather than months. (Production rates must be expressed in "units per day" rather than "units per month," since not all months have the same number of days.)

From the diagram in Figure 2 it is obvious that Plan I gives rise to very sizable inventories throughout the year, which, of course, are costly. In this simplified example, Plan II requires no inventory, since as soon as the units are completed, they are sold. Perhaps not so obvious, but nonetheless important, is the magnitude of the required production rates shown by this diagram. Plan I calls for production at the rate of 231 units per day throughout the year; whereas the production rate under Plan II varies from month to month. The Plan II production rate is 45 units/day in January, 174 units/day in June, 525 units/day in September, and 95 units/day in December. Since the peak production rate under Plan II occurs during the month of September, the production facility must have a capacity of 525 units/day if Plan II is to be satisfied. This capacity is more than twice that required by Plan I and, like inventory, productive capacity is expensive.

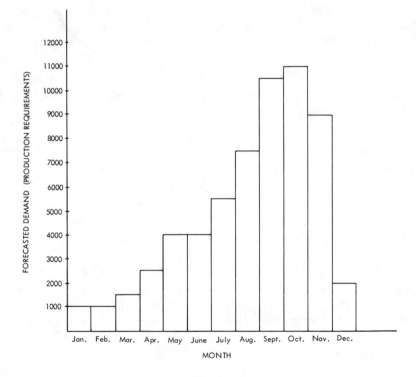

FIGURE 1

Specific costs attached to carrying inventory, size of plant, and changing production rates would enable us to determine an optimal production plan which, no doubt, would lie somewhere between the two extremes discussed here. Considerations other than costs, such as company policy toward the labor force, the labor-management agreement, desired customer service, and community relations, might also have considerable effect on the production planning operation.[1]

---

[1] The problem of the effect of uncertainty in production and inventory control is examined in more detail in Chapter 10, "Uncertainty Problems in Inventory Control."

The most popular schematic scheduling and control technique currently in use is the Gantt Chart. There are many forms of the basic Gantt Chart available, each with specific variations on the main theme to suit particular needs. The Produc-trol Board, Remington Rand's Sched-U-Graph, and the Boardmaster are three popular varieties.

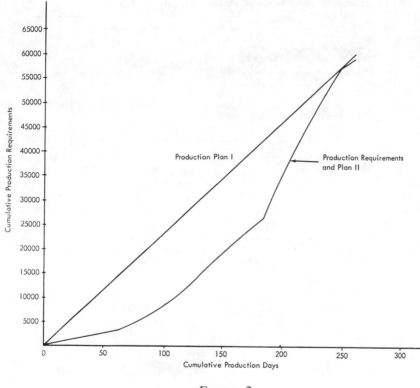

FIGURE 2

There are two basic types of Gantt Charts—the load chart and the planning chart. The most important contribution of the load chart is in keeping track of previous schedules and available machines; while the planning or progress chart is used mainly as a control device to plan and measure actual performance against the plan.

In the Gantt Load Chart, light lines indicate work actually scheduled. In Figure 3, for example, Machine A is fully loaded for all of week #1. Machine B, on the other hand, has slightly less than a 50 percent load. The heavy bars indicate cumulative production capacity for the period covered by the chart. The cumulative load lines are often used to balance loads among machines and in conjunction with maintenance programs.

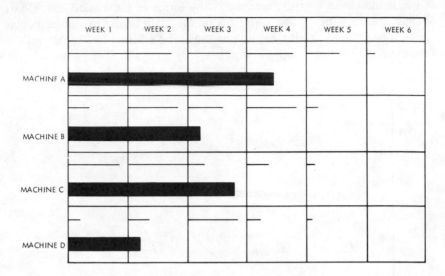

FIGURE 3. GANTT LOAD CHART

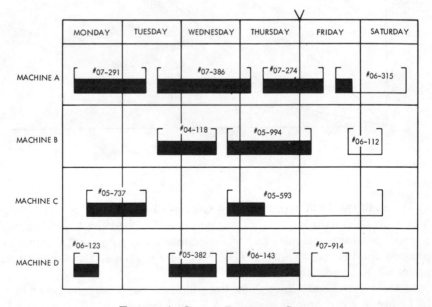

FIGURE 4. GANTT PROGRESS CHART

In the Gantt Progress Chart (Figure 4), the lines have similar meanings. The light lines indicate jobs scheduled; the brackets denote the scheduled beginning and end of each job, the number of which is given above the line. The heavy line indicates the fraction of the job completed at a given time. The present date is noted with a V at the top of the chart.

Figure 4 shows Machine A working well ahead of schedule. Machine B is also ahead of schedule. Machine C, which should be half finished with job #05–593, is almost a day behind. Machine D is right on schedule. This chart focuses attention on the delay at Machine C and should suggest action to expedite job #05–593.

Charts, and in fact many graphical techniques, are often difficult to handle. The Gantt Chart, for example, requires constant attention to keep the information timely. Corrections and changes in schedules and plans are difficult to make, and, as a result, Gantt Charts are often rather messy.

Another weakness of Gantt Charts and similar planning devices is that they handle only one dimension—time. Quite often there are other important factors which should be considered. For example, in deciding whether to assign a specific job to Machine A or Machine B, the most important consideration (when there is time available on both machines) is the relative cost of producing on one machine rather than the other. At the present time, graphical techniques do not take cost considerations into account.

MODERN ANALYTICAL METHODS

The past several years have evidenced the development of a rigorous, yet practical technique which solves the time problem in planning and scheduling, and also considers cost. The method, called *linear programming,* has proven an extremely useful addition in this area.

Developed during the Second World War for the Air Force, linear programming has been widely accepted and applied to a broad variety of problems. As a planning and scheduling technique, it assigns production to machines or production centers in a manner that yields least-cost production plans. The linear programming model takes into account the fact that different machines have different efficiencies, require different amounts of maintenance and operator time, and therefore have different operating costs. As a planning technique, linear programming not only allows an optimal allocation of products to machines, but also aids in deciding which of many possible products to produce.

An introduction to the elements of linear programming is presented in Appendix A. Basic linear programming can be mastered without an extensive knowledge of mathematics. It is this reason, perhaps, that has made linear programming so popular. Appendix A concentrates on building a

maximum facility for handling linear programming problems while using a
minimum of mathematics. Students interested in a more rigorous and complete treatment of linear programming fundamentals are referred to the
many excellent texts currently available on this subject.[2] Having mastered
Appendix A, the reader is equipped to study the application of linear programming methods to production planning problems in Chapters 2 and 3.

It has been found that some linear programming problems can be solved
by a relatively simple technique known as the transportation method. The
name springs from the fact that the first problems solved by this method
involved transportation or distribution plans. Chapter 4 presents an excellent description of the transportation method of linear programming and
several realistic examples of the types of problems that can be handled by
this method. This Chapter also demonstrates the significant advantages in
scheduling by programming rather than by chart or graph.

Granted that mathematical programming represents a significant improvement over schematic and graphical analysis, there still remain many
unsolved problems—especially in the area of production control. Linear
programming is of little value when planning broad production strategy
for the future and adapting production plans to sales forecast errors. Such
problems become quite involved, and the element of uncertainty disrupts
an orderly analysis by programming techniques.

To cope with large, complex production problems, a faculty group from
the Carnegie Institute of Technology developed a mathematical technique
to adapt plans to changing conditions. The end result of this research was
the formulation of decision rules for setting and controlling both production
and inventory levels and the size of the work force. Chapter 5 describes the
result of this research and presents an application.[3]

Another recent development has proven successful in control and scheduling problems. The development is usually called PERT for Programming
and Evaluation Review Technique. The Air Force uses a version called
PEP. Civilian applications, until recently found mostly in the construction
industry and in research and development planning, use the term "Critical
Path Scheduling." "Arrow Diagramming" is a term also used in connection
with this technique.

---

[2] Three texts on basic linear programming are A. Charnes, W. W. Cooper, A. Henderson, *An Introduction To Linear Programming,* John Wiley & Sons, Inc., 1953; S. I.
Gass, *Linear Programming Methods and Applications,* McGraw-Hill Book Co., Inc.,
1959; and An-min Chung, *Linear Programming,* Columbus, Ohio: Charles E. Merrill
Books, Inc., 1963.

[3] The methodology is analyzed more thoroughly in C. C. Holt, Franco Modigliani,
J. F. Muth, H. A. Simon, *Planning Production, Inventories and Work Force,* Prentice-
Hall, Inc., 1960. See especially Chapters 2, 3, and 4.

To understand PERT more fully, consider the information shown in Figure 5.

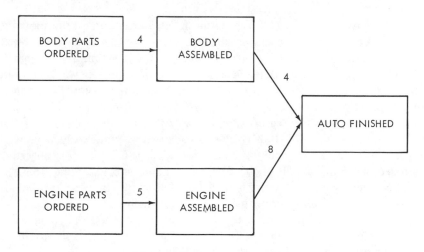

FIGURE 5. ARROW DIAGRAM

This diagram shows, in over-simplified form, the steps necessary to produce an automobile. Constraints on the sequence of steps are shown (i.e., the engine cannot be assembled before the engine parts are ordered; the body cannot be assembled before the body parts are ordered; and the finished automobile results from assembled engines and bodies). An estimate of the required time is given on the arrow connecting the steps. The arrow diagram is basic to all PERT applications.

Two paths lead to the finished automobile. The top path requires no less than eight days: assuming that the body parts are ordered at a zero point in time, the parts will be available four days later, and assembly will require an additional four days. The total time required by the top path, therefore, is no less than eight days.

The bottom path takes at least thirteen days, five for parts to arrive and eight for assembly. The bottom path is, therefore, the critical path in terms of slack time or cushion. Progress on the top path could be delayed up to five days and the automobile would still be produced in thirteen days. However, any delay in the critical path would mean that the automobile would not be produced in that amount of time.

With a knowledge of the critical path, planners can be made aware of possible delays and can expedite progress by using resources from slack paths. In our example, manpower could be transferred from body assembly to engine assembly. Engine assembly might be cut to six days, and body assembly increased to six days. In this way, two days could be cut from the final date for the finished automobile. The revised top path would be $4 + 6$ or ten days. The revised bottom path, still the critical path, would be $5 + 6$ or 11 days.

As a control device, a PERT program focuses attention on the most important areas for management action—the steps in the critical path. Small delays on slack or non-critical paths usually are not significant enough to affect the final completion date. Delays on the critical path, however, require immediate attention and effective follow-up if the target completion date is to be met.

Chapter 6 presents a case example indicating the method for defining the critical path. Careful study of this article will result in excellent grounding in the basic PERT technique. Also included in Chapter 6 is an article with a broader discussion of the PERT technique and its applications.

Sometimes problems exist which defy solution by standard techniques. A sub-set of scheduling problems called "sequencing" or "line balancing" problems often fall into this category. A general method called heuristic programming or, more simply, heuristics, has been found very useful in attacking problems of this type. The strict definition of heuristics is, literally, that it "serves to find out and encourages further investigation." When applied to production problems, heuristic techniques lead to solutions by trying "common sense" rules and procedures rather than rigorous optimality criteria. Heuristic results are usually not optimal; but, since optimal solutions are very difficult or impossible to find in some problems, heuristic solutions are very useful.

Chapter 7 applies heuristics to a typical production problem. We might suggest that whereas the conventional techniques described early in Chapter 1 are quite popular, there is strong evidence that certain formal techniques are often more likely to lead to practical, rigorous answers to planning and control problems. These formal methods include linear programming, linear control rules, PERT, and heuristics, all of which are thoroughly examined in Chapters 2 through 7.

Chapter 2

PRODUCTION PLANNING
WITH LINEAR PROGRAMMING

I.

Do You Want Production or Profit?[*]

Nyles V. Reinfeld

Manufacturing management is often in a position where it can choose between two roads of action—increase production, or increase profits. The first does not necessarily provide the latter. The difference between these viewpoints was clearly pointed out in a Linear Programming study recently made in the Tube Mill of a large midwest manufacturer.

The study showed that scheduling for maximum profit would increase company profits by close to $350,000 over last year.[1] On the other side of the ledger, scheduling for maximum output would increase the quantity by 22% but profits would decrease 23% below the maximum profit, or about $300,000 a year! This increase in profit was the direct result of a selection of products, using Linear Programming, and is based on the same production costs in both cases. The analysis considered such factors as plant and machine capacity, sales forecasts by various warehouses, shipping rates by items to the various distribution centers, and present and proposed company policies.

---

[*] From *Tooling and Production Magazine* (August 1954), 1–6. Reprinted by permission of Huebner Publications, Inc.

[1] All figures have been changed to retain the confidential nature of the findings. They are, however, representative of the true picture.

THE TUBE MILL STUDY

The problem in the Tube Mill consists of an overload on present production capacity. This overload creates a conflict between Standard and Capped sizes of tubing. The result has been a tendency toward purchasing some sizes of Standard and Capped tubing for resale through the company's various warehouses. Purchased items can be bought at a slight discount; but, after handling costs, they are resold at just about breakeven. In other words, there is no profit in purchasing tubing to fill orders. It is merely done as a customer convenience. The company's customers are serviced by nine warehouses scattered across the country. Due to the increase in shipping costs, the farther the warehouse from the factory, the greater is the tendency to purchase tubing from outside sources close to the warehouse.

The method of supplying tubing to the customer as originally proposed was to manufacture everything for the home warehouse. All Capped tubing for the remaining warehouses was to be bought and resold. Any remaining production capacity would then be used to fill orders for Standard tubing for nearby warehouses. All other tubing would be bought and resold. The pattern, here, is clear. The company was following the logical pattern which would reduce shipping costs and therefore increase profits.

At first view, this seems to be a good policy. Actually, it was not until Linear Programming was applied that it could be shown that a far more profitable policy was possible.

To set the problem up for Linear Programming, it was necessary to gather a large amount of data about every machine in the plant and about every product to be produced on the equipment. In some cases, the data was not directly available and had to be developed.

The plant handled several thousand products which represented many variations of approximately a hundred standard sizes of tubing. Each piece of tubing passed through a series of operations such as the piercer, pointers, saws, annealing furnaces, draw benches and straighteners. In many cases, it passed through some operations several times. On the draw benches, for example, some pieces of tubing required as high as 13 separate draws in bringing them down to size.

BASIC PRINCIPLES

Clearly, there are machines and factors that do not play a material role in determining which products should be produced and which should be bought. One of the problems, therefore, in formulating the attack, is to determine which data is essential.

The philosophy that underlies the application of Linear Programming to the Tube Mill problem is based on the concept of a bottleneck. A bottleneck is a condition which limits the total plant output. The bottleneck may be a certain operation or a group of operations or machines. In the case of the Tube Mill, draw benches limit the tube capacity. All other functions of that department, such as sawing and piercing, are limited in their output by the draw benches. Most of these "before-and-after" operations are working six or eight hours a day, while the benches are busy continuously, around the clock. Everything we can get through the benches, we can easily get through the rest of the department. Therefore, the bottleneck determines the ultimate profit that we can make by operating the Mill.

We can increase the dollar output of the bottleneck in two ways: We can buy new equipment and enlarge the capacity at the point of the bottleneck, or we can increase the earning power of the present equipment.

We can relate profit to time in the bottleneck. Last year approximately 1,400,000 minutes of draw bench productive capacity was used on standard tubing. If the profit from standard tubing was about $1,000,000 last year, the company made $.714 for each minute the draw benches were operating. If we could increase this to $1.00 per minute, the company's profit for the year would be $1,400,000.

You will soon see how it is possible to increase the profit-per-minute by means of Linear Programming.

What is true of profit is also true of production. If we wish to increase the quantity through the bottleneck, we must then work in terms of quantity-per-minute. In either case, it is possible to achieve a considerable increase, without any change in equipment. (This statement is not intended to minimize the importance of equipment modernization, methods improvement, etc.—when necessary.)

To increase the profit-per-minute involves the concept of opportunity profit. Opportunity profit is the increase in profit that can be made by running one part instead of another, and is determined by the profit-per-piece divided by the pieces-per-minute. It is seen from this fact, that the piece with the highest unit profit will not necessarily give the highest profit-per-minute.

Let us exaggerate this concept for purposes of illustration. Suppose that one piece of tubing makes a profit of $6.00, with a running time of 10 minutes. The profit-per-minute would be $.60. Another piece of tubing may make a profit of $5.00, with a running time of 8 minutes. In this case the profit-per-minute would be $.625.

In other words, if we could sell all we could make of either product, we would make the greatest profit by making the latter item. That such cases actually exist in Industry is shown by the solution we arrived at in the case of our Tube Mill example (see Table I). It is more profitable to make some items for the West Coast and pay the shipping cost than it is to make others for the home warehouse. The same thing is true for home warehouse items only—namely, some prove to be more profitable than others, without direct regard to the unit price tag attached to each.

SOLVING THE TUBE MILL PROBLEM

Working with the basic principles just discussed, the first step, after isolating the bottleneck equipment (draw benches) was to gather the relative data and organize it into a coherent picture.

Gathering the data essentially amounted to getting a list of the benches, utilization figures, available time on each, a list of all the tubing produced in the Mill, a standard operational breakdown for each size, and a list of all the equipment alternates and times for making each single draw. Since time was given in terms of draws, which represented any number of pieces, it was necessary to determine the number of pieces that were involved in each draw. In this way we were able to get the time per piece per draw.

A list of the warehouses, and sales forecasts by warehouses by products, were obtained along with shipping rates and the profit-per-piece at the plant before shipping costs were deducted. Whereas profit is normally based upon total cost variance including shipping charges, what we need is the profit at each specific warehouse.

Shipping rates were given in terms of weight minimums and destination. The rates for a specific destination were then deducted from the factory profit on each product to give the profit at each warehouse.

The next step was to set up the matrix for solving the problem. (A matrix is a mathematical arrangement of the coefficients of algebraic equations.) Figure 1 shows a part of the simplex matrix as it appears for one size of tubing and the three warehouses requisitioning that particular product.

The matrix is designed to convert normal profit into opportunity profit, and to compare for profitability of producing various products. We don't know what the opportunity profit is by direct inspection, because we don't know what combinations of machines will be used to make the products. The only approach is to solve all possible combinations of time, profit, and product that are relevant to obtaining the best answer.

The matrix in Figure 1 would normally require solution by electronic computers. It is possible, however, to perform a transformation on the data which will convert the matrix to a method suitable for hand calculation. The transformation is possible because of the type of data involved. The new (distribution) matrix, Figure 2, is much simpler to work with. In some instances, the distribution matrix can be set up directly without actual construction of the simplex matrix.

In constructing the distribution matrix, the vertical columns are arranged in descending order by relative profit. In scheduling the utilization of available capacity to meet forecast requirements, assignments are made on the matrix, working from left to right—giving priority to those product orders having the greatest relative profits. The complete conversion of the simplex matrix required two weeks, at which time the answer was obtained directly by setting up the distribution matrix, without further solution.

The rules for performing these operations are quite simple and can be readily taught to clerical workers.

The peculiarity of the data which made this type of matrix solution possible is the fact that there is a bottleneck within the bottleneck machine group. This bottleneck exists on the last four machine groups. When these machines were loaded, there was still open capacity on the first machines. This meant that we could solve the problem for the smaller bottleneck and then finish using our capacity on the first machines with products that can be made on them alone.

Caution must be exercised in working with bottlenecks of this sort since there is a tendency for the bottleneck to shift as the mix changes. In this case, were the mix to change over a period of time to where the first machines became the bottleneck, then the present solution would no longer be valid. However, since this solution is for a year in advance, it would normally be safe to assume that a regular pattern of sales would not affect it. In the case of other plants that have been analysed, bottlenecks of this type have shifted from week to week.

DIFFERENT SOLUTIONS

In arriving at the solutions, we approached the problem from the standpoint of the forecasted sales and also from the standpoint of both increased capacity and expanded sales forecasts. We will not go into how these variations were handled other than to emphasize the generality of the final answers.

In arriving at the solution of what products to make and which to buy, we ended up with a priority of products. This priority lists the most profitable products first and the least profitable last. A part of this table is given in Table I. It will be noted that warehouse No. 3 items are included right down the line with home warehouse items, despite the difference in shipping costs. It will also be noted that the profits-per-piece are not directly aligned with the profitability as indicated by the priority.

Because of the general approach that was used, the answers obtained cover a wide range of variation in sales and capacity. The solution is true for the present capacity as well as the expanded, and has the additional virtue of considering the course of action to pursue as sales increase. Since the answer is given in terms of priority of one product over another,

FIGURE 1

These are the machine groups that will draw the tubing. The available minutes-per-year must be substituted here for each machine group

"Operation" refers to a group of comparable draws

Four choices for doing operation No. 5. The cap "5", means that there is more than one machine that can perform these draws

Normal profit after shipping to the specific warehouse

3/16" CAPPED 50' COIL	OPERATION									NORMAL PROFIT		
	2	2	3	3	4	4	5	5	5	Plant Whse .444	Whse #2 .418	Whse #3 .393
Machine 1, 2	.107											
3		.028	.056									
5, 6		.045	.052	.076								
7, 8					.056							
9						3.16	2.60					
10								2.65	2.18			
Relation of Output	0	1	−1									
	0	1	−1									
	0	1		−1	−1							
	0	1			−1	−1						
							−1	−1	−1	−1	−1	−1
										✓	✓	✓
Forecast pcs/whse										600	1150	1100

Difference between number of pieces produced on one operation and another

Forecasted one-year sales for the specific warehouse— See check mark over to the right .. 1100 in the forecast for Whse No. 3

This is the time it takes to perform the draws that are grouped into Oper. 5. The final solution may show this operation being done on another machine

FIGURE 2

		k89	k90	k91	k92	k93	k94	k95	k96	Relative profit obtained by transforming the Simplex matrix. These figures indicate which product should be produced
		.160	.157	.148	.144	.136	.131	.122	.113	
R1	0	.160	.157	.148	.144	.136	.131	.122	.113	10,000
R2	0	.160	.157	.148	.144	.136	.131	.122	.113	1,670
		358	98	382						
R3	0	.160	.157	.148	.144	.136	.131	.122	.113	3,320
				383	18	886	19	36	15	
R4	0	.160	.157	.148	.144	.136	.131	.122	.113	2,760
Converted forecast		358	98	765	18	886	19	36	15	

Raw number, keyed to a specific machine group

Number determined by the solution to indicate degree of improvement. (Not part of basic data.)

Column number, keyed to a specific product by warehouse

Production assignment. Total assignments in each row must not exceed the machine capacity shown at right end of row. Total assignments in each column must not exceed the forecast shown at bottom of column

Available time has been converted for solution by the Distribution matrix quantity and capacity determine only how many of the products on the bottom of the list are to be purchased. In other words, on the basis of the load ahead of the equipment, the overload is purchased from outside sources in order of lowest priority.

TABLE I.   HIGHEST-PROFIT PRIORITIES

Product*	Location (Whse)	Priority	Profit/Pc. /Whse
1–1/4B3	2	10	4.50
1–1/4B	1	11	2.03
1–1/4A3	1	12	4.48
1–1/2A	2	13	2.23
1–1/2B	2	14	2.20
1–1/4B	2	15	1.85
1–1/4A	1	16	1.89
1A3	1	17	3.99
1–1/4B3	3	18	3.94

° A partial list of all the products, arranged in order of the priority applicable when objective is to use present capacity for making highest profit.

TABLE II.   HIGHEST PRODUCTION PRIORITIES

Product*	Priority†
1–1/4B	4
1–1/4A	5
3/4B	6
1C	7
3/8A	8
1/2B	9
3/4A	10

° A partial list of all the products, arranged in order of the priority applicable when objective is to increase output.
† No distinction made as to location, since profitability is not considered.

Price changes affecting profit on one single item will require special analysis of that one product, which will probably be shifted in the priority table. Cost changes affecting all products equally, such as increases in pay scale, generally will not affect the status of the priority table.

Several different solutions were made for comparative purposes. These solutions were given in terms of a list of products, such as the ones shown in Tables I and II. Products were listed by priority and showed what should be produced to accomplish a certain objective. In all cases for comparative purposes, the same capacity and forecast figures were used.

Similar tables were made up showing comparisons of the highest-possible profits with last year's production (Table III) and with the proposed method of purchasing which was outlined earlier and designed to reduce shipping costs.

	Table I (Highest-Profit)	Table II (Highest-Production)
Pieces Produced	820,000	1,000,000
Increase in Pieces		180,000
Profit Produced	$1,300,000	$1,000,000
Increase in Profit	300,000	

TABLE III. COMPARISON OF RESULTS*

* Based upon use of same capacity.

It was found that shipping costs are not a major factor in determining maximum profit. This is shown by the fact that use of the highest-profit table would increase profits by $300,000 over the original proposed policy and by $350,000 over profits realized by last year's production. The $300,000 profit increase constitutes the cumulative opportunity profit. This profit is not realized by cost reduction or by increased production, but so v the opportunity profits of all items considered simultaneously.

CONCLUSIONS

ata, that we have just discussed, are ready for use as is handed in to management. In spite of the rather nvolved, the only requirement on the part of management the use of the tables.

is possible to work from either the highest profit or pending on your objective) to determine the whole year. Once a policy has been established, it is a o the table when making a decision between pro-

re based on present capacity and forecasts. Natuty are expanded, the same possibilities exist on a

profits study, Linear Programming is now being uild weekly schedules for maximum utilization of ogram ties together the allocation procedure and h are normally treated separately.

one example of the many ways in which Linear d to increase company profits or reduce costs. be applied to any industry which has the probrchases to supplement their line, or the comparable problem of subcontracting many of the components for an end product.

Linear Programming is being used successfully for a wide range of management problems other than direct profit studies. Examples include salary evaluation, production scheduling, inventory control, and market research.

II.

*Applying Linear Programming to the Plywood Industry**

Ernest Koenigsberg

The applications of linear programming to the plywood industry, in particular the softwood industry, have recently been studied. This pape
cusses the preliminary examination, augmented by actual data wh
possible. The general value of linear programming in these appli
having been confirmed by this early study, more extensive work
being carried out for specific companies.

The studies made have shown that, when costs are express
way in terms of some volumetric measure, the very significant c
of grade and other factors (sanding, glue, and so forth) which
surface measure, are hidden. Costs should rather be consider
Mayhew system, in terms of the product specifications and la
a plywood panel. The method of extending the cost studies t
should therefore provide better rules and guides to aid
decisions, such as log purchases, veneer production, and p
of these problems (product mix and log purchases) are t
pendently of one another, to show how the use of mathe
improve the profitability of a plywood manufacturi
models demonstrated are somewhat simplified but tha
realistic and lead to meaningful and valuable results. S
treated because of the limitations imposed by a small
of necessary data for a full-scale calculation, or bot
now being investigated for specific companies.

_____
* From *Forest Products Journal,* Vol. 10, No. 9 (1960
mission of *Forest Products Journal.*

PROBLEM I–PRODUCT MIX

Softwood Plywood Production: A mill purchases (or obtains from government or owned land) logs that can be peeled in several thicknesses. Any log yields veneer of 6 or more grades, the percentage yield among grades varying from log to log even when logs of a single grade are peeled to the same thickness. Veneer costs then are subject to a somewhat arbitrary distribution among the various grades (which are the "joint products"). Even the best system of allocating veneer costs, that of assigning costs according to the "realization" on the finished products containing the grade, is subject to merited criticism. Another company using the same logs and peeling in the same way could conceivably have different veneer costs if the product mix were different. Further, the same logs could be peeled differently to obtain still a third set of veneer costs by grade. Since the assignment of veneer costs depends on the final product mix, these costs cannot be used to determine an "optimal" product mix.

Consider the "X Plywood Company." In 1956, this company produced 44 products in the quantities listed in Table 1. Each final product required three or more sheets of veneer of the following grades and thickness:

Thickness	Grades used†
1/10″	A, B, C, D, Cx, Dx
1/8″	A, B, C, D, Cx, Dx
3/16″	C, D, Cx, Dx

† The subscript x indicates crossband.

Assume that the available logs give the mixture of grades and sizes required for the listed quantities of final product. The available veneer supply is fixed; it is listed in Table II. Since we cannot justify costing veneer by grade and thickness, we cannot calculate a profit per unit of product. Instead we shall use "return" as a measure of profitability. "Return" is defined as the selling price minus standard trade discounts and those cost contributions (other than veneer) which are product-dependent (labor, glue, and so forth). The problem can then be expressed in the following way:

"Which product and how much of each should be produced from a known distribution of veneers of various grades and thicknesses so that the return is maximized?"

It must be tacitly assumed that we can market any products manufactured without further discounts. This latter assumption will be modified later.

Now, an A grade sheet of a given thickness can be used for any product that requires the A grade sheet. The amount of A grade sheets is limited; if we use the sheets for AD panels, we restrict the possible production of AA, AB and AC panels. Similarly the use of Dx sheets in AD panels restricts the possible production of other products requiring the Dx sheets of the same thickness. Hence all products are intimately connected. These restrictions can be expressed mathematically in a simple form, and the resulting mathematical equations can be manipulated by the method of linear programming.

TABLE I. PRODUCTION OF PLYWOOD PANELS IN S.M.

Grade and Size		X Company	Average Company
AA Interior	1/4"	49,300	288,200
	3/8"	65,500	117,000
	1/2"	139,400	208,500
	5/8"	49,700	58,900
	3/4"	696,800	1,052,000
BB Interior	1/4"	230,000	366,400
	3/8"	83,100	168,100
	1/2"	476,500	438,600
	5/8"	122,800	150,900
	3/4"	1,175,200	1,766,800
AD Interior	1/4"	6,017,700	10,502,800
	3/8"	1,085,900	2,468,000
	1/2"	1,301,200	3,159,400
	5/8"	784,100	1,432,200
	3/4"	2,798,800	6,579,100
CD Interior	5/16"	324,500	2,962,400
	3/8"	1,031,300	5,992,900
	1/2"	1,271,800	5,393,700
	5/8"	2,466,000	6,635,900
	3/4"	78,300	596,300
AA Exterior	1/4"	133,200	149,700
	3/8"	60,600	116,800
	1/2"	48,500	83,900
	5/8"	18,000	22,000
	3/4"	87,100	143,900
AB Exterior	1/4"	223,200	298,100
	3/8"	147,400	130,300
	1/2"	164,400	186,500
	5/8"	17,300	40,800
	3/4"	147,200	172,800
AC Exterior	1/4"	2,945,500	3,707,000
	3/8"	3,280,400	4,761,500
	1/2"	961,200	1,396,100
	5/8"	264,300	411,500
	3/4"	626,400	1,253,400
BB Exterior	1/4"	115,500	69,100
	3/8"	—	13,300
	1/2"	30,700	12,500
	5/8"	472,400	2,359,600
	3/4"	920,300	2,546,100
CC Exterior	5/16"	38,100	158,200
	3/8"	136,400	338,800
	1/2"	65,900	342,400
	5/8"	142,000	262,400
	3/4"	29,800	66,200

TABLE II. VENEER AVAILABLE IN S.M.

Grade and Thickness		X Company	In Decimal Fraction	Average Company	In Decimal Fraction
1/10"	A	9,781,000	.0786	15,750,000	.0550
	B	683,000	.0055	803,000	.0028
	C	6,021,000	.0484	15,086,000	.0527
	D	10,804,000	.0868	28,059,000	.0981
	Cx	5,897,000	.0474	8,425,000	.0294
	Dx	12,998,000	.1045	32,520,000	.1137
1/8"	A	15,776,000	.1268	28,119,000	.0983
	B	5,179,000	.0416	12,938,000	.0452
	C	9,464,000	.0761	22,655,000	.0792
	D	12,011,000	.0965	33,710,000	.1178
	Cx	1,962,000	.0158	5,735,000	.0200
	Dx	7,877,000	.0633	27,549,000	.0963
3/16"	C	2,581,000	.0207	7,016,000	.0245
	D	5,656,000	.0455	11,636,000	.0407
	Cx	7,108,000	.0571	13,387,000	.0468
	Dx	10,632,000	.0854	22,742,000	.0795
TOTAL		124,430,000	1.0000	286,130,000	1.0000

Let X_i be the fraction of product i produced (for example $i = 17$ indicates AA $\frac{1}{4}$ inch Interior, $i = 18$ indicates AA $\frac{3}{8}$ inch Interior . . . $i = 56$ indicates CC $\frac{5}{8}$ inch Exterior), and b_j be the fraction of veneer j available ($j = 1$ indicates A $\frac{1}{10}$ inch, $j = 2$ indicates B $\frac{1}{10}$ inch, . . . $j = 16$ indicates D_x $\frac{3}{16}$ inch). Now, the total production requiring j grade veneer cannot exceed the available quantity of that veneer, or

$$(1) \quad \sum_i a_{ij} X_i \leq b_j$$

where a_{ij} is the number of sheets of j grade veneer required for product i. For example, $a_{17 \cdot 1} = 2$, means two A $\frac{1}{10}$ inch sheets are required for each panel of AA $\frac{1}{4}$ inch; $a_{18 \cdot 1} = 2$, two A $\frac{1}{10}$ sheets are required for each panel of AA $\frac{3}{8}$ inch, $A_{56 \cdot 1} = 0$, no A $\frac{1}{10}$ inch sheets are required for CC $\frac{5}{8}$ inch.

There are 16 such requirement equations connecting the 40 to 45 product variables. These equations plus one more

$$(2) \quad Z = \sum_i R_i X_i = \text{Maximum},$$

define the problem. Here R_i is the return on the ith product. In effect equation (2) states that we want to maximize the return on the available raw materials. The return on all products is listed in Table III.

Solution of linear programming problems of this order are time-consuming if done by hand. Solutions have been obtained on the IBM 650 computer (using a modified H. Smith program) in about 30 minutes of machine time. The solutions show that considerable savings are possible. For "X Plywood Company" we find the return (per 1,000 S.M. of veneer) is

$22.47; this is to be compared with $21.16 obtained from their actual production. The difference, $1.31, when applied to the annual production of about 120,000,000 Surface Measures of veneer could result in increasing the return by about $150,000 per year. The bulk of the increase in return

TABLE III.   IDEAL SOLUTION FOR X PLYWOOD COMPANY

Product			Percent of Total Production	"Shadow Price"	"Return"	Raw Materials		Shadow Price
Interior AA	1/4"	17	—	$22.42	$ 72.61	1/10"	A	$35.72
	3/8"	18	—	13.59	101.21		B	22.25
	1/2"	19	—	3.55	120.63		C	19.81
	5/8"	20	—	17.24	132.03		D	—
	3/4"	21	.1078	—	157.93		Cx	16.32
							Dx	23.60
AB	1/4"	22	—	16.77	64.79	1/8"	A	38.49
	3/8"	23	—	14.83	85.24		B	24.43
	1/2"	24	—	6.67	102.78		C	9.93
	5/8"	25	—	5.09	129.45		D	4.43
	3/4"	26	—	6.47	136.73		Cx	35.42
							Dx	33.49
AD	1/4"	27	—	7.02	52.30	3/16"	C	17.60
	3/8"	28	—	8.16	72.58		D	5.32
	1/2"	29	.0810	—	90.74		Cx	31.10
	5/8"	30	.0739	—	115.21		Dx	37.82
	3/4"	31	—	3.93	119.94			
CD	5/16"	32	.1099	—	43.41			
	3/8"	33	.1049	—	48.69			
	1/2"	34	.0727	—	67.01			
	5/8"	35	—	9.69	76.08			
	3/4"	36	.0628	—	94.43			
Exterior AA	1/4"	37	.1569	—	87.75			
	3/8"	38	.0527	—	108.07			
	1/2"	39	—	4.85	124.58			
	3/4"	40	.0049	—	156.77			
AB	1/4"	41	—	5.29	68.99			
	3/8"	42	—	1.55	92.42			
	1/2"	43	.0107	—	114.70			
	3/4"	44	—	7.45	141.30			
AC	1/4"	45	—	12.62	59.23			
	3/8"	46	.0100	—	79.51			
	1/2"	47	—	4.85	96.02			
	5/8"	48	—	26.47	110.38			
	3/4"	49	—	1.34	126.87			
BB	1/4"	50	.0110	—	60.81			
	5/8"	51	—	17.59	118.37			
	3/4"	52	.0777	—	127.32			
CC	1/4"	53	—	6.84	49.10			
	3/8"	54	.0631	—	55.27			
	1/2"	55	—	12.91	79.16			
	5/8"	56	—	10.57	90.04			

is profit, because the fixed costs will be practically unaffected by changes in the product mix. The form of the results of the linear programming computation is shown in Table III. The "ideal" solution calls for the production of only the 15 products listed here:

Interior grades: AA $\frac{3}{4}$, AD $\frac{1}{2}$, AD $\frac{5}{8}$, CD $\frac{5}{16}$, CD $\frac{3}{8}$, CD $\frac{1}{2}$, CD $\frac{3}{4}$.

Exterior grades: AA $\frac{1}{4}$, AA $\frac{3}{8}$, AA $\frac{3}{4}$, AB $\frac{1}{2}$, AC $\frac{3}{8}$, BB $\frac{1}{4}$, BB $\frac{3}{4}$, CC $\frac{3}{8}$.

The production of any other items must lead to a reduction in return. These reductions can be discussed in terms of the third column of Table III marked "Shadow Price." The shadow price is the loss in return per 1,000 S.M. of plywood panels produced (since this can only be produced by reducing the production of at least one of the ideal products). In this case, the production of 1,000 S.M. panels of interior AA $\frac{1}{4}$ inch would produce a loss in return of $22.42 while the production of 1,000 S.M. of exterior AB $\frac{3}{8}$ would only produce a loss in return of $1.55. The value of the shadow prices is that they allow one to determine how the return is affected by deviation from the "ideal" product mix.

The "solution" of the problem consists of more than the quantities to be produced and the shadow prices. We also obtain a matrix or table of numbers that shows the best way (that is, the cheapest) to introduce a product not included in the basic solution. This is demonstrated by example later. Further, by using the shadow prices we can determine if a new product is profitable or if it is profitable to make an established product in another manner.

The solution here is not completely practical in that market restrictions have been ignored. For example, about 11 per cent of production is interior AA $\frac{3}{4}$. The market for this product is relatively small. Similarly, there is no production of exterior BB $\frac{5}{8}$, which is a popular product. These restrictions can be incorporated in the original set of equations, in which case we would have found a different solution (and, of course, a lower value of the return). We can, however, within a fairly wide range use the shadow prices and the final "matrix" to determine the effect of modifying the production. For example, our solution results in an excess of 2.6 S.M. of $\frac{1}{10}$ inch D veneer per 1,000 S.M. of initial product. This could be used as $\frac{1}{10}$ inch Dx and give a slight increase in our return (increased by $23.60 $\times$ 0.0026 = $0.06, making the return $22.53).

The value of $23.60 is the shadow price associated with $\frac{1}{10}$ inch Dx veneer. The shadow price of the raw material is the added return that can be obtained if there were an additional 1,000 S.M. of the raw material available. These shadow prices are indications of how peeling can be modified in order to produce greater returns, or how one might improve the return by changing the quantity peeled in each thickness. A study of Table III, for example, shows that Dx has a greater shadow price than D for all thicknesses. In an actual problem a result of this form would indicate that downgrading D to Dx may be profitable. A large difference in shadow price between B and C grades would indicate that more labor on patching grade C to B might be profitable. The differences in shadow prices also give indications of changing the peeling distribution.

Table IV shows the solution obtained for the "Average Company." The "ideal" return for the Average Company is $21.22 as compared with the actual return of $20.08 per 1,000 S.M. of veneer. We obtained $.2504 units of product for each unit of veneer. This is a difference of $1.14 per 1,000 S.M. of veneer produced. The ideal production for this company differs from the previous example for two reasons: (1) the return (and cost) structure is different (Tables III and IV) and (2) the raw product mix is different (Table II). X Company uses logs that yield more A and B grade and also peel more $3/16$ inch, hence the greater return.

We can examine the changes implied by altering the production. Let us assume that we must produce interior AB $3/4$ inch (product 26). To do this we must change our production of other products. The final matrix for product 26 gives the values shown in Table V, Column 1. The values show that, for each unit of product 26 produced, the output of product 40 is increased by 0.5 units, the output of product 52 is reduced by 0.5 units, and the output of product 21 is reduced by 1.0 unit. (A plus sign in the matrix column indicates a reduction and a minus sign indicates an increase.) For each 1,000 S.M. so changed, the shadow price tells us that we will lose $6.47 in return. If we do this for 4 per cent of production our return will be reduced by (0.04) × (0.2504) × 6.47. (0.2504 is the number of 1,000 S.M. panels produced per 1,000 S.M. of veneer.) Thus the return is reduced by about six cents per 1,000 S.M. of veneer. Column 3 of Table V shows the final production if this change is made.

We can make further modifications based on the information generated by our final matrix. Suppose that in addition to interior AB $3/4$ inch we must produce exterior BB $5/8$ inch (product 51). The 5th column of Table V shows the final matrix column for product 51. Each unit of product 51 produced results in an increase of 1 unit of product 38 and a decrease of 1 unit each for products 46 and 40. Now, since we only produce

1 percent of product 46, we cannot produce more than 1 percent of exterior BB ⅝ inch (or else we would have a "negative" production). If we

TABLE IV. SOLUTION FOR AVERAGE PLYWOOD COMPANY

Product			Percent of Total Production	"Shadow Price"	"Return"	Raw Materials		Shadow Price
Interior AA	{	1/4"	17	—	$10.57	$ 81.16	1/16" {	A	$39.92
		3/8"	18	—	8.31	101.22		B	26.34
		1/2"	19	—	.65	120.34		C	21.65
		5/8"	20	—	2.21	132.99		D	11.45
		3/4"	21	—	3.09	151.67		Cx	10.31
								Dx	11.90
AB	{	1/4"	22	—	10.70	67.45	1/8" {	A	42.87
		3/8"	23	—	8.11	84.64		B	26.09
		1/2"	24	.0682	—	104.20		C	20.27
		5/8"	25	.0757	—	118.42		D	14.61
		3/4"	26	—	2.97	135.00		Cx	19.48
								Dx	14.01
AD	{	1/4"	27	—	9.71	53.56	3/16" {	C	19.30
		3/8"	28	—	7.85	73.42		D	21.43
		1/2"	29	—	.18	92.55		Cx	28.15
		5/8"	30	.1023	—	106.95		Dx	23.79
		3/4"	31	—	2.63	123.87			
CD	{	5/16"	32	.0980	—	45.00			
		3/8"	33	.0105	—	48.90			
		1/2"	34	.1315	—	68.35			
		5/8"	35	.0273	—	77.53			
		3/4"	36	.1739	—	97.08			
Exterior AA	{	1/4"	37	.1203	—	90.15			
		3/8"	38	.0105	—	113.89			
		1/2"	39	—	.84	127.18			
		3/4"	40	.0808	—	161.97			
AB	{	1/4"	41	—	.49	76.08			
		3/8"	42	—	1.95	95.16			
		1/2"	43	.0011	—	111.23			
		3/4"	44	—	—	145.89			
AC	{	1/4"	45	—	12.08	59.80			
		3/8"	46	—	8.92	82.37			
		1/2"	47	—	5.63	99.78			
		5/8"	48	—	6.32	115.71			
		3/4"	49	—	5.39	133.98			
BB	{	1/4"	50	.0061	—	62.99			
		5/8"	51	.0101	—	111.06			
		3/4"	52	.0163	—	128.40			
CC	{	1/4"	53	—	3.14	50.47			
		3/8"	54	.0674	—	60.02			
		1/2"	55	—	4.92	80.65			
		5/8"	56	—	8.01	91.76			

TABLE V

Product			Matrix Column Product 26	Ideal Production (Percent of Total)	Modified Production	Matrix Column Product 51	Modified Production
Interior							
CD	3/8"	33	0	.1049	.1049	0	.1039
Exterior							
BB	1/4"	50	0	.0110	.0110	0	.0110
Interior							
CD	5/16"	32	0	.1099	.1099	0	.1099
Exterior							
AA	3/8"	38	0	.0527	.0527	−1.000	.0627
	1/4"	37	0	.1569	.1569	0	.1569
Interior							
CD	1/2"	34	0	.0727	.0727	0	.0727
AD	1/2"	29	0	.0810	.0810	0	.0810
Exterior							
AC	3/8"	46	0	.0100	.0100	1.000	0
CC	3/8"	54	0	.0631	.0631	0	.0631
D 1/10*		4	0				
Interior							
AD	5/8"	30	0	.0739	.0739	0	.0739
Exterior							
AA	3/4"	40	−.5000	.0049	.0249	1.000	.0149
AB	1/2"	43	0	.0107	.0107	0	.0107
BB	3/4"	52	.5000	.0777	.0577	0	.0577
Interior							
CD	3/4"	36	0	.0628	.0628	0	.0628
AA	3/4"	21	1.000	.1078	.0678	0	.0678
AB	3/4"	26	—		.0400		.0400
Exterior							
BB	5/8"	51					.0100
Shadow price			$6.47			$17.59	
Total return				$22.47	$22.41		$22.37

* Unused raw material.

produce 1 percent of exterior BB ⅝ inch we end up with the production listed in the last column of Table V. The return is reduced by (0.01) × (.2504) × 17.59 = 0.04.

The process can be carried on to include as many essential products as necessary. This substitution process is extremely useful for determining the return for various combinations of production. The changes made in production quantities are those which would introduce the products at minimum loss in return. The alternative to this method is the re-evaluation with added market condition equations. The program can be set up so that the effect of price changes can be treated starting from an existing solution. The latter requires much less computer time for the new calculations. One can define condition equations for the size of price change necessary to require a new solution. The method is extremely flexible to almost all possible changes.

The example shown here illustrates that improved production performance is possible. The tables also show the data for an "Average Company," the data for which has been generated from a cost study of some dozen companies for 1957. The results for the average company show savings of the same order of magnitude as the example company. We have carried out other calculations with the same sort of results. In our calculations, we were restricted somewhat by the available data and more by the restrictions in the computer program. Because of the latter limitation we only considered 41 final products. A more extensive program for the IBM 650 is available that will allow about 55 products and 20 raw material and market restriction equations. For larger-scale problems, the IBM 700 series, the UNIVAC, DATATRON, and other computers are available. If such machines are used there would be no need to omit such factors as sales potential, interchangeability of raw materials, alternate methods of making the same final products, and so forth.

Hardwood Plywood Production: No thorough analysis of hardwood plywood production has been made thus far. The differences between hardwood and softwood production are those of complexity and variety rather than differences in principle. In hardwood, one deals with a number of varieties of wood in a range of grades rather than a single variety. Logs are also purchased in a greater multiplicity of log grades. The complexity introduced by the numerous varieties and grades, and the fact that the products and veneers have much higher values, makes the selectivity, that is, the decision on product mix, a more critical problem.

The basis of any analysis of production mix, by purchases, veneer peelings, and so forth, is a good cost system. Without knowledge of the costs of various alternatives one can make only rough guesses as to the relative value of a given production, peeling or purchasing policy. Such cost systems are not firmly established in the hardwood industry and examples are therefore hard to come by. We shall, however, discuss the application of linear programming methods to a number of possible problems in the manufacture of hardwood panels.

First, let us consider the softwood producer who also manufactures hardwood panels with softwood centers. The hardwood panels "compete" for softwood centers and cores and thus interact with all the softwood products. If a Cx core is used for $\frac{5}{8}$ inch AC Exterior panel it is not available for a $\frac{3}{4}$ inch Birch panel; a B grade center used for a hardwood panel restricts the production AB and BB products that require the same thickness sheet of veneer.

Assuming that the variable costs of hardwood panels are known, we can treat the hardwood panels in the same way as other products. We shall consider two cases.

1. Hardwood veneer purchased outside and no limit on available supply (that is, a free market with adequate sources of veneers).

In this case the problem can be set up in the same way as problem 1. The various hardwood products are introduced only through the softwood components of the layups. The return on a hardwood product is defined as

$R_i =$ (Selling price) — (discounts) — (variable costs of manufacture) — (cost of the hardwood veneers).

2. Hardwood veneers manufactured by the company or purchased in a restricted market (that is, the quantity of hardwood veneer in each grade is limited).

This case differs from the example above in that the hardwood panels "compete" for both softwood and hardwood components. If the hardwood veneers are purchased, then the return R_i is as defined above. If hardwood veneers are manufactured, then we use the earlier definition of R_i given in Problem 1. In both cases one must introduce the hardwood components of the layups in establishing the matrix. We will then have equations of the form of Eq. 1 for the hardwood veneer supply as well as for the softwood veneer supply. The hardwood products may also be included in or subject to market restrictions of the same form as have already been presented.

Thus, the introduction of hardwood veneers and panels does not alter the problem in any serious manner, when one is concerned with the production of combined hardwood and softwood panels. One would expect this to be true, since the production method is similar and the interactions are not different in principle. In fact, the principles are even much the same for plants which produce entirely hardwood panels, as we shall show.

Let us now consider a company that produces only hardwood panels from a number of different species (oak, birch, maple, white pine, lauan, and so forth). Centers and cores are obtained from the hardwood (or perhaps by purchases of softwood panels or veneers). As in the softwood case, there are a number of different raw materials (veneers by species, grade and thickness) obtained by peeling logs. These are to be used to produce plywood panels of various thicknesses and quality in such a way as to maximize profits, subject to the limitations of marketability of products, plant capacity and other plant restrictions. One can set up a layup and restriction "matrix" just as in the case of softwood production. Because of the larger variety of raw materials (veneers) and finished products one will have a "larger" problem for a single plant. Within limits the size of the problem is no obstacle; problems involving a number of integrated plants in one system are already being studied. Given a good cost system, this problem can be treated quite readily and perhaps yield even greater increases in return than in softwood production because of the higher costs of peeling and grading in the hardwood industry.

PROBLEM 2—LOG PURCHASES

In the previous example, we were concerned with obtaining the best mix of final products from a group of sheets of veneer. This is equivalent to obtaining the best product mix from a set of logs. The connection lies in the relationship between grades produced from a log of given quality. A study made by the U.S. Forest Service[1] indicates that such relations exist. For Southwest Oregon the report gives the results below.[2]

Log Grade	% A Veneer	% B Veneer	% C Veneer	% D Veneer
#1 peeler	37	11	32	20
#2 peeler	28	9	33	30
#3 peeler	17	8	34	41
Special peeler	8	7	44	41

Given these values and a panel recovery ratio (panels $\frac{3}{8}$ inch equivalent per board foot of lumber) we can evaluate the number of sheets of veneer of each grade from the logs purchased. The DFPA Manual lists an average industry recovery ratio of 2.2. Converting this to $\frac{1}{8}$ inch equivalent veneer we have a veneer recovery ratio of 6.6. We can use the figure above in an example to show how the logs purchased tell us what veneer is available and the average cost per 1,000 board feet.

Suppose we purchase 1,000, 1,000, and 2,000 M board feet of #1 peeler, #3 peeler, and special peeler, respectively. The number of M $\frac{1}{8}$ inches sheets obtained in A grade is

$$(1,000 \times 0.37 + 1,000 \times 0.17 \div 2,000 \times 0.08)\ 6.6 =$$
$$(370 + 170 + 160)\ 6.6 = 4,620 \text{ M sheets of } \tfrac{1}{8} \text{ inch A.}$$

Similarly, we have

$$6.6\ (1,000 \times 0.11 + 1,000 \times 0.08 + 2,000 \times 0.07) =$$
$$2,178 \text{ M sheets } \tfrac{1}{8} \text{ inch B,}$$
$$6.6\ (1,000 \times 0.32 + 1,000 \times 0.34 + 2,000 \times 0.44) =$$
$$10,614 \text{ M sheets } \tfrac{1}{8} \text{ inch C,}$$
$$6.6\ (1,000 \times 0.20 + 1,000 \times 0.41 + 2,000 \times 0.41) =$$
$$9,438 \text{ M sheets } \tfrac{1}{8} \text{ inch D.}$$

---

[1] U. S. Forest Services, Report R–6, "West Side Plywood-Lumber Appraisal Base," Table 8 (October 22, 1957).

[2] The results are the average for large and small logs rounded off to the nearest percent.

If, for the log cost, the listed values for the Example Plywood Co. in the DFPA Manual, are used:

#1 peeler	$90/M bd. feet
#2 peeler	$80/M bd. feet
#3 peeler	$70/M bd. feet
Special peeler	$53.72/M bd. feet

we obtain for the average log cost/M board feet

$$\text{Average cost} = \frac{1,000 \times 90 + 1,000 \times 70 + 2,000 \times 53.72}{4,000}$$
$$= \$66.86/M \text{ bd. feet.}$$

Recognizing the fact that the purchased logs define the distribution of veneer by grades (assuming, at this stage, no substitution of one grade for another), we can define the second problem:

"Given a distribution of final products (and hence the required number of veneer sheets in each grade), what is the best combination of logs to purchase; that is, how many #1 peelers, #2 peelers, #3 peelers, and special peelers should be purchased?"

Therefore, this problem is just the reverse of the first problem that was treated by linear programming techniques.

Assume that we want to satisfy the demands for $1/10$ inch veneer listed in Table VI. For $1/10$ inch veneer the veneer return ratio is 8.25 (6.6/0.8; see DFPA Manual). The log prices are those given previously and we want to minimize the cost of logs to meet our demands. Let P_1 be the quantity of #1 peeler, P_2 the quantity of #2 peeler, P_3 the quantity of #3 peeler, and P_4 the quantity of special peeler. We need 10,591 M sheets of $1/10$ inch A. Then:

$$8.25 \ (0.37P_1 + 0.28P_2 + 17P_3 + 0.08P_41) \geqq 10,591$$
$$\text{(A) or } 3.069P_1 + 2.32P_2 + 1.40P_3 + 66P_4 \geqq 10,591$$

Similarly, for the other grades we obtain

$$\text{(B)} \quad 0.91P_1 + 0.74P_2 + 0.66P_3 + 0.58P_4 \geqq 627$$
$$\text{(C)} \quad 2.64P_1 + 2.72P_2 + 2.81P_3 + 3.63P_4 \geqq 11,905$$
$$\text{(D)} \quad 1.65P_1 + 2.48P_2 + 3.38P_3 + 3.38P_4 \geqq 25,531$$

(Note: In the absence of more complete data we have lumped the requirements for C and Cx and D and Dx.) We want to minimize the total cost of logs: that is, find the values of P_1, P_2, P_3, and P_4 which satisfy

equations (A), (B), (C), and (D) and minimize the cost K given by
(E) $K = 90P_1 + 80P_2 + 70P_3 + 53.72P_4$.

This, too, is a problem in linear programming that is solved more simply by using the so-called "dual."[3]

TABLE VI.   AVERAGE PLYWOOD COMPANY

1/10″ Veneer in Products Using
Only 1/10″ Veneer (in 1,000 S.M.)

Grade	
A	10,591
B	627
C	7,938
D	12,318
Cx	3,967
Dx	13,213

Because of the small amount of B required, any solution of the problem as stated must result in an excess quantity of B. Since A can be (and often is) downgraded to B grade, and in most cases there is an excess of C grade, we will solve a simpler problem; that is, consider only two grades, $A^1 = $ surface grade, either A or B, and $C^1 = $ back grade, either C or D. In this case our equations become

$$(A^1)\quad 3.97P_1 + 3.06P_2 + 2.06P_3 + 1.24P_4 \geqq 11,218$$
$$(C^1)\quad 4.29P_1 + 5.20P_2 + 6.19P_3 + 7.01P_4 \geqq 37,436$$
$$(E^1)\quad K = 90P_1 + 80P_2 + 70P_3 + 53.72P_4.$$

Our solutions are

$P_1 = 1,435$ M bd. feet
$P_2 = 0$
$P_3 = 0$
$P_4 = 4,535$ M bd. feet

The total cost is

$$K = \$368,500$$

and the average lumber cost is

$$\text{Average cost} = \frac{368,500}{5,970} = \$61.80/\text{M bd. feet}$$

If more A^1 grade is used, the average cost will increase; the average cost increases with increasing ratio of $A^1/(A^1 + C^1)$ and decreases with in-

---

[3] For technical reasons we cannot follow the same techniques as in the previous example. We make use of the fact that every minimizing problem has a "dual" which is a maximizing problem. The solutions are related in a simple manner and the total cost is identical for the problem and its dual. See, for example, Gass, S., *Linear Programming*, McGraw-Hill, New York (1958).

creasing ratio of $C^1/(A^1 + C^1)$. We can illustrate this with another example drawn from the data for the Example Plywood Company (DFPA Manual).

The total requirements of $\frac{1}{10}$ inch veneer are listed in Table VII (these include $\frac{1}{10}$ inch with $\frac{1}{8}$ inch and $\frac{3}{16}$ inch veneer). In this case, the equations are

$$(A^1, \tfrac{1}{10})\ 3.97P_1 + 3.06P_2 + 2.06P_3 + 1.24P_4 \geqq 11{,}218,$$
$$(C^1, \tfrac{1}{10})\ 4.29P_1 + 5.20P_2 + 6.19P_3 + 7.01P_4 \geqq 49{,}437,$$
$$(E^1, \tfrac{1}{10})\ \text{remains unchanged. The solution is}$$

$$P_1 = 750 \text{ M bd. feet} \qquad P_3 = 0$$
$$P_2 = 0 \qquad\qquad\qquad P_4 = 6{,}570 \text{ M bd. feet}$$

The total cost is

$$K = \$432{,}000,$$

and the average cost is

$$\text{Average cost} = \frac{432{,}000}{7{,}320} \text{ or } \$59.00, \text{ about } \$2.80 \text{ less per M bd. feet.}$$

We have examined the solutions for the other thicknesses. Since there is no $\frac{3}{16}$ inch surface grade (A or B), one can use only special peelers. There will be considerable downgrading, that is 15 percent of the output is surface grade that will be used as C grade, and some of the C grade will be used as D grade, but the average price is not affected. For $\frac{3}{16}$ inch the average cost is therefore $\$53.72/$M bd. feet.

The $\frac{1}{8}$ inch veneer differs from the $\frac{1}{10}$ inch in that a large percentage of surface grade is required—about 40 percent. This must increase the cost of logs and hence the cost of veneer. For $\frac{1}{8}$ inch veneer, the veneer recovery ratio is 6.6 and, using the data from Table VII, we get

$$(A^1\ \tfrac{1}{8})\ 3.17P_1 + 2.44P_2 + 1.65P_3 + 0.99P_4 \geqq 35{,}450$$
$$(C^1\ \tfrac{1}{8})\ 3.43P_1 + 4.16P_2 + 4.96P_3 + 5.62P_4 \geqq 53{,}450$$

Equation E^1 remains unchanged. The solutions are

$$P_1 = 10{,}250 \text{ M bd. feet} \qquad P_3 = 0$$
$$P_2 = 0 \qquad\qquad\qquad\quad P_4 = 3{,}200 \text{ M bd. feet}$$

The total cost is

$$K = \$1{,}119{,}000$$

The average cost is

$$\text{Average cost} = \frac{1{,}119{,}000}{13{,}450} = \$83.00/\text{M bd. feet}$$

Thus the lumber costs of $\frac{1}{8}$ inch veneer are almost 50 percent more than those of $\frac{1}{10}$ inch veneer. This is not suprising, since in $\frac{1}{8}$ inch 40 percent of the veneer is surface grade, while only 17 percent of the $\frac{1}{10}$ inch veneer is surface grade. It does suggest, however, that wherever possible alternate layups be used (assuming, of course that the veneer used for the products by the Average Plywood Company represents exactly what is desired for a customer and/or profit point of view) such that $\frac{1}{10}$ inch surface grade sheets replace $\frac{1}{8}$ inch sheets and the thicker sheets be of the lower grades.

For the total veneer supply we have the following results:[4]

	1/10 inch	1/8 inch	3/16 inch
Total veneer required	60,104	88,883	41,109
Logs used (M bd. feet) ..	7,285	13,467	9,343
Average cost of logs (per M bd. feet)	$59.00	$83.00	$53.72

$$\text{Average lumber cost} = \frac{7,285\ (59.00) + 13,467\ (83.00) + 9,343\ (53.72)}{7,285 + 13,467 + 9,434}$$

$$= \frac{2,049,481.96}{30,095}$$

Average log cost = $68.10/bd. feet.

The application of linear programming to the log purchase problem is more limited than in Problem 1 above because:

(1) There is a relatively small "free" market in logs; purchases are mainly by contract for a tract;

(2) There has been far too little analysis for grade recovery from logs of various grades; more precise data, including the variations in grade recovery by thickness of peeling, are required.

Should the second restriction be overcome, the linear programming technique can provide a measure of the recovery value of a timber tract, given good survey values.

CONCLUSIONS

The value of linear programming to plywood enterprises extends beyond providing the solutions to specific problems. As by-products of the solution, the technique generates information on such decision-factors as:

(1) The cost or loss in return due to a capacity or market restriction and hence the value of new equipment or extended sales promotion (of

---

[4] The solutions are given in rounded-off numbers obtained from sliderule calculations. The values listed here are from Table IV.

TABLE VII. AVERAGE PLYWOOD COMPANY

Total Veneer Production By Size and Grade

Grade	Veneer in 1,000 S.M.	1,000 Bd. Feet	Veneer in 1,000 S.M.	1,000 Bd. Feet	Veneer in 1,000 S.M.	1,000 Bd. Feet
	Factor 8.25		Factor 6.6		Factor 4.4	
A	10,591	1,283.76	20,706	3,137.27	–0–	
B	627	76.00	14,761	2,236.51	–0–	
C	9,347	1,132.97	15,252	2,310.90	7,278	1,654.09
D	15,000	1,818.18	17,535	2,656.81	7,667	1,742.50
Cx	6,784	822.30	8,815	1,335.61	10,873	2,471.13
Dx	18,303	2,218.54	11,814	1,790.00	15,290	3,475.00
TOTAL	60,652	7,351.75	88,883	13,467.10	41,108	9,342.72

specific products) which would cancel the restrictions.

(2) The cost of producing certain "unprofitable" products to satisfy demands or enter a market. These costs may be too high to merit retention of the customer or the market.

(3) The additional return that might be obtained by changing the peeling distribution or by changing the log distribution.

(4) The profitability or loss (in terms of production costs) of adding new products to the line or changing the layup for an existing product.

(5) The cost of minor adjustments to the ideal product mix and the range in which changes can be made without changing the total return.

(6) The effects of price changes or production costs on the product mix and on total realization.

All of these factors are of great importance to production and sales management. The existence of this information (which is not at present available in most companies) enables better operating and marketing decisions to be made. It is, in fact, possible that the availability of such information will prove of even greater value to the plywood manufacturer than actual solutions that linear programming can provide.

Chapter 3

MATERIALS PLANNING WITH LINEAR PROGRAMMING

III.

A Linear Programming Application to Cupola Charging*

R. W. Metzger and R. Schwarzbek†

Least cost cupola charging can be accomplished with a relatively new analysis tool called linear programming. The purposes of this presentation are to:

1. Present some general information about linear programming.

2. Describe the cupola charge problem and the required linear programming formulation.

3. Describe how linear programming has been successfully used in a production foundry making cast and malleable iron.

No attempt will be made to describe any of the methods of linear programming. While the problems discussed are concerned with making cast or malleable iron, the general approach is equally valid for any blending type problem, i.e., any problem where a variety of items are mixed, blended, or melted to form an end product.

* From *The Journal of Industrial Engineering,* Vol. 12, No. 2 (1961), 87–93. Reprinted by permission.

† Based upon a presentation to the Saginaw Valley Chapter of AIIE, April 19, 1960.

INTRODUCTION

Linear programming can best be defined as a group of mathematical techniques that can obtain the very best solution to problems which have many possible solutions. While a great many industrial problems fit this category of having many possible solutions, linear programming is not a magic panacea which will solve all problems. However, it can be used to solve a variety of industrial problems. For example, consider a four plant manufacturing system which manfactures an item and then ships it prepaid to a number of customers.

Historically, these four plants operated independently of one another. Linear programming was applied to the distribution of the product from these plants to the customers on the basis of the total four plant system, and resulted in a new distribution pattern.

This solution or pattern of shipping from the plants to the customers presents the lowest cost shipping program. If management deviates from this plan, the total costs would increase. For example, if management decided not to ship from the plant in Washington to the customer in Maine, but rather to ship to him from the plant in Pennsylvania, it would mean:

One or more changes in the shipments from the factory in Pennsylvania.
Several changes in the shipments from the factory in Indiana.
Several changes in the shipments from the factory in Kansas.
One or more changes in the shipments from the factory in Washington.

The net effect of all of the required shipping changes would result in increased total shipping costs.

This solution also illustrates the situation where the very best solution is not necessarily the one that would be obtained by "cut-and-try" or intuitive methods. This is sometimes the case when solving a problem with linear programming.

The methods of linear programming present a step-by-step approach which, when followed, will arrive at the best solution. Not only is the best solution obtained, but information is provided which permits a rather quick analysis of the less-than-best or alternative answers. In the preceding problem, if management said that they did not wish to distribute from Washington to the customer in Maine, the linear programming solution immediately shows how much the total costs will increase and indicates all the prescribed changes that must be made to obtain the less-than-best solution.

In problems like this, standard analytical procedures fail because all facets of the problem are so highly interrelated. In these kinds of problems, it soon exceeds human capabilities to be able to consider all facets of the problem at the same time. Linear programming, however, is a tool of analysis which can and does consider every facet of the problem simultaneously.

THE CUPOLA CHARGE PROBLEM

The problem of charging or loading materials into a cupola is one which has many possible solutions. One of the basic problems in charging materials into a cupola, in making either ferrous or nonferrous alloys, is in determining how much of the available materials to charge in order to obtain the proper chemical and metallurgical properties at the lowest possible cost. Linear programming can be used to obtain the lowest cost charge which meets all the specifications of the melt.

In order to illustrate the problem and to show the results that were obtained with linear programming, two typical cupola charging problems will be discussed. One is typical of cupola charging in a high volume production foundry while the other is more typical of a smaller or custom foundry operation.

The linear programming analysis requires much the same information as presently used in cupola charging, namely:

1. A list of charge materials, their chemical analysis and cost per ton.
2. Chemical specifications of the charge (percent range for each element).
3. Any additional restrictions on the usage of the various charge materials.

The last item of information will include limitations on the use of certain materials either because of limited supplies or because of metallurgy requirements.

Before we consider a specific problem it may be advisable to examine the general linear programming approach to the cupola charging problem.

In order to use linear programming one must first describe his problem mathematically, in a set of equations or formulas.

To illustrate this, assume we have several materials that can be put into a cupola and melted to make grey or malleable iron. We will call them materials Number 1, Number 2, etc. Since we wish to determine how much of the materials to charge, we can let:

x_1 = percent of charged material Number 1 actually used.

x_2 = percent of charged material Number 2 actually used.

$\bullet$

$\bullet$

$\bullet$

x_n = percent of charge material Number n actually used.

Then, what we want to do is calculate values for $x_1, x_2 \ldots x_n$ which will meet all the specifications of the charge at a minimum cost. Each specification takes the form of an equation or inequality. For example, suppose we consider the specifications for carbon obtained from the materials included in the charge. We can say:

$$ax_1 + bx_2 + cx_3 + \ldots nx_n \leqq \text{maximum carbon (percent)}$$

where a, b, c, etc., are the the percentages of carbon in each material 1, 2, 3, etc. This relationship says that the grand total of carbon which is contained in the various materials included in the charge cannot exceed the maximum carbon specification. A similar relationship must be expressed for the minimum carbon content namely:

$$ax_1 + bx_2 + cx_3 + \ldots nx_n \geqq \text{minimum carbon (percent)}$$

These two relationships together make certain that the carbon specification will be satisfied.

In a similar manner, we can express the limitations for all the other elements like silicon, manganese, chrome, etc. In this manner, we can consider any number of chemical elements.

In developing a cupola charge, certain of the charge materials may be in limited supply and it may be undesirable to use more than a limited amount of other materials for various metallurgical reasons. These restrictions must also be included in the mathematical statement of the problem. For example, suppose that material Number 5 (x_5) is in limited supply and we only have enough to permit charging 30 percent. Therefore, we want to limit x_5 to a maximum value of .3 which can be expressed:

$$x_5 \leqq .3.$$

In this way, we will permit no more than 30 percent of material Number 5 in the charge, if indeed it is profitable to use any of it at all. Similar restrictions can be placed on other materials in limited supply as well as those materials we wish to limit in the charge for metallurgical purposes.

A final equation is required in order to make certain that the solution gives percent of the various charge materials. The relationship:

$$x_1 + x_2 + x_3 + x_4 + \ldots x_n = 1$$

Finally the formulation requires an objective. In this case our objective is minimum cost. Hence we include:

$$px_1 + qx_2 + rx_3 + \ldots = \text{minimum}$$

where:

$p =$ the total cost per ton for material Number 1.
$q =$ the total cost per ton for material Number 2.

•
•
•

Now the formulation or mathematical statement of the problem includes:

1. The system of relationships describing the problem.
2. The desired objective.

In this way, then, the mathematical statement of the problem describes or defines the problem and its limits. What linear programming does is to seek the best solution in terms of the objective within the limits described by the system of relationships.

A PROBLEM

In order to better illustrate this formulation consider the following problem.

A metallurgist has this problem:

Size of total charge	5000 lbs.
Amount of sprue and iron briquettes charged	3000 lbs.
Amount of "other material" to be charged	2000 lbs.

This 2000 lbs. of "other material" must contain:

At Least		No More Than	
60 lbs. carbon	3.0 %	70 lbs. carbon	3.5 %
54 lbs. silicon	2.7 %	60 lbs. silicon	3.0 %
27 lbs. manganese	1.35%	33 lbs. manganese	1.65%
6 lbs. chrome	.30%	9 lbs. chrome	.45%

The materials to be considered are:

	Cost/ Ton	Carbon Percent	Silicon Percent	Manga- nese Percent	Chrome Percent
x_1 Pig Iron	$ 60	4.00	2.25	.90	0
x_2 Silvery Pig	129	0	15.00	4.50	10.00
x_3 Ferro-Silicon Number 1	130	0	45.00	0	0
x_4 Ferro-Silicon Number 2	122	0	42.00	0	0
x_5 Alloy Number 1	200	0	18.00	60.00	0
x_6 Alloy Number 2	260	0	30.00	9.00	20.00
x_7 Alloy Number 3	238	0	25.00	33.00	8.00
x_8 Silicon-Carbide	160	15.00	30.00	0	0
x_9 Steel Number 1	42	.40	0	.90	0
x_{10} Steel Number 2	40	.10	0	.30	0
x_{11} Steel Number 3	39	.10	0	.30	0

Maximum usages (either due to limited supply or due to metallurgy requirements):

Silicon carbide, 20 pounds per charge
Steel Number 1, 200 pounds per charge
Steel Number 2, 200 pounds per charge
Steel Number 3, 200 pounds per charge

The problem is then to determine how much of which materials (x_1 through x_{11}) should make up the 2000 pounds at a minimum cost.

The problem must be stated mathematically. For instance, the carbon content of the input must be in a certain range. Each possible material contains a certain amount of carbon. Therefore, one mathematical relationship would be:

The sum of carbon in each material times the quantity of that material, must be above the minimum requirement of carbon in the final blend.

Thus, in this problem the first relationship becomes:

$$4x_1 + 15x_8 + .4x_9 + .1x_{10} + .1x_{11} \geqq 3$$
(all numbers in percent)

where:

    x_1 = percent (decimal) of pig iron included in the charge.
    x_2 = percent (decimal) of silvery pig included in the charge.
    •
    •
    •
    x_{11} = percent (decimal) of Steel Number 3 included in the charge.

In order to assure that the carbon does not exceed the maximum specification we include:

$$4x_1 + 15x_8 + .4x_9 + .1x_{10} + .1x_{11} \leqq 3.4$$

Similar inequalities (relationships which have other than an equal sign) are established for all the chemical restrictions, i.e., silicon, manganese, and chrome.

The restrictions as to the use of these materials can be stated:

$$x_9 \leqq .1$$

which means that x_9 (percent of Number 1 steel to be included in the charge) cannot exceed 10 percent.

The entire problem is then stated mathematically as given below.

    Minimize:

$60x_1 + 129x_2 + 130x_3 + 122x_4 + 200x_5 + 260x_6 + 238x_7 + 160x_8 + 42x_9 + 40x_{10} + 39x_{11}$

    Subject to:

(Carbon)
$$4x_1 + 15x_8 + .4x_9 + .1x_{10} + .1x_{11} \geq 3.00$$
$$4x_1 + 15x_8 + .4x_9 + .1x_{10} + .1x_{11} \leq 3.5$$
(Silicon)
$$2.25x_1 + 15x_2 + 45x_3 + 42x_4 + 18x_5 + 30x_6 + 25x_7 + 30x_8 \geq 2.70$$
$$2.25x_1 + 15x_2 + 45x_3 + 42x_4 + 18x_5 + 30x_6 + 25x_7 + 30x_8 \geq 3.0$$
(Manganese)
$$.9x_1 + 4.5x_2 + 60x_5 + 9x_6 + 33x_7 + .9x_9 + .3x_{10} + .3x_{11} \geq 1.35$$
$$.9x_1 + 4.5x_2 + 60x_5 + 9x_6 + 33x_7 + .9x_9 + .3x_{10} + .3x_{11} \geq 1.65$$
(Chrome)
$$10x_2 + 20x_6 + 8x_7 \leq 3.0$$
$$10x_2 + 20x_6 + 8x_7 \leq .45$$
(Total Melt)
$$x_1 + x_2 + x_3 + x_4 + x_5 + x_6 + x_7 + x_8 + x_9 + x_{10} + x_{11} = 1.0$$

Maximum usages:
$$x_8 \leq .01$$
$$x_9 \leq .10$$
$$x_{10} \leq .10$$
$$x_{11} \leq .10$$

With this mathematical statement, the problem is ready for linear programming. The objective or cost equation indicates that we desire the answer with the lowest possible cost and one which is within the limitations described in the set of relationships. This formulation or mathematical statement of the problem can be solved with the simplex method of linear programming. While we will not consider the details of the simplex method here, let's take a look at the lowest cost solution which the simplex method provides.

The least cost solution is as follows.[1]

Variable	Value	Description	lbs./2000 lbs.
x_{11}	.10	10% Steel Number 3 in the charge	200.00
x_4	.011	1.1% FeSi Number 2 in the charge	22.0
x_5	.00711	.711% Alloy Number 1 in the charge	14.22
x_2	.03	3% Silvery Pig in the charge	60.0
x_1	.73713	73.713% Pig Iron in the charge	1474.26
x_{10}	.01472	1.472% Steel Number 2 in the charge	29.44
x_9	.10	10% Steel Number 1 in the charge	200.00
			1999.92 lbs.

Total Cost Per Ton $59.56.

This charge results in minimum amounts of the four elements carbon, silicon, manganese, and chrome. As mentioned earlier linear programming not only provides the best solution (lowest cost in the case) but it provides information about less than best or alternative solutions. The linear programming solution for this problem also gives the following information for those materials not in charge:

---

[1] It should be noted that the formulation of this problem can be reduced in size. The same solution can be obtained if we omit the upper limit relationships on carbon, silicon, manganese and chrome. In solving more than 30 similar cupola charging problems for both cast and malleable iron it was found that the optimum (lowest cost) solution always resulted in charges exactly at the lower limit specification. With this experience it seems reasonable to formulate a cupola charge problem without the upper limits and include these only if the solution demands them. This is a practical approach even when high speed computing equipment is readily available.

Material	Marginal Cost
(x_5) FeSi Number 1	$ 2.07
(x_6) Alloy Number 2	41.01
(x_7) Alloy Number 3	39.85
(x_8) SiC	6.71

These marginal costs indicate the amount of reduction in price per ton that must occur before these materials can be included in the charge, i.e., Alloy Number 2 will be profitable to use only if its price per ton is reduced by $41.01 per ton—from $260.00 to $218.99 per ton. These marginal costs give management an indication of the penalties incurred for deviating from the best solution. These can also be used very profitably by the purchasing agent in his dealings with suppliers.

Additional marginal costs are provided which can be used to study the effect of changing the chemical requirements of the charge. These marginal costs for this problem are:

Element	Marginal Cost
Carbon	3.67
Silicon	1.98
Manganese	2.09
Chrome	5.09

which can be interpreted:

Carbon—If we raise the minimum carbon content in the charge by 1 percent this will increase the charge cost by $3.67 per ton. An increase of .1 percent will increase the charge costs by $.37 per ton. Also a decrease of 1 percent in the minimum carbon content will decrease the charge cost by $3.67 per ton.

A similar interpretation can be developed for each of the other elements.

The analysis of the marginal cost provided by the linear programming solution are often of more value than the specific least cost charge in that they give management a quantitative measure of penalties and hence a measure of operating flexibility.

THE PROGRAM IN A PRODUCTION FOUNDRY

Aside from the mathematics involved in applying linear programming, many problems can be encountered in putting this into effect in a production foundry.

In the summer of 1958 a study was initiated in a production foundry to determine the feasibility of applying linear programming to the cupola charge problem. During the early stages of the study it became apparent that the linear programming calculations (for the simplex method) presented an enormous chore. Therefore, a high speed computer was used for these calculations. This is not to say that these calculations cannot be accomplished by hand. However a high speed computer can solve a problem like the one described previously in several minutes whereas it would require three to six hours to accomplish the same thing by hand.

In addition to the bulk of calculations other problems were encountered. Initially, the solutions which were obtained were not valid. Some of this was due to incorrect data, errors in the data, and omissions in the statement of the problem. In one case, a solution specified a relatively high usage of a certain scrap steel. This was not acceptable because the supply of this scrap steel was sufficient for only a few days of operation at the rate of usage indicated by the solution. Since a solution was desired which could be used throughout one production month, it was necessary to restrict the permissible amount of this scrap steel in the charge so that the available quantity would last for one month's operation.

In another case, a solution indicated sizable savings over the present charge. However this solution was not acceptable to the metallurgist because, while the low limit on one element was .65 percent, the metallurgist felt that the nature of the cupola operation required a charge with closer to .70 percent of this element. Since the linear programming solution usually develops a charge with exactly minimum amounts of the various elements, the data had to be revised so that in effect the minimum specification on this element was .70 percent. This type of thing may happen with the more expensive elements in a charge.

In still another case, the solution was invalid because the data ignored the fact that one charge material was not fully recovered in the melt. Neglecting losses in melting usually leads to an unusable solution.

Errors appeared in one solution because several charge materials were grouped together and handled collectively as if they were one material. This resulted in erroneous answers because the costs of each material as well as the chemical analysis was slightly different. It was just enough different that when the materials were handled individually, the linear programming solution used all of one and none of the other materials. Here it became apparent that in any solution, all possible materials should be considered individually as separate materials even though costs and analyses are nearly the same. These early solutions, even though invalid, were useful in demonstrating the sensitivity of the linear programming analysis and the need for a complete statement of the problem.

It is important to realize that anyone beginning an analysis of cupola charging via linear programming should not expect perfect results the first time. Indeed, it is only after several invalid solutions that one fully appreciates the ultimate value of the analysis.

In the early stages of the study, relatively few possible charge materials were considered. Many materials were omitted because at one time in the past they were evaluated and were not profitable to use at that time. However, as cupola charge specifications change, and with the fluctuations in material costs from time to time, it was found that several of these materials now could be profitably included in the charge. Hence, subsequent problems have considered all possible charge materials. Here, it is necessary for us to consider an important factor in understanding the application of linear programming. Intuitive or inspection method may often yield the best solution when relatively few charge materials are considered. These methods, however, become increasingly less effective as the number of materials to be considered increases. The larger the number of materials, the more difficult it becomes to analyze the complex interaction of material analyses and costs by cut-and-try methods. Linear programming can determine the lowest cost charge regardless of the number of charge materials to be considered.

Some of the results of the early parts of the study were useful in indicating the effects of a change in chemical specifications on charge cost. It was found that for certain elements a very slight change (in hundredths of percent) would show a marked increase or decrease in the cost and make-up of the least cost charge.

The initial study finally indicated that linear programming was feasible and savings from $.15 to $.45 per ton might be realized. Therefore, in the spring of 1959, it was decided to use linear programming for cupola charging. It was decided to solve the problem twice per month in order to:

Determine the lowest cost charge considering all the materials available for purchase;

Determine the lowest cost charge in terms of the materials on hand.

The first solution was developed from data prepared by the purchasing agent and the metallurgist. The purchasing agent indicated what materials were available, their delivered cost per ton, and available quantity. The metallurgist specified the desired minimum chemical content of the charge, the approximate chemical analyses of the charge materials, and any limitations on the use of certain charge materials. This solution was then used as a guide by the purchasing agent in buying materials.

Later in the month the second solution was obtained. Here the actual costs, quantities, and chemical analyses of the materials on hand were used to determine the least cost charge. This was used as a guide by the metallurgist in charging the cupola.

In putting the linear programming on a production basis a form was developed to facilitate data collection. Figure 1 illustrates the form that is used for the linear programming analysis. Space is provided for the data prepared by the purchasing agent, metallurgist, and the mathematician.

Material:		13M Sprue	Cam Sprue	M. I. Sprue	Soft Sprue	Ferro Carbo	Carbo Sil	C.I. Briq.	Purch. C.I. Briq.	Steel Briq.	M. I. Briq.	Mall. Pig	Ferro Mn	Ferro Silicon	Fe Cr	FeCr Si	Silvery Pig	Si Mn	Silico Mn	Speg.	Briq.	Fe Mn	Scrap	Flash.	Flash.	Plate	Plate	Plate	Bun-dles	Bun-dles	Bun-dles
Cost (Include Freight)																															
Code No.		X1	X2	~~X3~~	~~X4~~	X5	~~X6~~	X7	X8	~~X9~~	~~X10~~	X11	X12	X13	X14	X15	X16	X17	X18	X19	X20	X21	X22	X23	X24	X25	X26	X27	X28	X29	X30
Total Cost per Net Ton Delivered		0	0	0	0	171.80		35.00	39.00			62.50	1.98	134.00	422.00	429.00	126.40	187.20	205.00	104.00	205.00	429.00	80.00	45.00	42.00	43.00	40.00	37.00	42.00	39.00	36.00
Carbon: 3.00	≤	3.35	3.40	2.60	2.35	19.10		3.10	3.10	.10	2.35	4.00	7.00	0	4.25	.04	.75	1.50	1.50	4.25	0	7.0	1.85	.59	.59	0	0	0	−.09	−.09	−.09
Silicon: 2.50	≤	2.23	2.35	1.40	1.40	44.6		2.25	2.25	0	1.40	2.10	.80	45.0	3.25	40.0	15.25	13.75	19.00	2.00	31.50	2.75	10.30	1.02	1.02	−.32	−.32	−.32	−.70	−.70	−.70
Manganese: .820	≤	.68	.83	.43	.43	0		.70	.70	.30	.43	.88	75.00	0	0	0	4.65	66.50	66.50	20.00	9.20	87.50	1.92	1.09	1.09	.33	.333	.33	.18	.18	.18
Chrome: .300	≤	.31	.90	0	0	0		.24	0	0	0	0	0	0	62.0	40.0	9.20	0	0	0	19.20	0	0	.02	.02	0	0	0	−.02	−.02	−.02

				TONS AVAILABLE: (Show tons—available only on materials of limited availability)
.320	=	X_1	13M Sprue	
.020	=	X_2	Cam Sprue	
	=		Malleable Sprue	
	=		Soft Sprue	
.0075	≥	X_5	Ferro Carbo	
	≥		Carbo Sil	
	≥		Steel Briquettes	
	≥		M. I. Briquettes	
.200	≥	X_7	C.I. Briquettes	
.060	≥	X_8	Purch. C.I.B.	1860
.020	≥	X_{24}	Flashings	620
	≥		Plate	
.030	≥	X_{26}	Plate	930
.020	≥	X_{27}	Plate	620
	≥		Bundles	
.030	≥	X_{29}	Bundles	930
.020	≥	X_{30}	Bundles	620
1.00	=	ΣX_i		

DEFIANCE PLANT, CENTRAL FOUNDRY DIVISION, GENERAL MOTORS CORPORATION

COST MINIMIZATION OF METALS BY LINEAR PROGRAMMING

Date: X X X FOUNDRY: X X X X Tons Pour for Charge Period: 31,000

SOLUTION

MATERIAL	PERCENT	Dj	MATERIAL	PERCENT	Dj	MATERIAL	PERCENT	Dj
X1 13M Sprue	.320		X11 Malleable Pig	.209		X21 Fe Mn		207.86
X2 Cam Sprue	.020		X12 Ferro Manganese	—		X22 Scrap		16.25
~~X3 M.I. Sprue~~			X13 Ferro Silicon		38.05	X23 Flashings	.1158	
~~X4 Soft Sprue~~			X14 Fe Cr	—		X24 Flash	.020	
X5 Ferro Carbo	.0075		X15 Fe Cr Si		10.80	X25 Plate		3.94
~~X6 Carbo Sil~~			X16 Silvery Pig		3.46	X26 Plate		.94
X7 Cast Iron Briquettes	.200		X17 Si Mn		13.61	X27 Plate	.020	
X8 Purchased Cast Iron Briquettes	.060		X18 Silico Manganese		24.75	X28 Bundles		4.22
~~X9 Steel Briquettes~~			X19 Spegeleisen		8.80	X29 Bundles		1.22
~~X10 M.I. Briquettes~~			X20 C. M. Briquettes	.0084		X30 Bundles	.020	

TOTAL COST (EXCLUDING SPRUE) $32.685/TON

TOTAL COST (ASSUMING SPRUE COSTS $32.685/TON) $49.50/TON

FIGURE 1. THE DATA AND LEAST COST SOLUTION

The analysis of certain materials remains relatively constant, so its analysis is printed on the form. Each column in the upper half of the form represents a charge material or space for one. The rows represent (from top to bottom):

    1. The identification or name of the material.
    2. Cost (including freight)—this may be cost per ton or cost per car load.
    3. Code number—this identifies the material for the mathematician.
    4. Total cost per net ton delivered—this is the numerical quantity used in the linear programming analysis.
    5–8. Four rows for the chemical content for carbon, silicon, manganese, and chrome in the various materials and the charge.

You will note that plate (X25, X26, X27) and bundles (X28, X29, X30) seem to have negative amounts of the various elements. During the course of the study it was found that the use of plate and bundles in a charge tends to reduce the recovery of certain of the elements in the final melt. The negative numbers reflect the influence of these materials on the recovery of the chemical elements. These corrections or modifications were made after several months of operating experience with linear programming. It is interesting to note, here, that these corrections came to light primarily due to the fact that the charges developed by linear programming always result in exactly the minimum chemical content. Without these correction factors some charges resulted in melt which was below the minimum specification on certain elements.

This form is started by the purchasing agent who fills in data concerning the cost and availability of materials for charging the cupola. The form is then sent to the metallurgist, who indicates the minimum chemical specifications, chemical analyses of the available charge materials, any limitations on the use of charge materials, and the total tonnage projected for the period.

The form is then sent to the mathematician who checks the data to see that they are complete and converts the availability of the materials in limited supply from tons to percent. The data are then ready for linear programming.

The solution obtained with a high speed computer is recorded by the mathematician on the data form. The solution is in two parts. First, the percent of the various materials in the charge is noted in the Percent column. The D_j column is used to record the marginal costs of the materials not used in the charge. As mentioned earlier, linear programming not only determines the best solution but it also provides information about less-than-best solutions. The numbers (D_j) for those materials not used in the charge indicate the reduction in price per ton required before these materials could be profitably used in the charge. This is commonly called a marginal cost. This, then, provides the purchasing agent with a bargaining point when talking with the scrap dealers. If prices can be obtained which are lower than the original quoted prices, by the amount of the marginal cost, then the purchasing agent purchases the lower priced material. When this happens it becomes necessary to resolve the problem after the materials are delivered in order to determine the cupola charge.

The second solution per month, if necessary, is handled by the metallurgist and the mathematician since they are considering only those materials available in inventory.

After four months of operation, a cost and savings analysis was made. To be certain, it is difficult to exactly determine what might have been done without linear programming. However, the analysis indicated savings from $.10 to $1.40 per ton with the average at $.51 per ton for the entire four month period. The cost of linear programming solutions must be deducted from the foregoing. However, since the total cost per solution is only about $25.00, this is quite negligible. Each problem would require a day or more to solve by hand, but requires less than one minute on an IBM 704 computer.

This application of linear programming has not only reduced cupola charge costs, but it has opened the door to other operating cost reductions. In fact, the other cost reductions in materials and operating procedures have been several times the savings obtained by linear programming.

These savings have been realized in making malleable iron where we are concerned with only a few chemical elements. In making aluminum alloys, usually a greater number of elements with much closer specifications must be considered. Here linear programming is even more valuable for determining the least cost charge which satisfies all the specifications.

SUMMARY

In the past decade, technological progress has been made in mathematics as well as in other fields of science. The results obtained by using linear programming in cupola charging reflect the advantages of this new mathematical technique. Essentially, linear programming does the clerical task that used to require a sizeable portion of the metallurgist's time and energy. Linear programming has become an important new tool which depends very heavily upon the close cooperation of metallurgist, purchasing agent, and mathematician. This is a new addition to the many mathematical and statistical tools available for analyzing foundry operating problems.

References

(1) METZGER, R. W., *Elementary Mathematical Programming,* John Wiley & Sons, 1958.
(2) METZGER, R. W., AND SCHWARZBEK, R., "Least Cost Cupola Charging," presented before the General Motors Foundry Committee (Restricted for General Motors distribution only).

Chapter 4

PRODUCTION PLANNING WITH THE TRANSPORTATION MODEL

IV.

Mathematical Programming: Better Information for Better Decision Making*

Alexander Henderson and Robert Schlaifer†

In recent years mathematicians have worked out a number of new procedures which make it possible for management to solve a wide variety of important company problems much faster, more easily, and more accurately than ever before. These procedures have sometimes been called "linear programming." Actually, linear programming describes only one group of them; "mathematical programming" is a more suitable title.

Mathematical programming is not just an improved way of getting certain jobs done. It is in every sense a *new* way. It is new in the sense that double-entry bookkeeping was new in the Middle Ages, or that mechanization in the office was new earlier in this century, or that automation in the plant is new today. Because mathematical programming is so new, the gap between the scientist and the businessman—between the researcher

* From the *Harvard Business Review,* Vol. 32, No. 3 (1954), 73–100. Reprinted by permission of the *Harvard Business Review.*

† Authors' note: The authors wish to express their gratitude to Charles A. Bliss, W. W. Cooper, and Abraham Charnes for their invaluable assistance in the preparation of this article.

and the user—has not yet been bridged. Mathematical programming has made the news, but few businessmen really understand how it can be of use in their own companies.

This article is an attempt to define mathematical programming for businessmen, describe what it means in practice, and show exactly how to use it to solve company problems. We have divided the article into four sections:

Part I is addressed specifically to the top executive. Here are the salient points about mathematical programming which the man who makes company policy needs to know.

Part II is addressed to executives directly responsible for the organization and administration of operations where mathematical programming could be used and to the specialists who actually work out the problems. This part is based largely on case examples which are typical of the kinds of problems that can be handled.

Part III shows management how to use mathematical programming as a valuable planning tool. In many situations programming is the only practical way of obtaining certain cost and profit information that is essential in developing marketing policy, balancing productive equipment, making investment plans, and working out rational decisions on many other kinds of short-run and long-run problems.

In addition, to be used in connection with Part II, there is an appendix providing actual instructions for working through the most frequently useful, quick procedure for solving a common class of business problems.

PART I. BASIC PRINCIPLES

Production men usually have very little trouble in choosing which machine tool to use for a given operation when there is free time available on every tool in the plant. Traffic managers usually have little trouble in choosing which shipping route to use when they are able to supply each of their customers from the company's nearest plant. The manager of a refinery usually has little trouble in deciding what products to make when he has so much idle capacity that he can make all he can sell and more.

Except in the depths of depression, however, the problems facing management are usually not this simple. Any decision regarding any one problem affects not only that problem but many others as well. If an operation is assigned to the most suitable machine tool, some other operation on some other part will have to be performed on some other, less suitable tool. If Customer A is supplied from the nearest plant, that plant will not have sufficient capacity to supply Customer B, who also is closer to that plant than to any other. If the refinery manager makes all the 80-octane gasoline he can sell, he will not have capacity to satisfy the demand for 90-octane gasoline.

BUSINESS PROGRAMS

The general nature of all these problems is the same. *A group of limited resources must be shared among a number of competing demands, and all decisions are "interlocking" because they all have to be made under the common set of fixed limits.* In part, the limits are set by machine-tool capacity, plant capacity, raw materials, storage space, working capital, or any of the innumerable hard facts which prevent management from doing exactly as it pleases. In part, they are set by policies established by management itself.

When there are only a few possible courses of action—for example, when a company with only two plants wants to supply three or four customers at the lowest possible freight cost—any competent scheduler can quickly find the right answer. However, when the number of variables becomes larger—when a company has a dozen factories and 200 or 300 customers scattered all over the country—the man with the job of finding the best shipping pattern may well spend many days only to end up with a frustrated feeling; though he thinks he is close to the right answer, he is not at all sure that he has it. What is worse, he does not even know how far off he is, or whether it is worth spending still more time trying to improve his schedule. The production manager who has 20 or 30 different products to put through a machine shop containing 40 or 50 different machine tools may well give up as soon as he has found *any* schedule that will get out the required production, without even worrying whether some other schedule would get out the same product at a lower cost.

Under these conditions business may incur serious unnecessary costs because the best program is not discovered. Another kind of cost is often even more serious. The few direct tests which have been made so far show that intelligent and experienced men on the job often (though by no means always) come very close to the "best possible" solution of problems of this sort. But since problems of such complexity can almost never be handled by clerical personnel, even these good cut-and-try solutions are unsatisfactory because they take up a substantial amount of the time of supervisory employees or even of executives.

The time of such men is the one thing that management cannot readily buy on the market. If it is all used up just in getting the necessary information, there is nothing left for the next step, making sound decisions. Often this produces a sort of inertia against *any* change in the status quo; it is so hard to find out the cost or profit implications of a proposed change or series of changes that management simply gives up and lets existing schedules and programs stand unchanged. Conversely, if better information were available more easily, management would be less tempted to drop important questions without investigation or could make better decisions as a result of investigation.

A ROUTINE PROCEDURE

Many of these complex and time-consuming problems can in fact be solved today by mathematical programming. The purely routine procedures of which it is comprised can be safely entrusted to clerical personnel or to a mechanical computer. Such procedures have already been successfully applied to practical business problems, some of which will be described in the course of this article.

The word mathematical may be misleading. Actually the procedures go about solving problems in much the same way as the experienced man on the job. When such a man is faced by a problem with many interlocking aspects, he usually starts by finding a program that meets the minimum requirements regardless of cost or profit, and then tries out, one by one, various changes in this program that may reduce the cost or increase the profit. His skill and experience are required for two reasons: (a) to perceive the desirable changes and (b) to follow through the repercussions of a single change on all parts of the program.

What "mathematical" programming does is to reduce the whole procedure to a simple, definite routine. There is a rule for finding a program to start with, there is a rule for finding the successive changes that will increase the profits or lower the costs, and there is a rule for following through all the repercussions of each change. What is more, it is *absolutely certain* that if these rules are followed, they will lead to the best possible program; and it will be perfectly clear when the best possible program has been found. It is because the procedure follows definite rules that it can be taught to clerical personnel or handed over to automatic computers.

COST INFORMATION

Quick and inexpensive calculation of the best possible programs or schedules under a particular set of circumstances is not the only benefit which management can obtain from this technique. The same complex situation which makes it difficult to find the best possible schedule for the entire operation makes it difficult to get useful cost information concerning details of the operation. When every operation in the shop can be performed on the most suitable machine tool, the cost of any particular operation can be obtained by the usual methods of cost accounting. But if capacity is short, then the true cost of using a machine for one particular operation depends in a very real sense on the excess costs incurred because some *other* part has to be put on a less suitable machine. To illustrate further:

If the production of 80-octane gasoline is carried to a point where less 90-octane can be produced than can be sold, the profits which failed to be made on 90-octane must certainly be kept in mind when looking at the stated profits on the 80-octane.

When a company is supplying some (but not all) of its eastern customers by bringing in supplies from the West Coast, additional cost will be incurred by giving one of these customers quick delivery from a nearby plant, even though the actual freight rate from the nearby plant is lower than the rate from the West Coast.

Any time that the programming procedure will solve the basic problem of determining the most profitable over-all schedule, it will also produce *usable* cost information on parts of the whole operation. In many cases this information may be even more valuable than the basic schedule. It can help management decide where to expand plant capacity, where to push sales, and where to expend less effort, or what sorts of machine tools to buy on a limited capital budget. In the long run, sound decisions in matters of this sort will pay off much more substantially than the choice of the best shipping program in a single season or the best assignment of machine tools for a single month's production.

LIMITATIONS

Mathematical programming is not a patented cure-all which the businessman can buy for a fixed price and put into operation with no further thought. The principal limitations of the technique today lie in three areas:

1. *Cost or revenue proportional to volume*—Problem-solving procedures have been well developed only for problems where the cost incurred or revenue produced by every possible activity is strictly proportional to the volume of that activity; these are the procedures that belong under the somewhat misleading title of *linear* programming. This limitation, however, is not so serious as it

seems. Problems involving nonproportional costs or revenues can often be handled by linear programming through the use of special devices or by suitable approximations, and research is progressing on the development of procedures which will handle some of these problems directly.

2. *Arithmetic capacity*—Even when the procedure for solving a problem is perfectly well known, the solution may involve such a sheer quantity of arithmetic that it is beyond the capacity even of electronic computing machinery. However, the problem can sometimes be set up more simply so that solution is practical. For instance, careful analysis may show that the really essential variables are relatively few in number, or that the problem may be split into parts of manageable size.

3. *Scheduling problems*—A third limitation is often the most serious, particularly in the assignment of machine tools. So far very little has been accomplished toward the solution of *scheduling* problems, where certain operations must be performed before or after other operations. Mathematical programming can indicate, within the limits of available tool capacity, which operations should be performed on which tools, but the arrangement of these operations in the proper sequence must usually be handled as a separate problem. Again, however, research is attempting to find procedures which will reduce even this problem to a straightforward routine, and some progress in this direction has already been made.

APPLICATION

In Part II of this article we describe a series of cases which should suggest to the reader the sort of problems where mathematical programming can be of use in his own business. Included are both actual cases and hypothetical examples. The hypothetical examples are purposely made so simple that they could be solved *without* the use of these procedures; in this way the reader can better see the essential nature of the analysis which programming will accomplish in more complex problems.

Top executives may want to turn a detailed reading of this section over to specialists, but they will find the major points as set forth below of practical interest. Very briefly, the discussion of case examples will show that mathematical programming can be used to decide:

1. *Where to ship*—Here the problem is to find the shipping program that will give the lowest freight costs. It has been demonstrated by the H. J. Heinz Company that linear programming can save thousands of dollars on a single scheduling problem alone. By virtue of its greater ease and accuracy, linear programming has also enabled the company to schedule on a monthly rather than quarterly basis, thus taking advantage of new information as soon as it becomes

available.

2. *Where to ship and where to produce*—A complete program to determine the most economical program of production or procurement *and* freight costs can be developed so quickly and inexpensively that every possible alternative can be taken into account without throwing a heavy burden on senior personnel.

3. *Where to ship, where to produce, and where to sell*—Here the problem is further complicated. Such factors as a management policy regarding minimum supplies for dealers and a varying price schedule should and can be taken into account.

4. *What the most profitable combination of price and volume is*—At present mathematical programming can provide the answers only under certain conditions, but progress is being made in broadening its applicability.

5. *What products to make*—Problems that can be solved range from the most economical use of scarce raw materials to the most profitable mix in gasoline blending. If automatic computers are necessary because of the sheer bulk of arithmetic, the small or medium-size firm can turn to a central service bureau; the company does not have to be so large that it can afford its own computers.

6. *What products to make and what processes to use*—This problem arises when machine capacity is limited. Here mathematical programming may produce surprising results. For example, a certain amount of idle time on one machine may be necessary for the greatest production. Without mathematical programming, there is a real danger that personnel will use every machine all the time to satisfy management pressure, and thus defeat the company's real objective.

7. *How to get lowest cost production*—Here the problem is to determine the most economical production when the company can produce all it can sell. In these days of growing cost-consciousness, mathematical programming may become one of management's really valuable cost-reduction tools.

The businessman who recognizes or suspects that he has a problem which can be solved by mathematical programming will usually have to consult with specialists to learn how to use the technique. But an even greater responsibility will reman with the businessman himself. Like the introduction of a variable overhead budget, each application of mathematical programming will require careful study of the particular circumstances and problems of the company involved; and, once installed, the technique will pay off only in proportion to the understanding with which management makes use of it.

PART II. EXAMPLES OF OPERATION

The case examples to be presented here illustrate some of the uses of mathematical programming. Although limited in number, the examples are so arranged that the reader who follows them through in order should gain an understanding of the situations in which mathematical programming can and cannot be helpful and of how to set up any problem for accurate solution. The exhibits accompanying the text set forth the mathematical solution of the problems posed in the cases, while the appendix gives specific directions on how to work through a procedure for handling some of the problems that may arise in the reader's own business.

WHERE TO SHIP

As our first example of the uses of mathematical programming, let us look at a case where the technique is currently in use as a routine operating procedure in an actual company:

The H. J. Heinz Company manufactures ketchup in half a dozen plants scattered across the United States from New Jersey to California and distributes this ketchup from about 70 warehouses located in all parts of the country.

In 1953 the company was in the fortunate position of being able to sell all it could produce, and supplies were allocated to warehouses in a total amount exactly equal to the total capacity of the plants. Management wished to supply these requirements at the lowest possible cost of freight; speed of shipment was not important. However, capacity in the West exceeded requirements in that part of the country, while the reverse was true in the East; for this reason a considerable tonnage had to be shipped from western plants to the East. In other words, the cost of freight could not be minimized by simply supplying each warehouse from the nearest plant.

SIMPLEST PROBLEM

This problem can immediately be recognized as a problem of *programming* because its essence is the minimization of cost subject to a fixed set of plant capacities and warehouse requirements. It can be handled by *linear* programming because the freight bill for shipments between any two points will be proportional to the quantity shipped. (The quantities involved are large enough so that virtually everything will move at carload rates under *any* shipping program which might be chosen.)

This is, in fact, the simplest possible kind of problem that can be solved by this method. Certain complexities which make solution by trial and error considerably more difficult than usual—in particular, the existence of water-competitive rates, which make it practical to send California ketchup all the way to the East Coast—add no real difficulty to the solution by linear programming. Given the list of plant capacities and warehouse requirements, plus a table of freight rates from every plant to every ware-house, one man with no equipment other than pencil and paper solved this problem for the first time in about 12 hours. After H. J. Heinz had adopted the method for regular use and clerks had been trained to become thoroughly familiar with the routine for this particular problem, the time required to develop a shipping program was considerably reduced.

The actual data of this problem have not been released by the company, but a fair representation of its magnitude is given by the similar but hypo-thetical examples of Exhibits I and II, which show the data and solution of a problem of supplying 20 warehouses from 12 plants.

Exhibit I shows the basic data: the body of the table gives the freight rates, while the daily capacities of the plants and daily requirements of the warehouses are in the margins. For example, Factory III, with a capacity of 3,000 cwt. per day, can supply Warehouse G, with require-ments of 940 cwt. per day, at a freight cost of 7 cents per cwt.

Any reader who wishes to try his hand will quickly find that without a systematic procedure a great deal of work would be required to find a shipping program which would come reasonably close to satisfying these requirements and capacities at the lowest possible cost. But with the use of linear programing the problem is even easier than the Heinz problem.

Exhibit II gives the lowest-cost distribution program. For example, Warehouse K is to get 700 cwt. per day from Factory I and 3,000 cwt. per day from Factory III. On the other hand, Factory III ships nothing to Warehouse A, although Exhibit I shows that Factory III could ship at less expense to this warehouse than to any other. (The "row values" and "column values" are cost information, the meaning of which is explained on p. 94.)

EXHIBIT I. TABLE OF RATES, REQUIREMENTS, AND CAPACITIES

Factory	I	II	III	IV	V	VI	VII	VIII	IX	X	XI	XII	Daily requirements (cwt.)
					Freight rates (cents per cwt.)								
Warehouse A	16	16	6	13	24	13	6	31	37	34	37	40	1,820
B	20	18	8	10	22	11	8	29	33	25	35	38	1,530
C	30	23	8	9	14	7	9	22	29	20	38	35	2,360
D	10	15	10	8	10	15	13	19	19	15	28	34	100
E	31	23	16	10	10	16	20	14	17	17	25	28	280
F	24	14	19	13	13	16	18	9	14	13	29	25	730
G	27	23	7	11	23	8	16	6	10	11	16	28	940
H	34	25	15	4	27	15	11	9	16	17	13	16	1,130
J	38	29	17	11	16	27	17	19	8	18	19	11	4,150
K	42	43	21	22	16	10	21	18	24	16	17	15	3,700
L	44	49	25	23	18	6	13	19	15	12	10	13	2,560
M	49	40	29	21	10	15	14	21	12	29	14	20	1,710
N	56	58	36	37	6	25	8	19	9	21	15	26	580
P	59	57	44	33	5	21	6	10	8	33	15	18	30
Q	68	54	40	38	8	24	7	19	10	23	23	23	2,840
R	66	71	47	43	16	33	12	26	19	20	25	31	1,510
S	72	58	50	51	20	42	22	16	15	13	20	21	970
T	74	54	57	55	26	53	26	19	14	7	7	6	5,110
U	71	75	57	60	30	44	30	30	41	8	15	37	3,540
Y	73	72	63	56	37	49	40	31	31	10	8	25	4,410
Daily capacity (cwt.)	10,000	9,000	3,000	2,700	500	1,200	700	300	500	1,200	2,000	8,900	40,000

EXHIBIT II. LOWEST-COST DISTRIBUTION PROGRAM
(Daily shipments from factory to warehouse in cwt.)

Factory	I	II	III	IV	V	VI	VII	VIII	IX	X	XI	XII	Total	Row value
Warehouse A	1,820												1,820	16
B	1,530												1,530	20
C		2,360											2,360	28
D	100												100	10
E		280											280	28
F		730											730	19
G	940												940	27
H				1,130									1,130	28
J		4,150											4,150	34
K	700		3,000										3,700	42
L	1,360					1,200							2,560	44
M		140		1,570									1,710	45
N	580												580	56
P								30					30	51
Q		1,340			500				500			500	2,840	59
R	810						700						1,510	66
S								90				880	970	57
T												5,110	5,110	42
U	2,160							180		1,200			3,540	71
Y											2,000	2,410	4,410	61
Total	10,000	9,000	3,000	2,700	500	1,200	700	300	500	1,200	2,000	8,900	40,000	
Column value	0	—5	—21	—24	—51	—38	—54	—41	—49	—63	—53	—36		

ADVANTAGES GAINED

One of the most important advantages gained by the H. J. Heinz Company from the introduction of linear programming was relief of the senior members of the distribution department from the burden of preparing shipping programs. Previously the quarterly preparation of the program took a substantial amount of their time; now they pay only as much attention to this problem as they believe necessary to keep the feel of the situation, while the detailed development of the program has been handed over to clerks. Freed from the burden of working out what is after all only glorified arithmetic, they have this much more time to devote to matters which really require their experience and judgment.

An equally important gain, in the opinion of these officials themselves, is the peace of mind which results from being sure that the program *is* the lowest-cost program possible.

The direct dollars-and-cents saving in the company's freight bill was large enough by itself to make the use of this technique very much worth while. The first shipping program produced by linear programming gave a projected semi-annual freight cost several thousand dollars less than did a program prepared by the company's previous methods, and this comparison is far from giving a full measure of the actual freight savings to be anticipated.

Shipping schedules rest on estimates which are continuously subject to revision. The capacity figures in part represent actual stocks on hand at the plants, but in part they are based on estimates of future tomato crops; and the figures for requirements depend almost wholly on estimates of future sales. The fact that schedules are now quickly and accurately prepared by clerks has enabled the company to reschedule monthly rather than quarterly, thus making much better use of new information on crops and sales as it becomes available.

Furthermore, the risk of backhauling is very much reduced under the new system. It had always been company practice early in the season to hold "reserves" in regions of surplus production, in order to avoid the danger of shipping so much out of these regions that it became necessary to ship back into them when production and sales estimates were revised. In fact, these reserves were largely accidental leftovers: when it became really difficult to assign the last part of a factory's production, this remainder was called the reserve. Now the company can look at past history and decide in advance what reserve should be held at each factory and can set up its program to suit this estimate exactly. Since the schedule is revised each month, these reserves can be altered in the light of current information until they are finally reduced to nothing just before the new pack starts at the factory in question.

SIMILAR PROBLEMS

Many important problems of this same character unquestionably are prevalent in business. One such case, for instance, would be that of a newsprint producer who supplies about 200 customers all over the United States from 6 factories scattered over the width of Canada.[1]

Similar problems arise where the cost of transportation is measured in time rather than in money. In fact, the first efforts to solve problems of this sort systematically were made during World War II in order to minimize the time spent by ships in ballast. Specified cargo had to be moved from specified origins to specified destination; there was usually no return cargo, and the problem was to decide to which port the ship should be sent in ballast to pick up its next cargo. An obviously similar problem is the routing of empty freight cars,[2] and a trucker operating on a nationwide scale might face the same problem with empty trucks.

WHERE TO PRODUCE

When ketchup shipments were programmed for the H. J. Heinz Company, factory capacities and warehouse requirements were fixed before the shipping program was worked out, and the only cost which could be reduced by programming was the cost of freight. Since management had decided in advance how much to produce at each plant, *all* production costs were "fixed" *so far as the programming problem was concerned.*

The same company faces a different problem in connection with another product, which is also produced in a number of plants and shipped to a number of warehouses. In this case, the capacity of the plants *exceeds* the requirements of the warehouses. The cost of production varies from one plant to another, and the problem is thus one of satisfying the requirements at the least *total* cost. It is as important to reduce the cost of *production* (by producing in the right place) as it is to reduce the cost of *freight* (by supplying from the right place.) In other words, management must now decide two questions instead of one: (a) How much is each factory to produce? (b) Which warehouses should be supplied by which factories?

It is tempting to try to solve these two problems one at a time and thus simplify the job, but in general it will *not* be possible to get the lowest total cost by first deciding where to produce and then deciding where to ship. It is obviously better to produce in a high-cost plant if the additional cost can be more than recovered through savings in freight.

METHOD OF ATTACK

This double problem can be handled by linear programming if we may

---

[1] R. Dorfman, "Mathematical, or 'Linear' Programming," *American Economic Review,* Dec. 1953, p. 797.

[2] Cf. *Railway Age,* April 20, 1953, pp. 73–74.

assume (as businessmen usually do) that the cost of production at any one plant is the sum of a "fixed" cost independent of volume and a "variable" cost proportional to volume in total but fixed per unit, and if these costs are known. The variable cost is handled directly by the linear programming procedure, while the fixed part is handled by a method which will be explained later.

Actually, the problem can be much more complicated and still lend itself to solution by linear programming. For example, we can bring in the possibility of using overtime, or of buying raw materials at one price up to a certain quantity and at another price beyond that quantity. (Although there is no longer a constant proportion between production and variable cost, we can restore proportionality by a device described in the Appendix, p. 101.)

Exhibit III shows the cost information needed to solve a hypothetical example of this sort. It is assumed that there are only four plants and four warehouses, but any number could be brought into the problem.

In our first approximation (which we shall modify later) we shall assume that no plant will be closed down entirely and, therefore, that "fixed costs" are really fixed and can be left out of the picture. Like Exhibit I, Exhibit III shows the freight rates from each plant to each warehouse, the available daily capacity at each plant, and the daily requirements of each warehouse; it also shows the "variable" (fixed-per-unit) cost of normal production at each plant and the additional per-unit cost of overtime production. The total capacity is greater than the total requirements even if the factories work only normal time.

EXHIBIT III. COST INFORMATION FOR DOUBLE PROBLEM

A—Warehouse Requirements (tons per day)

Warehouse	A	B	C	D	Total
Requirements	90	140	75	100	405

B—Factory Capacities (tons per day)

Factory	I	II	III	IV	Total
Normal capacity	70	130	180	110	490
Additional capacity on overtime	25	40	60	30	155

C—Variable Costs (per ton)

Factory	I	II	III	IV
Normal production cost	$30	$36	$24	$30
Overtime premium	15	18	12	15
Freight rates to:				
Warehouse A	$14	$ 9	$21	$18
B	20	14	27	24
C	18	12	29	20
D	19	15	27	23

On the basis of these data, the lowest-cost solution is given by Part A of Exhibit IV. It is scarcely surprising that this solution calls for no use of overtime. So long as fixed costs are taken as really fixed, it turns out that it is best to use the entire normal capacity of Factories I, II, and III, and to use 25 tons of Factory IV's normal capacity of 110 tons per day. The remaining 85 tons of normal capacity at IV are left unused. The total variable cost under this schedule (freight cost plus variable production cost) will be $19,720 per day.

EXHIBIT IV.   LOWEST COST DISTRIBUTION PROGRAM
(Daily shipments in tons from factory to warehouse)

A—With All Four Factories Open

Factory	I	II	III	IV	Total
Warehouse A			90		90
B		80	60		140
C		50		25	75
D	70		30		100
Idle normal capacity				85	85
Total	70	130	180	110	490

B—With Factory I Closed

Factory	II	III	IV	Total
Warehouse A		90		90
B	130	10		140
C			75	75
D		80	20	100
Idle normal capacity			15	15
Total	130	180	110	420

C—With Factory IV Closed

Factory	I	II	III	Total
Warehouse A			90	90
B		55	85	140
C		75		75
D	70		30	100
Total	70	130	205	405

FINAL DETERMINATION

Presented with this result, management would certainly ask whether it is sensible to keep all four factories open when one of them is being left about 80% idle. Even without incurring overtime, Factory I, the smallest plant, could be closed and the load redistributed among the other plants. If this is done, the lowest-cost distribution of the requirements among Factories II, III, and IV is that given by Part B of Exhibit IV. Under this program the total variable cost would be $19,950 per day, or $230 per day more than under the program of Exhibit IV, A, which depended on the use of all four plants. If more than $230 per day of fixed costs can be saved by closing down Factory I completely, it will pay to do so; otherwise it will not.

It might be still better, however, to close down some plant other than Factory I even at the cost of a certain amount of overtime. In particular, a very little overtime production (25 tons per day) would make it possible to close Factory IV. A person asked to look into this possibility might reason as follows: Under the shipping schedule of Exhibit IV, A, the only use of Factory IV's capacity is to supply 25 tons per day to Warehouse C. Looking at Exhibit III for a replacement for this supply, he would get the following information on costs per ton:

Factory	Normal cost of production	Overtime premium	Freight to Warehouse C	Total
I	$30	$15	$18	$63
II	36	18	12	66
III	24	12	29	65

Apparently the cheapest way of using overtime, if it is to be used at all, would be to produce the needed 25 tons per day at Factory I and ship them to Warehouse C at a total variable cost of $63 per ton. Under the program of Exhibit IV, A, with all plants in use, Warehouse C was supplied from Factory IV at a total variable cost of $30 for production plus $20 for freight, or a total of $50 per ton. The change would thus seem to add a total of $325 per day (25 tons times $13 per ton which is the difference between $63 and $50 per ton).

But, in fact, closing Factory IV need not add this much to the cost of the program. If we take Factory IV out of the picture and then program to find the best possible distribution of the output of the remaining plants, we discover that the program of Part C of Exhibit IV satisfies all requirements at a total variable cost of $19,995 per day, or only $275 per day more than with all plants in use. The overtime is performed by Factory III, which does not supply Warehouse C at all.

DIFFICULTIES AVOIDED

This last result deserves the reader's attention. *Once a change was made in a single part of the program, the best adjustment was a general readjustment of the entire program.* But such a general readjustment is impractical unless complete programs can be developed quickly and at a reasonable cost. It is rarely clear *in advance* whether the work will prove profitable, and management does not want to throw a heavy burden of recalculation on senior personnel every time a minor change is made. Mathematical programming avoids these difficulties. Even minor changes in the data can be made freely despite the fact that complete recalculations of the program are required, because the work can be done quickly and accurately by clerks or machines.

We can proceed to compute the lowest possible cost of supplying the requirements with Factory II or Factory III closed down completely. We can then summarize the results for all alternatives like this:

Total freight plus variable production cost

All four factories in use	$19,720
Factory I closed, no overtime	19,950
Factory II closed, overtime at Factory III	20,515
Factory III closed, overtime at Factories I, II, and IV	21,445
Factory IV closed, overtime at Factory III	19,995

Management now has the information on variable costs which it needs in order to choose rationally among three alternatives: (1) operating all four plants with a large amount of idle normal capacity; (2) shutting down Factory I and still having a little idle normal capacity; (3) shutting down Factory II, III, or IV and incurring overtime. Its choice will depend in part on the extent to which fixed costs can be eliminated when a particular plant is completely closed; it may depend even more on company policies regarding community relations or some other nonfinancial consideration. Mathematical programming cannot replace judgment, but it can supply some of the factual information which management needs in order to make judgments.

RELATED PROBLEMS

Problems of this general type are met in purchasing as well as in producing and selling. A company which buys a standard raw material at many different geographical locations and ships it to a number of scattered plants for processing will wish to minimize the total cost of purchase plus freight; here the solution can be obtained in exactly the same way as just discussed. The Department of Defense is reported to have made substantial savings by using linear programming to decide where to buy and where to send certain standard articles which it obtains from a large number of suppliers for direct shipment to military installations.

WHERE TO SELL

In our first case, we considered a situation where management had fixed the sales at each warehouse and the production at each plant before using programming to work out the best way of shipping from plant to warehouse. In the second example, management had fixed the sales at each warehouse in advance, but had left the decision on where and how much to produce to be made as a part of the program. Let us now consider a case in which sales are not fixed in advance, and management wants to determine where to sell, as well as where to produce and where to ship, in order to give the greatest possible profits.

Such a problem often arises when sales would exceed a company's capacity to produce unless demand were retarded by higher prices, yet management does not wish to raise prices because of the long-run competitive situation. Under these circumstances some system of allocating the product to branch warehouses in the different market areas (or to individual customers) will be necessary. One way of doing this is simply to sell wherever the greatest short-run profits can be made. Often, however, management will not want to take an exclusively short-run view and will want to provide each warehouse or customer with at least a certain minimum supply, with only the remainder over and above these minimum allocations being disposed of with a view to maximum short-run profits.

One additional complication will often be present in real problems of this sort. The selling price of the product may not be uniform nationally, but may vary from place to place or from customer to customer. In addition, there may well be present the complication we dealt with in the last example: it may be desirable to have some plants working overtime while others are working at only a part of their normal capacity or are even closed down entirely.

Thus a production and distribution program must be prepared which answers all the following questions in such a way as to give the greatest possible profits, subject to the requirement of supplying certain warehouses with at least a specified allocation of product:

(1) How much shall be produced at each plant?

(2) How much, if any, above the predetermined minimum shall be delivered to each warehouse?

(3) The above questions being answered, which plants shall supply which warehouses?

As in the previous example, all three questions must be answered simultaneously; it is not possible to work them out one by one. The problem can still be handled by linear programming, however, despite the additional complications which have entered the picture; in fact, it is no harder to solve than the previous problem. The only difference is that we now look directly at the profit resulting from supplying a particular warehouse from a particular plant, rather than looking at the costs involved. We shall not even work out an example, since the solution would appear in the same form as Exhibit IV of the previous case, while the required data would look the same as Exhibit III with the addition of the selling price at each warehouse.

PRICE, VOLUME, AND PROFIT

In all the previous examples it was assumed that management had set selling prices before the production and distribution program was worked out. The quantity to be produced and shipped followed from the predetermined prices. This is certainly a common situation, but it is also very common for management to want to consider the effect of prices on volume *before* prices are set. This means, of course, that sales volume must be forecast at each of a variety of possible prices, and we assume that such forecasts have been made separately for each of the branch warehouses of our previous examples.

Under these conditions the problem can no longer be handled *directly* by linear programming, since the margin, or difference between the selling price at a particular warehouse and the variable cost of producing at a particular plant and shipping to that warehouse, is no longer in a constant ratio to the quantity produced and sold. As quantities go up, prices go down, and the ratio of total margin to quantity sold declines. Even so, we can still use linear programming to solve the problem quickly, accurately, and cheaply *if* there is to be a single national selling price. We can compute the best program for each proposed price, determine the total profits for each program, and select the most profitable alternative.

However, linear programming becomes virtually impossible if prices can vary from place to place and management wishes to set each local price in such a way as to obtain the greatest total profits. Even if there are only ten distribution points for which price-quantity forecasts have to be considered, and even if each branch manager submits forecasts for only five different prices, we would have to compute nearly 10 million different programs and then select the most profitable one.

In practical cases it will often prove possible with a reasonable amount of calculation to find a program which is probably the best program or very close to it, but in general the solution of this problem of mathematical programming, like many others, depends on further research to develop methods for attacking nonlinear problems directly. As mentioned, progress in this direction is already being made.

WHAT AND HOW TO PRODUCE

All the cases discussed so far have involved problems of *where* (as well as how much) to buy, sell, produce, and ship. Mathematical programming can be of equal use in deciding *what* and *how* to produce in order to maximize profits or minimize costs in the face of shortages of raw materials, machine tools, or other productive resources. Some problems of this kind may be solved by clerks using procedures such as those previously discussed;

others, however, may require new procedures and automatic computing equipment.

A representative problem in the first category is the following one, which involves the selective use of scarce raw materials:

A manufacturer produces four products, A, B, C, and D, from a single raw material which can be bought in three different grades, I, II, and III. The cost of processing and the quantity of material required for one ton of end product vary according to the product and the grade of material used, as shown in Exhibit V.

EXHIBIT V.   COSTS, AVAILABILITIES, AND PRICES

A—Yields and Processing Costs

Grade	I	II	III
Product	Tons of material per ton of product		
A	1.20	1.80	2.00
B	1.50	2.25	2.50
C	1.50	2.25	2.50
D	1.80	2.70	3.00
	Processing cost per ton of product		
A	$18	$30	$ 42
B	30	60	69
C	57	63	66
D	54	81	126

B—Material Cost and Availability

Grade	I	II	III
Normal price per ton	$48	$24	$18
Quantity available at normal price (tons)	100	150	250
Premium price per ton	$72	$36	$24
Quantity available at premium price (tons)	100	150	400

C—Product Prices and Sales Potentials

Product	A	B	C	D
Price per ton	$96	$150	$135	$171
Potential sales (tons)	200	100	160	50

If unlimited supplies of each grade of material were available at a fixed market price, each product would be made from the grade for which the total purchasing-plus-processing cost was the smallest; but the amount of each grade obtainable at the "normal" price is limited as shown in the exhibit. Additional quantities of any grade can be obtained, but only at the premium shown.

The products are sold f.o.b. the manufacturer's single plant; the selling prices have already been set and are shown in the exhibit, together with the sales department's forecasts of the amount of each product which can be sold at these prices.

The problem, then, is to determine *what* products to make and how much of each, and *how* to make them—in other words, which grade of material to use for which products. The solution is shown in Exhibit VI.

EXHIBIT VI. MOST PROFITABLE PRODUCTION PROGRAM

	Tons of product		Tons of material used		
Product	Sales potential	Production	Grade I	Grade II	Grade III
A	200	200		210	167
B	100	100	100		83
C	160	160			400
D	50	0			
Total material usage			100	210	650
Bought at normal price			100	150	250
Bought at premium price			0	60	400

USE OF COMPUTERS

It will be remembered that, in discussing the use of mathematical programming by the H. J. Heinz Company, we emphasized the fact that shipping programs are produced by a clerk with nothing but paper and pencil in a very reasonable amount of time. This is true even though the existence of about 6 plants and 70 warehouses makes it necessary to choose 75 routes for actual use from the 420 possible routes which might be used. This ease of solution, even in cases where a very large number of variables is involved, applies to the selective use of raw materials just discussed as well as to the other problems taken up in earlier sections. They are all problems which can be solved by what is known as the "transportation-problem procedure."

By contrast, other problems usually require the use of high-speed computing machinery. They are problems requiring the use of what might be called the "general procedure." While the mathematics involved here is at the level of grade-school arithmetic, the sheer *bulk* of arithmetic required is very much greater than under the transportation procedure. This means that, unless a skilled mathematician finds some way of simplifying a particular problem, it will be impossible for clerks to obtain a solution by hand in a reasonable amount of time when the number of variables is such as will be encountered in most practical situations.

Whether a given problem can be solved by the transportation-problem procedure or will require the use of the general procedure does not depend on whether the problem actually involves transportation or not, but rather on the *form* of the data. The raw material problem discussed just above, for example, could be solved as a transportation problem because *any* product would require 50% more material if Grade II was used instead of Grade I, or 67% more if Grade III was used instead of Grade I. But if the inferiority of yield of the lower grades had varied depending on the particular end product, it would have been necessary to use the general procedure.

The fact that the general procedure usually requires an automatic computer by no means implies that this procedure can be profitably applied only by very large firms with computers of their own. Fortunately, all problems which call for the use of this procedure are *mathematically* the same, even though the physical and economic *meaning* of each problem may be completely different. And since they are mathematically the same, a machine at a central service bureau can be coded once and for all to carry out the general procedure for any problem up to a certain size. The machine can then be used to solve the varying problems of many different companies promptly and inexpensively. Such a service can already be purchased from at least one source by the hour, and the time required to solve a problem is usually surprisingly short.

MOST PROFITABLE BLEND

Now let us turn to a case requiring the use of the general procedure:

Gasoline sold as an automobile or aviation fuel is ordinarily not the product of a single refining process but a blend of various refinery products with a certain amount of tetraethyl lead added. To a certain extent each of the various constituents requires peculiar refining facilities. Consequently, the management of a refinery may well be faced with the following problem: given a limited daily supply of each of various constituents, into what end-product fuels should they be blended to bring in the maximum profits? The problem is made additionally complicated by the fact that there is no single "recipe" for any particular end product. In general, the end product may be blended in any of a large number of different ways, provided only that certain performance specifications are met.

This is clearly a problem of programming, both because the use of a given constituent in one end product means that less is available for use in another, and also because the use of one constituent to produce a given kind of performance in a particular end product means that less of other constituents is needed to produce that performance in the end product. But is the problem linear? We must look a little more closely at the relation between the characteristics of the constituents and the characteristics of the resulting blends:

The two most important measures of the performance characteristics of a gasoline fuel are its performance number (PN), which is a development of the octane number and describes antiknock properties, and its vapor pressure (RVP), which indicates the volatility of the fuel. In the case of most high-grade aviation gasolines there are actually two PN's specified: the 1-c PN, which applies to lean mixture, and the 3-c PN, which applies to rich mixture. Each of the various constituents has its own RVP and PN.

The PN and RVP required in the end product are produced by proper blending of the constituents and by the addition of tetraethyl lead (TEL) to improve the PN. The amount of TEL which can be used in any fuel is limited for various reasons; and since TEL is often the cheapest way of obtaining the desired PN (particularly in the case of aviation fuels), it is a common practice to use the maximum permitted amount of this chemical.

It appears from the above that the problem will be linear provided that the RVP and PN of any end product are simply weighted averages of the RVP's and PN's of the various constituents (each PN being calculated for the predetermined amount of TEL to be used in the end product). While not perhaps strictly true as regards PN, this proposition is close enough to the truth to serve as the basis for ordinary blending calculations. Therefore the problem can be handled in a straightforward manner by linear programming.

A. Charnes, W. W. Cooper, and B. Mellon have applied linear programming to the choice of the most profitable mix in an actual refinery; and although they were forced to simplify the problem somewhat in order to do the computation with nothing but a desk calculator, the results of their calculations were of considerable interest to the company's management.[3]

(With modern computing equipment, of course, much more data could be handled in much less time, and various large oil companies are currently trying out the use of such equipment for this purpose.)

The figures which Charnes, Cooper, and Mellon present to show the nature of the calculations, and which we use below, are of course largely disguised:

The refinery in question is considered as having available fixed daily supplies of one grade of each of four blending constituents: alkylate, catalytic-cracked gasoline, straight-run gasoline, and isopentane. The quantities available and the performance specifications are shown in Exhibit VII. These constituents can be blended into any of three different aviation gasolines, A, B, or C, the specifications and selling prices of which are also shown in Exhibit VII.

[3] A. Charnes, W. W. Cooper, and B. Mellon, "Blending Aviation Gasolines—A Study in Programming Interdependent Activities in an Integrated Oil Company," *Econometrica,* April 1952, p. 135.

EXHIBIT VII.   QUANTITIES AVAILABLE AND PERFORMANCE SPECIFICATIONS

A—Product Specifications

Product	Maxi-mum RVP	Mini-mum 1-c PN	Mini-mum 3-c PN	Maximum TEL cc. per gal. of product	Price per bbl. of product	Cost of TEL per bbl. of product
Avgas A	7.0	80.0	—	0.5	$4.960	$0.051770
Avgas B	7.0	91.0	96.0	4.0	5.846	0.409416
Avgas C	7.0	100.0	130.0	4.0	6.451	0.409416
Automobile	—	—	—	3.0	4.830	0.281862

B—Constituent Specifications

Constituent	Supply bbl. per day	RVP	1-c PN 0.5 cc. TEL	1-c PN 4.0 cc. TEL	3-c PN 4.0 cc. TEL
Alkylate	3,800	5.0	94.0	107.5	148.0
Catalytic	2,652	8.0	83.0	93.0	106.0
Straight-run	4,081	4.0	74.0	87.0	80.0
Isopentane	1,300	20.5	95.0	108.0	140.0

Any supplies not used in one of these three aviation gasolines will be used in premium automobile fuel, the selling price of which likewise appears in the exhibit. Performance specifications for automobile fuel are not shown since this product will be composed primarily of constituents not included in this study; these constituents will be added in the proper proportions to give the desired performance specifications.

Management has decided to use the entire available supply of the constituents in one way or another. Their costs can therefore be neglected in selecting the blending program since they will be the same whatever program is chosen. The costs of blending itself are also about the same whatever end product is produced and can, therefore, be neglected in solving this problem, too. The only variable cost factor is the TEL (since some end products use more of this than others), and its cost per barrel of product is shown in Exhibit VII.

The solution of the problem is given in Exhibit VIII. In the actual case, however, precise determination of the most profitable blending program was not the result which was of most interest to the management concerned. After all, the company's experienced schedulers *could,* given sufficient time, arrive at programs as profitable or nearly as profitable as those derived by mathematical programming—although the tests which seemed to show this were perhaps unduly favorable to the traditional methods because the schedulers were given the results of the programming calculations in advance, and thus knew what they had to try to attain.

EXHIBIT VIII.   MOST PROFITABLE PRODUCT MIX

Product	Total amount produced	Composed of these constituents:			
		Alkylate	Catalytic	Straight-run	Isopen-tane
Avgas A	0	0	0	0	0
Avgas B	5,513	0	2,625	2,555	333
Avgas C	6,207	3,800	27	1,526	854
Automobile	113	0	0	0	113
Total	11,833	3,800	2,652	4,081	1,300

The indirect results were what really impressed management. For one thing, just as in the case of the Heinz Company, it was clear that the time and effort of experienced personnel would be saved if the job were routinized by the use of mathematical programming. This, in turn, now made it practical to compute programs for a variety of requirements and assumptions not previously covered. To illustrate:

The most profitable product mix as shown in Exhibit VIII contains no Avgas A. However, company policy called for the production of 500 bbl. per day of this product for goodwill reasons. When the problem was recomputed taking this factor into account, it was found that the most profitable mix containing the required 500 bbl. of Avgas A yielded profits about $80,000 per year less than those resulting from the program of Exhibit VIII.

This loss was considerably higher than management had believed. Presumably the cost could have been computed with adequate accuracy by the company's schedulers, but *when such calculations are expensive in terms of the time of senior personnel, they simply do not get made.*

"CONCAVE" PROGRAMMING

The field of gasoline refining is perhaps the one in which the most extensive work has been done in trying out actual applications of mathematical programming to practical operations. One interesting type of *non*linear programming has been tried on actual data in this field. The method has been called "concave" programming.

In our gasoline case, the problem could be solved by linear programming because it was assumed that the RVP and PN of any product would be a simple weighted average of the RVP's and PN's of the constituents, the PN's being calculated for a predetermined amount of TEL in the product. We have already suggested that under some conditions this assumption is not strictly true. Linear programming is particularly inapplicable when the problem involves the blending of automotive rather than high-grade aviation fuels. In such a case it is not at all clear in advance that it will be economical to use the maximum permitted amount of TEL, and PN is definitely not proportional to the amount of TEL in the fuel.

The procedures which have been developed to cope with situations like this have at least approximately solved the problem in a number of actual cases.[4] The results show the most profitable amount of TEL to use in various end products as well as the most profitable way to blend the refinery stocks.

WHAT PROCESSES TO USE

Some of the most perplexing problems of limited resources which management commonly faces do not concern materials but the productive capacity of the plant. A good example is the problem of choosing what products to make and what processes to use for manufacturing them when a shortage of machine capacity restricts production. The problem may arise because of a shortage of only a few types of machine in a shop which is otherwise adequately equipped. The SKF Company, for example, has reported savings of $100,000 a year through the use of scheduling techniques developed from linear programming.[5]

Rather than describing the SKF application, however, let us take a hypothetical example which will give an opportunity to show one of the ways in which setup costs can be handled by mathematical programming. Setup costs cannot be handled directly by linear programming because they are not proportional to volume of production. However, they can be handled indirectly by the same means used to deal with the fixed costs that can be avoided by closing down a plant completely (see the case described under the heading Where to Produce). Here is an illustrative situation:

A machine shop has adequate machine-tool capacity except for three types of machine, I, II, and III. These machines are used (in conjunction with others) to make three products, A, B, and C. Each product can be made in a variety of ways. It is possible, for example, to reduce the amount of time required for

---

[4] See A. S. Manne, *Concave Programming for Gasoline Blends,* Report P-383 of The Rand Corporation, Santa Monica, 1953.

[5] *Factory Management and Maintenance,* January 1954, pp. 136–137. The technique there described is very close to the "profit-preference procedure" mentioned in the Appendix, p. 94.

grinding by closer machining, but this requires more machining time. To be specific, let us suppose that for each product there are three alternate operation sheets, which we shall call processes 1, 2, and 3.

If sufficient time were available on all machines, the most economical process would be chosen for each product individually, and the company would then make all it could sell of that product. But because of the shortage of capacity the process to be used for any one product must be chosen with regard to its effect on machine availability for the other two products, and the quantity to be produced must be calculated for all products together in such a way as to obtain the greatest profit from the total production of all products.

The demands of each process for each product on the three critical types of machine are shown in Exhibit IX; these are pre-unit times (standards duly adjusted for efficiency). For example, if Product B is produced by Process 3, each unit will require 0.2 hour on a machine of Type II and 1.0 hour on a machine of Type III, but no time on Type I. The weekly available machine hours are also shown in the exhibit, after deduction of estimated allowances for repair and maintenance, but with no deduction for setup.

Exhibit IX also shows the number of units of each product which must be produced each week to fill orders already accepted, together with the "margin" which will be realized on any additional units that can be produced. This margin is the selling price less all out-of-pocket costs of production *except* the costs of operating the machines being programmed. Since these machines are the "bottlenecks," they will be used full time or virtually full time in any case, and, therefore, the costs of operating them will be virtually the same regardless of the program chosen.

SOLUTION OF PROBLEM

To solve the problem, we start by neglecting the setup times for the machines (shown in Exhibit IX) just as we first neglected fixed costs in deciding where to produce ketchup. We simply deduce a roughly estimated flat six hours from each of the weekly machine availabilities and then develop a program based on the assumption that any program would involve exactly six hours total setup time on each type of machine. We can subsequently adjust for the number and kind of setups actually called for by the program.

EXHIBIT IX.   MACHINE-SHOP REQUIREMENTS

A—Per-Unit Machine Times

Machine type		I	II	III
Product	Process	Machine hours per unit		
A	1	0.2	0.2	0.2
A	2	0.4	—	0.3
A	3	0.6	0.1	0.1
B	1	0.2	0.3	0.4
B	2	0.1	0.1	0.8
B	3	—	0.2	1.0
C	1	0.2	0.1	0.7
C	2	0.1	0.6	0.4
C	3	—	0.8	0.2

B—Total Machine Hours Available per Week

Machine type	I	II	III
Hours	118	230	306

C—Product Requirements and "Margins"

Product	A	B	C
Minimum units required per week	100	200	300
Margin per unit on additional production	$10	$20	$30

D—Machine Setup Times

Machine type		I	II	III
Product	Process	Machine hours per setup		
A	1	2.4	0.6	1.2
A	2	1.8	—	1.8
A	3	1.2	1.8	1.2
B	1	3.0	1.2	2.4
B	2	0.6	3.0	1.2
B	3	—	3.6	1.2
C	1	2.4	1.8	3.0
C	2	1.2	1.2	1.2
C	3	—	2.4	2.4

Exhibit X shows the program which would be the most profitable *if this assumption concerning setup were true.* It calls for the production of only the required 100 units per week of Product A and 200 units of B, but it calls for 394 units of Product C instead of just the required 300. In other words, the calculation indicates that the most profitable use which can be made of the available capacity after fulfilling contractual obligations is to produce Product C.

Checking to see how much setup time is actually implied by this program, we discover that it exceeds the six-hour estimate on all three types of machine (see the totals shown in the table under B, Exhibit X). We could adjust for this by simply reducing the available machine hours accordingly and then recalculating the program, but examination of the program of Exhibit X brings to light another fact of which we ought also to take account. This is the fact that only 8 units per week of Product A are to be manufactured by Process 3.

EXHIBIT X.   MOST PROFITABLE USE OF CAPACITY ASSUMING SIX HOURS SETUP PER MACHINE

A—Program Based on Six Hours Setup per Machine

Machine type		I	II	III	
Product	Process	*Productive machine hours*			*Units produced*
A	1	18.4	18.4	18.4	92
A	3	4.8	0.8	0.8	8
B	1	40.0	60.0	80.0	200
C	1	48.8	24.4	170.8	244
C	3	—	120.0	30.0	150
	Total	112.0	223.6*	300.0	

B—Actual Setup Times Implied by Program

Machine type		I	II	III
Product	Process	*Hours of setup time*		
A	1	2.4	0.6	1.2
A	3	1.2	1.8	1.2
B	1	3.0	1.2	2.4
C	1	2.4	1.8	3.0
C	3	—	2.4	2.4
	Total	9.0	7.8	10.2

* Discrepancy from 306.0 due to rounding of figures.

Since these are bottleneck machines, we do not really need a cost calculation to decide that it is wasteful to tie them up in setup for this almost negligible amount of production. (This decision can be checked, as will be shown shortly.) Therefore we eliminate Process 3 for Product A before adjusting the available machine hours for the amount of setup time actually required, and then recalculate the program, again excluding the unwanted process. One of the more useful features of linear programming is the fact that the calculation need not be purely mechanical, but can always be controlled to agree with common sense.

The resulting revised program is shown in Exhibit XI, together with some related cost information which corresponds to the "row values" and "column values" of the ketchup problems. This information will be discussed more fully in Part III of this article. For the moment we may observe that it confirms our decision to reject Process 3 for Product A. Use of this process for 8 units would save running time worth $51.20 (8 × $6.40) but would cost nearly $100 in setup (1.8 hours on a Type II machine worth $27.80 per hour plus 1.2 hours on a Type III machine worth $38.80 per hour).

We could at this point ask whether it might also be better to use only a single process for Product C. Common sense tells us, however, that the production of Product C by each of the two methods is large enough to make setup cost negligible, and again this can be confirmed by analysis of the by-product cost information and other data on the worksheets underlying

---

EXHIBIT XI.　MOST PROFITABLE USE OF AVAILABLE CAPACITY

A—Revised Program Based on Actual Setup Requirements

Machine type			I	II	III	
Product	Process			Machine hours		Units produced
A	1	setup	2.4	0.6	1.2	100
		run	20.0	20.0	20.0	
B	1	setup	3.0	1.2	2.4	200
		run	40.0	60.0	80.0	
C	1	setup	2.4	1.8	3.0	238
		run	47.6	23.8	166.6	
C	3	setup	—	2.4	2.4	150
		run	—	120.2	30.0	
	Idle time		2.6	—	—	
	Total		118.0	230.0	305.6*	

B—Additional Margin Which Would Be Made Possible by One Additional Machine Hour

Machine type	I	II	III
Margin	—	$27.80	$38.80

C—Loss of Margin Which Would Result from Production of One Unit by Processes Other than Those Selected†

		Process	
Product	1	2	3
A	—	$(1.70)‡	$(6.40)‡
B	—	10.00	20.80
C	—	2.20	—

D—Loss of Margin Which Would Result from Production of One Extra Unit of Product Other than Product C

Product	Loss
A	$3.30
B	3.00

° Discrepancy from 306.0 due to rounding of figures.
† This table gives the loss which would arise from the running time of the process in question. The loss due to setting up for the additional process can be calculated from the value of one machine hour shown in the previous table.
‡ Minus quantity.

Exhibit XI. However, the argument is a little more complex than the one concerning Process 3 for Product A and will not be given here.

FEATURES OF PROGRAM

The final program still calls for only the required amounts of Products A and B; proper choice of processes for all products makes it possible to produce 88 units per week of Product C above the minimum requirements. This figure of 88 units is not greatly different from the 94 units shown in the first-approximation program (Exhibit X). That program, despite the rough-and-ready assumption on which it was based, proved in fact to be a very good guide to the proper use of the available capacity, and only minor refinements were required to make it into the genuinely most profitable program. A more complex problem might, of course, call for several successive approximations instead of just two as in this simple case.

One significant feature of the final program is the fact that it calls for a certain amount of idle time on machines of Type I. Any program which used this type of machine fully would produce *less* profit than the program of Exhibit XI. In one actual application of mathematical programming to a machine shop, a result of exactly this sort proved to be of very considerable practical importance. Without some kind of provable justification, personnel were extremely hesitant to include idle time in the program when management was pressing for all possible production. There is a real danger under such conditions that personnel will produce a program less efficient than is possible simply because they concentrate their efforts on discovering a program which uses all machines 100% of the time.

LOWEST COST PRODUCTION

The last few examples have involved the problem of getting out the most profitable production when a company can produce less than it can sell. Mathematical programming can also be of value when the problem is one of getting out the required production at the lowest possible cost. Here is an interesting example:

One of the large meat packers is currently using linear programming to find the least expensive way of producing a poultry feed with all the required nutritive values. All that is needed to solve such a problem is: a list of the essential nutrients (minerals, proteins, and so forth) with the amount of each which should be contained in a pound of feed; a list of the possible materials which could be used to produce the feed, with the price of each; and a table showing the amount of each nutrient contained in a pound of each possible constituent for the feed.[6]

This problem is obviously very similar to the Avgas problem discussed above, except that here the object of the program is to supply a fixed output

---

[6] The use of mathematical programming in connection with a variety of problems in farm economics is described in a number of articles in the *Journal of Farm Economics*, 1951, p. 299; 1953, pp. 471 and 823; 1954, p. 78.

at lowest cost rather than to choose the output which will maximize revenue.

Exactly the same kind of problem can arise when there is more than a single end product involved. For instance, the manager of a refinery might be faced with this kind of problem:

Suppose that instead of having inadequate supplies, this manager has ample capacity to make all he can sell. As we have seen, each of the products which he sells can be blended in a variety of ways from intermediate products such as alkylates and catalytic-cracked gasolines, and each of these intermediate products can be produced out of various crudes in various proportions. The manager of the refinery must decide which crudes to buy and how they should be refined so as to produce the required end products at the lowest possible cost.

Charnes, Cooper, and Mellon have shown that it is possible to use linear programming to solve a still more complex problem than this, bringing in, for example, the possibility of using imported as well as domestic crudes, and considering even such factors as taxes, customs duties, and the cost differences between chartered and company-owned tankers.[7]

Programming can also assist in cost reduction in a machine shop when there is sufficient capacity to produce all that can be sold of every product; it can indicate how to produce each product by the most economical process. All that is required for a programming problem to exist is that the capacity of the company's *best* or most economical machines of a given type—for example, its highest-speed screw machine—be less than sufficient for the entire production requirements. To illustrate:

Suppose that a manufacturer wants to produce specified quantities of five different screw-machine parts, A through E, and has available three different

EXHIBIT XII. PRODUCTION RATES, REQUIREMENTS, AND COSTS

Machine	I	II	III	Average weekly production (units)
Part	*Per-unit machine time (minutes)*			
A	0.2	0.4	0.5	4,000
B	0.1	0.3	0.5	9,000
C	0.2	0.2	0.4	7,000
D	0.1	0.3	0.3	9,000
E	0.2	0.3	0.5	4,000
	Variable operating cost (Per hour)			
	$12	$9	$9	

screw machines, I, II, and III. Any of the machines can produce any of the parts, but the rates of operation are different, as shown by the per-unit times in

---

7 A. Charnes, W. W. Cooper, and B. Mellon, "A Model for Programming and Sensitivity Analysis in an Integrated Oil Company," circulated in mimeographed form by the Carnegie Institute of Technology, and to be printed in a forthcoming issue of *Econometrica*.

Exhibit XII. If Machine II were slower than Machine I by the same percentage on all parts, and the same were true of Machine III, this problem would not require much thought for its solution, but when the inferiority of a machine depends on the particular part, linear programming is of use.

The hourly variable cost (direct labor, power, repair and maintenance, etc.) of operating each machine is shown in the exhibit, since the machines are not *all* bottlenecks and the whole point of the problem is to avoid operating costs insofar as possible. The exhibit also gives the required average production of each part on a weekly basis, though we shall assume that management can make each part in long runs and thereby reduce setup cost to a point where it may be neglected in determining the program. Setup, maintenance, and repairs we shall assume to be performed on Saturday, and therefore we take each machine as being available 40 hours per week.

The lowest-cost program which will accomplish the required production is shown in Exhibit XIII together with the usual by-product cost information. As

---

EXHIBIT XIII.   LOWEST-COST PROGRAM AND BY-PRODUCT COST INFORMATION

A—Lowest-Cost Machine Assignments

| | | First Alternative Program | | | Second Alternative Program | |
| | | | | | | |
Machine	I	II	III	I	II	III
Part			*Average weekly minutes*			
A	600		500	467		833
B	900			900		
C		1,400			1,400	
D	900			900		
E		1,000	333	133	1,000	
Idle time			1,567			1,567
Total	2,400	2,400	2,400	2,400	2,400	2,400

B—Cost of One Additional Unit of Product

	A	B	C	D	E
Cost	$0.0750	$0.0375	$0.0500	$0.0375	$0.0750

C—Value of One Additional Machine Hour

Machine	I	II	III
Value	$10.50	$7.50	$0.00

---

previously stated, the production shown in the exhibit is in terms of weekly *averages;* the actual length of individual runs can be determined subsequently, in the usual way in which economic lot sizes are determined.

PART III. COST AND PROFIT INFORMATION

Determination of the most profitable program under a particular set of circumstances is by no means the only advantage which management can derive from the intelligent application of mathematical programming. In many situations the technique will be of equal or even greater value as the only practical way of obtaining certain cost and profit information that is essential for sound decisions on both short-run and long-run problems of many kinds.

NEED FOR PROGRAMMING

What kind of cost information will mathematical programming provide? The gasoline blending case described in Part II of this article is a good example.

In that instance the management learned that the manufacture of Avgas A was leading to a reduction of nearly $80,000 a year in profits, far more than had been believed. Now, "cost" in this sense—the difference between the profit which results from one course of action and the profit which would result from another course of action—is obviously a completely different thing from cost in the accounting sense. Information regarding this kind of cost cannot be provided by ordinary accounting procedures. In fact, mathematical programming is the only way to get it quickly and accurately when there are many possible combinations of the various factors involved.

COSTS FOR DECISION MAKING

In some situations the need for looking at the effect of a proposed action on over-all profits rather than at its accounting cost or profit is perfectly clear. In our gasoline blending case, management knew very well that money was being lost by the production of Avgas A even though the accounts showed a profit; it was only the extent of the loss that was unknown. In other situations, by contrast, accounting cost is really misleading in arriving at a sound decision, and it is easy to overlook this fact. An example should help make this point clear:

It would seem to be plain common sense that the cost of freight to a particular warehouse is simply the freight bill which is paid on shipments to that warehouse. But management will do well to think twice before acting on the basis of this "common-sense" view.

Suppose that the sales manager of the company whose shipping program is given earlier in Exhibit II finds that it is becoming very difficult and expensive to sell the supply allocated to Warehouse E, whereas sales could easily be increased at Warehouse T. Selling price is the same at both localities and, because of competition, cannot readily be changed. On inquiry the sales manager finds that Warehouse E is being supplied at a freight cost of 23 cents per cwt., whereas freight to Warehouse T is only 6 cents per cwt. He proposes, therefore, that supplies and sales be diverted from E to T, thus increasing the company's profits by the freight saving of 17 cents per cwt. as well as reducing the cost of advertising and other selling expense.

The traffic manager will probably counter that the two warehouses are not being supplied from the same factory, and that if the supplies now being sent from Factory II to Warehouse E are shipped to Warehouse T instead, freight costs will not fall to 6 cents per cwt., but will increase from the present 23 cents to 54 cents, making a loss of 31 cents per cwt.

Actually, neither of the two would be right. In the event that supplies are diverted from Warehouse E to Warehouse T, there will in fact be an extra freight cost rather than a saving. But *if the change is properly programmed* (the supplies formerly sent from II to E should be sent to Q, which can then take less from XII, which in turn can then supply the additional amount to T), then the extra cost will be only 14 cents per cwt. It is this cost which management should compare with the estimated extra cost of selling at Warehouse E.

The example just cited and the gasoline blending case are typical of the way in which mathematical programming can be used to calculate the cost or profit which results or will result from a management decision. Generally speaking, any program is determined in such a way as to produce the greatest possible profits under a certain set of fixed conditions. If management wishes to consider a change in any of these conditions, a new program can be computed and profits under the two sets of conditions can then be compared.

AVAILABLE FIGURES

In some cases it is not even necessary to compute a new program to find the cost or profit which applies to a proposed decision. The computation of the original program itself yields as a free by-product the cost or profit which will result from certain changes in the conditions underlying the program, *provided that these changes are not too great in extent*. In the jargon of the economists, these by-product figures are "marginal" cost or profit rates. To illustrate:

For diversion of sales from Warehouse E to Warehouse T, the marginal cost is given immediately by comparison of the "row values" shown in Exhibit II for the two warehouses. The value for E is 28 cents per cwt., the value for T is 42 cents, and the extra cost is therefore 14 cents per cwt. (42–28). We can be sure at once that this will be the extra cost if only a single cwt. is diverted from one warehouse to the other, but in order to find the cost of a larger diversion we must study the program itself. If we do so, we will find that the marginal rate will hold in this case even if the entire supply now allocated to E is diverted to T. If, on the contrary, we were considering diversion from Warehouse G to T, we would find that the marginal rate of 15 cents (42–27) would apply only to the first 180 cwt.

The "column values" of Exhibit II give similar information concerning the cost or saving which will result from shifting production from one plant to another. If production is increased at Factory V and decreased at Factory VI, there will be a saving of 13 cents per cwt. ($-38-[-51]$) up to a certain limit, and study of the program shows that this limit is again 180 cwt.

The costs shown in Exhibit XI and XIII are marginal rates of this same sort. In fact, such information could have been given in connection with all the programs developed in this article.

Probably the most important use of the marginal rates is that they immediately give a *minimum* figure for the cost of a change which *reduces* profits, or a *maximum* figure for the profitability of a change which *increases* profits. For example, when the program of Exhibit XI shows that an additional hour on a machine of Type III is worth $38.80, we can be sure that ten additional hours will be worth no more than $388, although they may be worth less. Inspection of the marginal costs can thus be of practical value in limiting the range of alternatives which are worth further investigation.

USES OF INFORMATION

Now let us turn to consider a number of examples of particular kinds of cost and profit information which can be obtained by mathematical programming and which will be of use in making management decisions.

PRODUCT COST

The gasoline blending case was as good an illustration as possible of the use of mathematical programming to find the true profitability of a particular product, but the technology of gasoline blending is so complex that it is not easy to see why the answer comes out as it does. Since it is difficult to make intelligent use of a technique without really understanding how it operates, let us look briefly at a much simpler example of the same kind of problem:

In the first case involving the assignment of machine tools in Part II, there was idle capacity available after meeting the contractual commitments (see Exhibit XIII). Suppose that, after this schedule has been worked out, a customer places an order for an additional 1,000 units of screw-machine Part D. What will be the cost of filling this order?

Machine III is the only machine with idle capacity; and if the additional quantity of Part D is made on that machine, it will cost $75 (500 minutes at $9 per hour). The most economical course of action, however, is to produce the additional 1,000 units of D on Machine I, obtaining the required 100 minutes by taking 500 units of Part A off this machine and putting them on Machine III. If this is done, the accounting cost of the 1,000 units of D will be only $20 (100 minutes at $12 per hour), but the actual addition to total cost will be $37.50 (250 minutes at $9 per hour to make the 500 units of A on machine III). Thus the true cost of the additional 1,000 units of D will be $0.0375 each, the value shown in Exhibit XIII. Any price above the sum of this figure and the material cost of the part will make a contribution to fixed overhead.

MOST PROFITABLE CUSTOMERS

The example of the diversion of sales from Warehouse E to Warehouse T previously discussed shows how programming can be used to determine which customers are the most profitable in a situation where the only difference among customers lies in the cost of freight. The question would be no harder to answer if some customers were supplied from plants with higher production costs than others. Actually, of course, there is very little difference between determining the profitability of a product and the profitability of a customer.

MARKETING POLICY

Cost and profit information calculated by mathematical programming can be of use to management in deciding what products to make, what prices to set, and where to expend selling effort. We wish to emphasize, however, that we are not proposing that management should build its entire marketing program on the basis of short-run profit considerations. Programming provides information; it does *not* provide answers to policy questions.

On learning that certain products or certain customers are relatively unprofitable under present conditions, it is up to management first of all to decide whether the situation is temporary or likely to continue for some time to come. This means that management should forecast future costs and future sales potentials under a variety of reasonable assumptions, and then calculate the profitability of the various products or markets under various combinations of these assumptions. It is here that mathematical programming will make its real contribution, since it is only when such calculations can be easily and cheaply carried out that management can afford to investigate a wide range of assumptions.

After such calculations have been made, management can decide to change prices, refuse certain orders, accept them at a short-run loss, or install new capacity of such a kind and at such places that the products or markets in question will become profitable.

COST OF IMPROVEMENTS

Another kind of cost which it is often important to know is the cost of an improvement in the quality of product or service rendered to the customer. A similar problem arises when it is necessary to decide whether improved materials acquired at higher cost will increase revenues or reduce other costs sufficiently to justify their higher cost. Here are some illustrative cases:

1. *Cost of quick delivery*—According to the shipping program of Exhibit II, Warehouse M is to be supplied partly from Factory II at a cost of 40

cents per cwt. and partly from Factory IV at 21 cents per cwt. Suppose that stocks are low at this warehouse and that the manager would like to obtain some supplies quickly from the nearest source, Factory V. Since this is the nearest plant, the freight rate to Warehouse M, 10 cents per cwt., is naturally lower than the rates from the factories currently supplying the warehouse; but use of this shorter route will necessarily result in an *increase* in total cost, since the program as it stands gives the lowest possible total cost.

Programming shows immediately that the extra cost will be 16 cents per cwt. for the first 140 cwt. shipped to M from Factory V. The higher cost applying to additional quantities could be readily calculated if it were needed.

2. *Choice of process in a machine shop*—In the case of the machine shop with limited total capacity, Exhibit XI showed that the most profitable course of action was to produce Product B by the use of Process 1. Suppose that while an adequate product results from this process, a better quality would result from the use of Process 3. Would it be worth using this process in order to increase customer satisfaction, or could the price be increased sufficiently to recover a part of the additional cost?

The program of Exhibit XI shows immediately that the extra cost resulting from the use of Process 3 for Product B will be at least $20.80 per unit. The cost arises because use of this process instead of Process 1 takes up capacity which is being used for the production of Product C, each unit of which produces a "margin" of $30 per unit. Up to 128 units of B can be made by Process 3 instead of Process 1 at the cost of $20.80 per unit. If 128 units are made, the entire capacity of the shop will be used up in producing the contractual commitments for the three products, and further use of Process 3 for Product B will be impossible.

3. *Cost of antiknock rating*—In the gasoline refinery studied by Charnes, Cooper, and Mellon, antiknock ratings (PN's) were specified for Avgas B and Avgas C for both rich and lean mixture. During the study an interesting question was raised as to the additional cost entailed by the rich-mixture specification. It was found to amount to over $1,000 per day. In other words, profits could have been increased by that amount if only a lean-mixture rating had been required in the products. A little further calculation with their data produced the equally interesting result that the lean-mixture requirement on these two fuels was costing nothing; satisfaction of the rich-mixture requirement automatically produced oversatisfaction of the lean-mixture requirement.

4. *Value of improved materials*—Engineers of this same refinery suggested that if the volatility of the straight-run gasoline being used in blending could be reduced, it would be possible to produce a product mix with a

considerably higher market value. Again, programming provided significant and accurate information. It was able to show that if the RVP of this stock could be reduced by one unit, from 4.0 to 3.0, the market value of the products could be increased by $84 per day. Thus, if the improved stock could be produced at an additional cost smaller than this, it would pay to do so; otherwise it would not.

CAPITAL INVESTMENTS

Some of the most important decisions that management has to make are those which involve the choice of the most profitable ways in which to invest new capital. The choice is usually made by comparing the cost of each proposed investment with the increase of income that it will produce. When several of the proposed investments are for use in the *same* productive process, and when this process produces a variety of different products, it may be extremely difficult to determine the additional income that will result from any one investment or from any combination of investments without the use of a systematic computing technique.

Machine Tools. Consider, for example, the machine-shop case described in Part II in which sales were limited by machine capacity. Under the program of Exhibit XI, all machines of Type II and Type III are loaded to capacity; and while there is idle time on machines of Type I, it is very small in amount and actually exists only because it was unprofitable to set up to produce just 8 units per week of Product A by Process 3. Under these conditions what would be the return on an investment in an additional machine of one of the three types? It will be enough to work out the answer to this question for just one of the three types as an example, assuming that management has forecast that present demand and present costs and prices will remain unchanged in the future:

Suppose that if the shop acquires one additional machine of Type III, it would be available for 38 hours per week (one shift with allowance for down time). We simply calculate a new program for the same conditions as shown in Exhibit IX, except that we increase the available time on machines of Type III from 300 to 338 hours. The resulting program shows a $960 per-week increase in "margin"—selling price less all costs of production except the costs on the bottleneck machines. (To find the additional *income* produced by the new machine, we would have to subtract the labor and overhead costs of operating the machine and the depreciation and other costs of owning it.)

The result is due to the fact that the additional machine will make it possible to produce 32 additional units of Product C per week. Note that the $960 margin on 38 hours of use amounts to only $25.30 per hour, considerably less than the $38.80 shown in Exhibit XI. As more time is made available on machines of Type III, the bottleneck on this type becomes relatively less important and the bottlenecks on the other two types become relatively more important.

Raw Materials. Without actually working out examples, we can point to either the gasoline refinery or the hypothetical case on the selective use of raw materials (both in Part II) as two other situations where the profitability of investment would be very difficult to calculate without the use of mathematical programming. The refinery problem discussed above involved only the most profitable way in which to blend *existing* supplies of materials. Mathematical programming would readily show the additional sales revenue which could be obtained (at present prices) if the refinery were to enlarge its facilities for production of one or more of the blending stocks.

In the case on selective use of raw materials, the materials had to be purchased in the market; and, as shown in Exhibit VI, it proved unprofitable to produce Product D because of the limited supplies of materials available at normal prices. Programming could readily show how much the company could afford to invest in a source of raw materials in order to obtain them at more reasonable cost.

Programming and Forecasts. In the case of investment decisions even more than in the case of the other types of decisions previously discussed, the relevant data are not so much the facts of the immediate present as they are forecasts of conditions which will prevail in the future. An investment decision cannot be made rationally unless it is possible to explore its profitability under a variety of assumptions about future costs and markets.

It is already difficult enough to make the necessary forecasts; without the use of a systematic technique for calculation, full exploration of their implications is virtually impossible because of time, trouble, and expense. It is for this reason that it seems likely that mathematical programming may be of even greater value to management in the field of planning than in the field of immediate operating decisions.

As in the case of its other applications, however, mathematical programming is not a cure-all. Management can use it to great advantage in planning and policy making, but executives must first understand it correctly and be able to use it intelligently in combination with the other tools of forecasting and planning. The fate of mathematical programming, in other words, lies today in management's hands. The scientists, the inventors, have done their work; it is now up to the users.

Appendix
DIRECTIONS FOR SOLVING PROBLEMS
BY A USEFUL SHORT PROCEDURE

There are several alternate procedures available for solving problems of linear programming. One of these will work in all cases but takes a long time to carry out—the "general procedure," which is discussed toward the end of this appendix. The others are relatively quick, but will work only in certain cases—e.g., the "profit-preference procedure" and the "transportation-problem procedure."

A very restricted class of problems can be solved by hand with remarkable ease through the use of the "profit-preference procedure." A good example of its use is the scheduling of two classes of machine tools which formed a bottleneck in the operations of one actual company. The example has been published, with clear instructions for carrying out the procedure.[8]

By far the most frequently useful of the shorter procedures is the one known as the "transportation-problem procedure."[9] As pointed out in the preceding text, it got this name because it was developed to determine lowest-cost shipping programs, but it can be used for problems not involving transportation (just as certain problems involving transportation cannot be solved by it). Because of its simplicity, we shall give full directions for its use, first working through a simple example and then giving some suggestions for reducing more complex problems to such a form that they can be solved in the same way.

Transportation-Problem Procedure

Our example consists of assigning the production of three plants to fill the requirements of four warehouses in such a way that the total cost of freight will be at a minimum. This example involves so few variables that it could be solved far more quickly by common sense than by the use of a formal procedure. The example is adequate, nevertheless, to explain the procedure, and the procedure can then be used to solve much larger problems that would be extremely difficult to solve by common sense. Furthermore, the procedure itself can be considerably short-cut once it is understood; some suggestions for doing that will be given.

TABLE A gives the data for the problem: the freight rates from each plant to each warehouse, the capacity of each plant, and the requirements of each warehouse. Now let us go through the various steps of the solution.

TABLE A.   RATES, REQUIREMENTS, AND CAPACITIES

Factory	I	II	III	Warehouse requirements (tons)
	Freight rates (dollars per ton)			
Warehouse A	1.05	.90	2.00	35
B	2.30	1.40	1.40	10
C	1.80	1.00	1.20	35
D	1.00	1.75	1.10	25
Factory capacity (tons)	5	60	40	105

Getting a Starting Program. We first get a shipping program which satisfies the fixed requirements and capacities, regardless of cost, by the following procedure. Take Factory I and assign its 5 tons of capacity to Warehouse A. Fill the remaining 30 tons of this warehouse's requirements from Factory II. Then use 10 more tons of Factory II's capacity to satisfy Warehouse B, and assign its remaining 20 tons in partial satisfaction of Warehouse C. Complete C's requirements from Factory III, and use the remainder of III's capacity to satisfy Warehouse D. This produces the starting program of TABLE B. The procedure could obviously be used to assign warehouses to factories in a problem of any size.

A starting program can be based on a guess at the best solution rather than on the "blind" procedure described in the text; and if the guess is any good at all, subsequent calculation will be materially reduced. Start with any factory at all and use its

8 See A. Charnes, W. W. Cooper, and D. Farr, "Linear Programming and Profit Preference Scheduling for a Manufacturing Firm," *Journal of the Operations Research Society of America I,* May 1953, pp. 114–129. (The reader should be warned that errors have crept into Tables III and IV of this publication.) The technique is similar to the one used by SKF: cf. above, p. 86.

9 This procedure was developed by G. B. Dantzig: see T. C. Koopman's, *Activity Analysis of Production and Allocation* (New York, John Wiley & Sons, Inc., 1951), pp. 359–373.

TABLE B.   INITIAL PROGRAM OF SHIPMENTS
(*Tons*)

Factory	I	II	III	Total
Warehouse A	5	30		35
B		10		10
C		20	15	35
D			25	25
Total	5	60	40	105

capacity to fill the requirements of those warehouses which it seems most economical to assign to this factory. When that factory's capacity has been used up, take any other factory; first use its capacity to complete the requirements of the warehouse which was left only partially satisfied at the end of the previous step, and then go on to fill any other warehouses which it seems sensible to assign to the second factory.

The only rule which should not be neglected is to finish filling the requirements of one warehouse before going on to a new one. If the number of plants is greater than the number of warehouses, it is perfectly legitimate, however, to reverse the procedure. Start by assigning one warehouse to a series of plants, and, when the warehouse's requirements are filled, take the next warehouse, use it to absorb the leftover capacity of the last factory previously used, and then go on to new factories.

The easiest way to do the work is on paper ruled into squares; and in the following discussion reference is made to locations in the tables as "squares"; for example, the number located in Row B and Column III is said to be in Square B III.

Row Values and Column Values. Next build up a "cost table" by the following procedure:

(1) Fill in the actual freight rates, taken from TABLE A, for those routes which are actually in use in TABLE B. This produces TABLE C except for the "row values" and "column values."

(2) Fill in the "row values" and "column values" shown in TABLE C. To do this, assign an arbitrary row value to Row A; we have chosen .00 for this value, but it might have been anything. Now under every square of Row A which contains a rate, assign a column value (positive or negative) such that the sum of the row and column values equals the value in the table. In Column I we put a column value of 1.05, since $1.05 + .00$ gives the value 1.05 found in Square A I; in Column II we put a value of .90, since $.90 + .00$ gives the .90 in Square A II.

(3) We have now assigned all the column values which we can assign on the basis of the row value for Row A. We must next assign additional row values on the basis of these column values. We therefore look for rows with no row value but containing rates in squares for which column values exist. We observe that Rows B and C both have rates in Column II, which has a column value of .90. The row value for Row B must be set at .50, since $.90 + .50 = 1.40$, which is the rate in B II. By the same reasoning, we arrive at .10 as the row value for Row C.

TABLE C.   RATES FOR ROUTES USED IN TABLE B
(*Dollars per ton*)

Factory	I	II	III	Row value
Warehouse A	1.05	.90		.00
B		1.40		.50
C		1.00	1.20	.10
D			1.10	.00
Column value	1.05	.90	1.10	

(4) No further row values can be assigned, so we go back to assigning column values by looking for rates which now have a row value but no column value. We

observe that there is a 1.20 in Square C III, which has a row value of .10 but no column value. The column value must be 1.10 in order to have $1.10 + .10 = 1.20$.

(5) Finally, we assign the one missing row value. In Row D there is 1.10 in Square D III, with a column value of 1.10 and no row value. The row value must be .00 if the total of the row and column values is to equal the value in the square.

This procedure of alternately assigning row and column values can always be extended to fill in the row and column values for any cost table provided that "degeneracy" is not present in the corresponding route table. Degeneracy will be explained and a method of dealing with it will be described subsequently. In the absence of degeneracy, inability to complete the row and column values, or the existence of contradictory evidence on row and column values, indicates that an error has been made either in drawing up the table of routes (TABLE B) or in putting down in the cost table (TABLE C) the rates which correspond to the routes in TABLE B. On the other hand, it is not essential to derive the row values in the order A, B, C, D and the column values in the order I, II, III; they may be derived in any order that is possible.

The Cost Table. We now proceed to make TABLE C into a complete cost table, TABLE D, by filling in all the blank squares with the total of the appropriate row and column values. For example, the 1.55 in Square B I is the total of the row value for Row B (.50) and the column value for Column I (1.05). The figures thus derived are shown in TABLE D in lightface type, whereas the figures taken from TABLE C and corresponding to routes actually in use (in TABLE B) are shown in boldface type. (In practice, the cost table can be made up directly without actually filling in the row and column values.)

TABLE D.   COSTS FOR ROUTES USED IN TABLE B
(Dollars per ton)

Factory	I	II	III	Row value
Warehouse A	**1.05**	**.90**	1.10	.00
B	1.55	**1.40**	1.60	.50
C	1.15	**1.00**	**1.20**	.10
D	1.05	.90	**1.10**	.00
Column value	1.05	.90	1.10	

Revising the Program. We now have a complete set of tables: a rate table, a route table, and a "cost" table. We proceed to look for the best change to make in the route table in order to reduce the cost of freight. To find this change, we compare the cost table, TABLE D, with the rate table, TABLE A, looking for the square where the figure in TABLE D is *larger* than the corresponding figure in TABLE A by the greatest difference. This is Square B III. The fact that TABLE D shows 1.60 while TABLE A shows 1.40 tells us (for reasons to be explained later) that if we make shipments from Factory III to Warehouse B, and make the proper adjustments in the rest of our program, we shall save 20 cents for every ton we can ship along this new route.

The next problem is to find out what adjustments will have to be made in the rest of the program and, thereby, to find out how much we *can* ship along the new route from III to B. To do this, we construct TABLE E by first copying TABLE B (in actual practice there would be no need to copy the table) and then going through the following procedure.

(1) In the Square B III write $+x$: this is the as yet unknown amount which will be shipped over the new route from III to B. We have now overloaded the capacity of Factory III by the amount x, and must therefore decrease by x the amount which III is to supply to some other warehouse. When this is done, it will be necessary to supply this warehouse from some other factory, and so on.

(2) To locate the factories and warehouses which will *not* be affected, look through TABLE E and put a star beside any number which is the only number in *either* its row *or* its column, but remember that the x in B III counts as a number. This leads to putting a star beside the 5 in A I and the 25 in D III. Considering the starred numbers as nonexistent, look through the table again and put a star beside any numbers which are now left alone in their row or column owing to the elimination of the starred numbers in the previous step. This leads to putting a star beside the 30 in A II, since with the 5 in A I starred, A II is alone in its row.

Now look through the table again for additional numbers which have been left alone in their row or column. In this case we can find none, so the operation is complete; otherwise, we would continue eliminating until no more isolated numbers could be found.

TABLE E. CHANGES TO BE MADE IN ROUTES OF TABLE B
(*Tons*)

Factory	I	II	III	Total
Warehouse A	5*	30*		35
B		10—x	+x	10
C		20+x	15—x	35
D			25*	25
Total	5	60	40	105

(3) Having completed the foregoing procedure, we now make all required adjustments by changing the amount to be shipped along those routes which have *not* been eliminated by a star. (Once a little experience has been gained, the routes affected by a change can easily be found without first starring the routes not affected.) The +x in B III overloads Factory III, so write —x beside the 15 in C III. Warehouse C is now short by x, so write +x beside the 20 in C II. Factory II is now overloaded, so write —x beside the 10 in B II. This last —x balances the +x in Row B with which we started, so that the effect of using the new route has been completely adjusted for throughout the program.

(4) Since we shall save 20 cents for every ton we ship along the new route from III to B, we wish to divert as much tonnage as possible to this route. We therefore look at all the squares in which we have written —x and discover that the smallest number with —x beside it is the 10 in B II. This is the limit to the diversion, and therefore the value for the unknown x. We now produce TABLE F by subtracting 10 in TABLE E wherever —x was written and adding 10 wherever +x was written. This is our first revised program of shipments. By multiplying the shipments along each

TABLE F. FIRST REVISED PROGRAM OF SHIPMENTS
(*Tons*)

Factory	I	II	III	Total
Warehouse A	5	30		35
B			10	10
C		30	5	35
D			25	25
Total	5	60	40	105

route by the rate for that route, the reader can check that the reduction in total freight cost has in fact been 20 cents per ton times the 10 tons diverted to the new route.

Repeating the Process. The rest of the solution proceeds by mere repetition of the process already followed for the first improvement in the program. We build up a new cost table, TABLE G, by first copying from TABLE A the rates for the routes used in TABLE F (these rates are shown in boldface type in TABLE G), then calculating the row and column values, and then filling in the other squares (lightface type). We next compare TABLE G with TABLE A square by square and find that the square with the largest difference in favor of G is D I (1.05 against 1.00). We therefore put +x in D I of TABLE H, remove the "isolated" squares with stars, and then follow around a circuit with +x and —x as indicated. The square with the smallest number with a —x beside it is A I, with a value of 5, and we therefore add or subtract 5 as indicated by +x or —x to produce TABLE J.

TABLE G.   COSTS FOR ROUTES USED IN TABLE F
(*Dollars per ton*)

Factory	I	II	III	Row value
Warehouse A	**1.05**	**.90**	1.10	.00
B	1.35	1.20	**1.40**	.30
C	1.15	**1.00**	**1.20**	.10
D	1.05	.90	**1.10**	.00
Column value	1.05	.90	1.10	

TABLE H.   CHANGES TO BE MADE IN TABLE F
(*Tons*)

Factory	I	II	III	Total
Warehouse A	5—x	30+x		35
B			10*	10
C		30—x	5+x	35
D	+x		25—x	25
Total	5	60	40	105

TABLE J.   SECOND REVISED PROGRAM OF SHIPMENTS
(*Tons*)

Factory	I	II	III	Total
Warehouse A		35		35
B			10	10
C		25	10	35
D	5		20	25
Total	5	60	40	105

TABLE K.   COSTS FOR ROUTES USED IN TABLE J
(*Dollars per ton*)

Factory	I	II	III	Row value
Warehouse A	1.00	**.90**	1.10	.00
B	1.30	1.20	**1.40**	.30
C	1.10	**1.00**	**1.20**	.10
D	**1.00**	.90	**1.10**	.00
Column value	1.00	.90	1.10	

From TABLE J we make up a new cost table, TABLE K. Comparing TABLE K with TABLE A, we find that *every* lightface figure in TABLE K is smaller than the corresponding figure in TABLE A. There is no further improvement that can be made; in fact, any change made in the program of TABLE J would result in an *increase* in the cost of freight. Had there been squares where the lightface figure in TABLE K was just equal to the rate in TABLE A, this would have indicated a route which could be used without either raising or lowering the total cost of freight.

Why the Procedure Works. To see why this method works, consider TABLE B. Now suppose that we ship x tons from Factory III to Warehouse B. Every ton that we ship will cost $1.40, the rate between these two points. But for every ton which B gets from III, one less ton from II will be needed, thereby saving $1.40 of freight. Factory III, on the other hand, cannot now supply both C and D as before, whereas Factory II now has an excess. The simplest solution is to have III ship less to C, thus saving $1.20 per ton, while II makes up the deficit at a freight cost of $1.00 per ton. The net effect is a saving of 20 cents per ton, even though the shipments from III to B cost just as much as the previous shipments from II to B.

This saving of 20 cents per ton is exactly the difference between the $1.60 in Square B III of TABLE D and the $1.40 in the same square of TABLE A. This is true in general; the lightface figures in a "cost table" show the *net* savings on *other* routes which can be made by readjusting the program if direct shipments are made along the route in question. In other words, the lightface figures show the cost of "not using" a route; the cost of using the route is, of course, simply the freight rate as shown in TABLE A.

The best possible program has not been reached until there is no unused route for which the cost of "using" is less than the cost of "not using." To be sure, at any stage in the process of arriving at a best program there may be more than one route for which the cost of not using is higher than the cost of using. We have given the rule of making the change by introducing the route for which the difference between the two costs is greatest. This rule is not necessary, but it is commonly believed that use of this rule will *usually* reduce the number of steps required to arrive at the best possible program.

Any program is a best possible program if there is no unused route for which the cost of using is less than the cost of not using. This is a rather important fact, since it means that a solution can be checked by simply building up the corresponding cost table. There is no need to check over the work which produced the solution. Furthermore, if there is an error in the solution, it is a waste of time to go back to find it; everything will come out all right if you simply go on making successive changes until the best possible program emerges. This is an additional reason why the transportation-problem procedure is really suited for hand computation while the general procedure is not; there is a reasonably simple check on the accuracy of the final solution obtained by the general procedure, but correction of any errors that may be present is far more difficult.

The map also shows why we arrived at the value 10 for the x in TABLE E. If we make direct shipments from III to B, we must reduce shipments from II to B and from III to C. We cannot reduce either of these below zero. The route from II to B carries the smaller traffic, 10 tons, and therefore 10 tons is the largest amount we can ship from III to B. TABLE E has —x beside each route that will be reduced as a result of the change, and a +x beside each route that will be increased. The routes which are starred in TABLE E are the routes which are *not* in the "circuit" III–B–II–C–III.

In some cases adjustments could be made which would give a greater saving per ton or make possible diversion of more tons than will result from the use of the rules given above. It is perfectly permissible to make more general changes in the program at any stage provided that they are made in accordance with the rule given previously for starting the program. On the other hand, such general adjustments are never *necessary,* since it is absolutely certain that the step-at-a-time method described above will ultimately lead to the best possible program.

Coping with Degeneracy. The procedure just described serves to solve any "transportation" problem of any size except when degeneracy appears in a route table at some stage in the solution of the problem.

A route table is degenerate if it can be divided into two or more parts each of which contains a group of factories whose combined capacity exactly satisfies the combined requirements of the warehouses assigned to them. TABLE L gives an example of such a situation which might have arisen in solving the example we have just worked out. Warehouses A and D exactly use up the capacity of Factory II, while Warehouses B and C exactly use up the capacity of Factories I and III. Under such circumstances the procedure breaks down because it is impossible to build up the cost table corresponding to a degenerate route table; that is, in this instance, the cost table corresponding to TABLE L.

TABLE L. PROGRAM OF SHIPMENTS WHICH *MIGHT* HAVE OCCURRED BEFORE REACHING SOLUTION

Factory	I	II	III	Total
Warehouse A		35		35
B	5		5	10
C			35	35
D		25		25
Total	5	60	40	105

The following simple device will take care of this difficulty: If the number of plants is smaller than the number of warehouses, divide one unit of shipment by twice the number of plants. (If shipments are to be measured to the tenth of a ton, for example, we divide $\frac{1}{10}$ ton, *not* 1 ton, by twice the number of plants.) Take any convenient number which is smaller than this quotient and add it to the capacity of each of the plants; add the same *total* amount to the capacity of any one warehouse. If the number of warehouses is less than the number of plants, then reverse the rule.

In either case, solve the problem as if the additional quantities were real parts of the requirements and capacities; then when the problem has been solved, round all numbers containing fractions to the nearest unit of shipment. (A route carrying less than one-half unit is rounded to zero.) *The solution thus obtained is not approximate; it is exact.*

When to Use

In its original application, as illustrated in the example worked through above, the transportation problem consists of assigning a set of sources to a set of destinations in such a way that the total cost of transportation from sources to destinations will be a minimum. The capacity of each individual source and the requirements of each individual destination are fixed in advance, and the total capacity equals the total requirements. A unit of requirements at any destination can be filled by the use of a unit of capacity at any source, and only the cost of freight varies according to which particular source is used.

This can easily be generalized as a problem of assigning a set of *inputs* of any nature whatever to a set of *outputs* of any nature whatever in such a way that the total *cost of conversion* is a minimum. The inputs might be the available supplies of various raw materials, for example, rather than the capacities of various factories, while the outputs might be the quantities produced of various products rather than the quantities of a single product shipped to various warehouses.

There is no real change when the problem is one of maximizing profits rather than minimizing costs. Instead of a "rate table" giving the cost of converting one unit of any input into one unit of any output, we have a "margin table" giving the margin which will be realized by such conversion, the margin being the revenue from selling the unit of output less the variable costs of producing it. The program is developed in exactly the same way as in the example worked through above, except that new "routes" are introduced when the margin from not using the route is less than the margin from using it, rather than when the cost of not using it is higher than the cost of using it.

The formal characteristics which a problem must have if it is to be solved by the transportation procedure are the following:

(1) One unit of *any* input can be used to produce one unit of *any* output.

(2) The cost or margin which will result from conversion of one unit of a particular input into one unit of a particular output can be expressed by a single figure regardless of the number of units converted.

(3) The quantity of each individual input and output is fixed in advance, and the total of the inputs equals the total of the outputs.

If a problem cannot be put into the form specified by these three characteristics, it cannot be solved by the transportation procedure. However, these are *formal* characteristics, and it is often possible to find devices or tricks which will put a problem into this form even though at first glance it seems quite different. It is impossible to give a complete list of such devices, but we shall describe here the more common ones, which make it possible to solve by the transportation procedure all the problems discussed on pages 59–73.

Inputs and Outputs Not Fixed in Advance. In many problems all that we know in advance is how much of a given input is *available* or how much of a given output *could* be sold. We wish the program to determine how much of each it will be profitable to use or make. This violates the third requirement stated above, but the difficulty is easily overcome by the introduction of "dummy" inputs and outputs.

If, for example, total factory capacity exceeds total warehouse requirements, we create a dummy warehouse and treat it exactly as if it were real. The cost or profit which will result from supplying a unit to the dummy warehouse from any factory is set down in the rate table as zero, and the requirements of the dummy warehouse are set equal to the difference between total capacity and total real requirements. That part of any factory's capacity which the final program assigns to the dummy warehouse is capacity which is actually to be left idle.

If total potential output exceeds total available input, we create a dummy input equal to the difference between the two. The cost or margin resulting from supplying a unit of output from the dummy input is set at zero in the cost or margin table; where the final program calls for producing all or a part of some output from the dummy input, that amount of this potential output is not really to be produced at all.

In a case such as that described in Part II under the heading Where to Sell, it is possible that potential inputs may be left unused at the same time that potential outputs are left unfilled. This calls for the use of both a dummy input and a dummy output. Since neither the total amount of real inputs which will be used nor the total amount of real outputs which will be produced is known until the program has been computed, the quantity of the dummy input must be set equal to or greater than the total of the potential real outputs, and the amount of the dummy output must be set equal to or greater than the total of the potential real inputs. With this proviso, the quantities assigned to the dummies are arbitrary, except that the total of the real plus dummy *in*puts must equal the total of the real plus dummy *out*puts. The final program will show a certain amount of dummy output to be supplied from the dummy input, but this figure has no real meaning whatever and should be disregarded.

Inputs and Outputs at Varying Prices. It may be that a factory can supply a certain amount of product at one cost and an additional amount at a higher cost (for example, by the use of overtime), or that a certain amount of a material can be obtained at one price and additional quantities at higher prices. Similarly it may be possible to sell a certain amount of product at one price and additional amounts only at lower prices. All such cases are handled by treating the input at each cost as a separate input, or the output at each price as a separate output. In this way we can still produce a cost or margin table which shows a single unchanging per-unit cost or margin for converting any particular input into any particular output.

Note that this method will *not* work if the price at which the *entire* output is sold depends on the quantity sold. As pointed out in Part II under the heading Price, Volume, and Profit, this is not a problem of *linear* programming.

Impossible Processes. The first formal requirement set forth above demands that one unit of any output be producible from one unit of any input. In some cases particular input-output combinations may be completely or practically impossible. For example, freight service uniting a particular factory with a particular warehouse may be so poor that management will in no case permit its use, or it may be simply impossible to make a particular product from a particular material. This situation causes no difficulty at all in the solution of the problem, since all we need to do is to assign a fictitious, extremely high "cost" to the conversion of this input into this output. In this way we can be sure that the unwanted process will not appear in the final solution.

Artificial Units. In other problems, the *amount* of output which can be obtained from a unit of input depends on the particular output and input in question. In problems involving the selective use of raw materials, for example, the yield of any material may depend on the product, and the amount of material required for a particular product may depend on which material is used. Usually such problems cannot be solved by the transportation procedure, but in some cases the data can be reduced to such a form that they can.

This was true in the first raw-material problem discussed above. The trick here was to express each output not in terms of the quantity of product but in terms of the amount of Grade I material which would be required to produce it, and to express the inputs of Grade II and Grade III material in terms of the amount of Grade I material which they could replace. This made it necessary, of course, to make corresponding changes in the per-unit purchase cost of Grades II and III material and in all pre-unit processing costs. TABLE M shows the form to which EXHIBIT V had to be reduced before computing the program of EXHIBIT VI.

TABLE M.   MARGINS, SALES POTENTIALS, AND AVAILABILITIES

Product	A	B	C	D	Quantity available (equivalent tons)
Material		Margin per equivalent ton			
I at $48/ton	$ 17	$ 32	$ 4	$ 17	100
I at $72/ton	(7)*	8	(20)*	(7)*	100
II at $24/ton	19	24	12	14	100
II at $36/ton	1	6	(6)*	(4)*	100
III at $18/ton	15	24	16 †	(5)*	150
III at $24/ton	5	14	6	(15)*	250
Potential sales (equivalent tons)	240	150	240	90	

* Minus quantity.

† *Derivation for Product C and Grade III material at normal price.* As shown by the yield table (EXHIBIT V), 2.5 tons of III replace 1.5 tons of I, so that 1 ton of III = .6 equivalent tons. As shown by the same table, 1.5 tons of I are required to produce 1 ton of C, so that 1 ton of C = 1.5 equivalent tons.
Material available: 250 tons, or .6 × 250 = 150 equivalent tons.
Sales potential: 160 tons, or 1.5 × 160 = 240 equivalent tons.
Product price: $135 per ton, or $135/1.5 = $90 per equivalent ton.
Processing cost: $66 per ton of product, or $66/1.5 = $44 per equivalent ton.
Material cost: $18 per ton, or $18/.6 = $30 per equivalent ton.
Margin: $90 (selling price) − $44 (processing cost) − $30 (material cost) = $16 per equivalent ton.

The reason why the subsequent cases discussed above could not be solved by the transportation procedure should now be clear. If the raw-material problem were changed so that the inferiority in yield of the lower-grade materials varied from product to product, it would no longer be possible to express these inputs in such a way that one unit of any input could produce one unit of any output. In the machine-shop problems, the amount of time on one machine which could be replaced by one hour on another varied according to the product and the process being used. The Avgas problem is still more complex, since a single unit of any output is blended from several inputs.

Such are the problems which call for the use of the general procedure.

The General Procedure

"Simplex method" is the technical name for the general procedure. Actually there are two slightly different versions. The original version[10] will really work well only for rather small problems because of the way in which rounding errors build up from step to step. Machine computation of large problems is better carried out by the modified method of Charnes and Lemke.[11]

The general procedure can be worked by hand with the aid of a desk calculator when the number of variables is small, as in the examples discussed in the main text. However, it requires the use of automatic computers in most practical problems owing not to the difficulty but to the sheer quantity of arithmetic involved. Even the simplified Avgas problem discussed above required several days of hand computation to solve by the general procedure, while the answer to a problem with twice as many blending stocks and twice as many end products could be obtained in an hour or less, on a good electronic computer.

There are still certain limitations on the size of problem which can be handled on existing computers with existing codes of instructions, and some problems which can be solved may cost too much time or money to be worth solving. In many cases, nevertheless, skilled mathematical analysis of a very large problem will show that it can be simplified or broken into manageable parts.

Some problems will undoubtedly remain intractable, but until many more practical applications have been made, it will not really be known whether this will prove to be a frequent obstacle or a very rare one. It should be remembered that rapid progress is being made both in mathematical research[12] and in the design of computers and computing codes. If business finds that it is important to solve problems of linear programming, it seems almost certain that means will be found of solving the great majority of the problems that occur.

V.

Production Scheduling by the Transportation Method of Linear Programming*

Edward H. Bowman

With fluctuating sales, a manufacturer must have fluctuating production, or fluctuating inventory, or both. Penalties are associated with either type of

10 See A. Charnes, W. W. Cooper, and A. Henderson, *An Introduction to Linear Programming* (New York, John Wiley & Sons, Inc., 1953).

11 See *Proceedings of the Association for Computing Machinery* (Pittsburgh, Richard Rimbach Associates, 1952), pp. 97–98.

12 An important recent advance is to be found in A. Charnes and C. E. Lemke, "Computational Theory of Linear Programming I: The 'Bounded Variables' Problem," O.N.R., Research Memorandum No. 10 (Pittsburgh, Graduate School of Industrial Administration, Carnegie Institute of Technology, 1954).

* From *Operations Research,* Vol. 4, No. 1 (1956), 100–103. Reprinted by permission of the author and the Operations Research Society of America.

fluctuation. Several papers place this problem into a conventional linear-programming framework. This paper suggests that the same problem may be placed into a transportation-method framework and, further, that many transportation problems may be extended to include multiple time periods where this is meaningful. A generalized scheduling problem is placed here into the standard form of the transportation table.

Many manufacturing firms have fluctuating sales patterns, particularly on a seasonal basis. Fluctuations in sales can be accommodated by fluctuations in production or fluctuations in inventory, or by some combination of the two. Penalties are associated with either type of fluctuation. The problem may be conceived as one of balancing production overtime-type costs with inventory-storage costs to yield a minimum total of these costs.

This problem has been placed by several papers[1,2] into a conventional linear-programming framework which may be solved by the Simplex method.[3,4]

It is the purpose of this paper to suggest that the same problem may be placed into a transportation-method framework, and further, that many "transportation problems" may be extended to include multiple time periods where this is meaningful.

TABLE I[a]   UNIT COSTS OF "SHIPMENT"

	Sales periods (destination)							Total capacities
	(1)	(2)	(3)	......	(n)	Inventory (n)	Slack	
Inventory (0)	0	C_I	$2C_I$	......	$(n-1)C_I$	nC_I	0	I_0
Regular (1)	C_R	C_R+C_I	C_R+2C_I	......	$C_R+(n-2)C_I$	C_R+nC_I	0	R_1
Overtime (1)	C_0	C_0+C_I	C_0+2C_I	......	$C_0+(n-2)C_I$	C_0+nC_I	0	O_1
Regular (2)	—	C_R	C_R+C_I	......	$C_R+(n-2)C_I$	$C_R+(n-1)C_I$	0	R_2
Overtime (2)	—	C_0	C_0+C_I	......	$C_0+(n-2)C_I$	$C_0+(n-1)C_I$	0	O_2
Regular (3)	—	—	C_R	......	$C_R+(n-3)C_I$	$C_R+(n-2)C_I$	0	R_3
Overtime (3)	—	—	C_0	......	$C_0+(n-3)C_I$	$C_0+(n-2)C_I$	0	O_3
...	...	...	...	......	...	...	...	...
Regular (n)	—	—	—	......	C_R	C_R+C_I	0	R_n
Overtime (n)	—	—	—	......	C_0	C_0+C_I	0	O_n
Total requirements	S_1	S_2	S_3	......	S_n	I_n	[b]	

Production periods (source)

Table I shows how the production-scheduling problem may be thrown into the standard form for the transportation method and hence may be solved by this method.[5,6] The values within the table represent the unit cost of "shipment" from the row source to the column destination. In effect, each type of production, regular or overtime, in each time period is considered a source of supply or input. Each period's sales requirement is considered a destination or output. It is possible to compute the cost of each possible shipment, which is a combination of production and storage costs.

Certain cell-routes, marked by dashes, are forbidden since it is, of course, not possible to produce in one period and sell (and deliver) the unit in a previous period. The conventional procedure can be used of assigning a cost M to these cell-routes, representing a very high cost, so that, in effect, economic considerations drive out of the solution a "shipment" that is impossible. Though the notation does not indicate it, the production and storage costs for each assignment or cell-route may be unique, i.e., production and storage costs need not be the same for different time periods.

[a] *Notation:*

I_i = inventory at the end of the ith time period.

R_i = maximum number of units which can be produced during ith time period on regular time.

O_i = maximum number of units which can be produced during ith time period on overtime.

S_i = number of units of finished product to be sold (delivered) during ith time period.

C_R = cost of production per unit on regular time.

C_O = cost of production per unit on overtime.

C_I = cost of storage per unit per time period.

[b] Slack total $= I_0 + \Sigma R + \Sigma O - \Sigma S - I_n$.

ADVANTAGES

The computational advantages of the transportation method of linear programming are fairly well known. Practically, a further advantage is that organizations with such a scheduling problem may have some facility with the transportation method, and not with one such as the Simplex method.

The method can be readily extended to several products. Each product in each sales period becomes a separate destination (or column). Sources would remain the same. Units of sales and production would, then, probably be given in hours or other time units, and the appropriate cost of production and storage of an hour's output would be used in the computation.

Possibly the most important point to be made here is that many diverse problems now taking the transportation framework may be extended to include time periods. For instance, where a number of plants supply a number of warehouses with given requirements, capacities, and costs, some routings become advantageous (as revealed by the conventional transportation method). However, the sales requirements of many firms fluctuate, possibly to different extents in different areas and for different warehouses. The question arises as to whether it is better to use some of the less costly "routes" during the slack periods and thus incur the associated storage costs, or to use the more costly routes during the peak periods and so save those storage costs. The same general methodology presented here can be used in such a problem. Each plant in each time period becomes a source, and each warehouse in each time period becomes a destination. The appropriate storage or time-period costs are added to the conventional manufacturing and shipping costs in the cost matrix. This problem can also be further extended to more than one product.

A class at M.I.T.'s School of Industrial Management was given a relatively simple scheduling problem to solve by the general Simplex method, and then by the transportation method. The first solution took two to three hours, the second fifteen to thirty minutes. Among other reasons, this was due to the fact that in a problem of this type (with almost half of the "routes" forbidden because of impossible time sequences) short cuts and partial solutions by inspection become possible.[7] Though it is felt that the method has merit, it is quite difficult to get *meaningful costs* (linearity?), *capacities* (homogeneity?), and *requirements* (certainty?) Research involving the application of this model to several companies in the Boston area is currently underway.

References

(1) J. F. MAGEE, *Studies in Operations Research I: Application of Linear Programming to Production Scheduling,* Arthur D. Little, Inc., Cambridge, Massachusetts.

(2) JOSEPH O. HARRISON, JR., "Linear Programming and Operations Research," J. F. McCloskey and F. N. Trefethen (eds.) *Operations Research for Management,* pp. 231–33, The Johns Hopkins Press, Baltimore, 1954.

(3) G. B. DANTZIG, "Maximization of a Linear Function of Variables Subject to Linear Inequalities," T. C. Koopmans (ed.) *Activity Analysis of Production and Allocation,* Cowles Commission Monograph 13, Chap. XXI, Wiley, New York, 1951.

(4) A. CHARNES, W. W. COOPER, AND A. HENDERSON, *An Introduction to Linear Programming,* Wiley, New York, 1953.

(5) A. CHARNES AND W. W. COOPER, "The Stepping Stone Method of Explaining Linear Programming Calculations in Transportation Problems," *Management Science* 1, 49–69 (October, 1954).

(6) A. HENDERSON AND R. SCHLAIFER, "Mathematical Programming, Better Information for Better Decision Making," *Harvard Business Review* 32, 3 (May–June, 1954).

(7) H. S. HOUTHAKKER, "On the Numerical Solution of the Transportation Problem," *J. Opns. Res. Soc. Am.* 3, 210 (1955).

Chapter 5
PRODUCTION CONTROL WITH LINEAR DECISION RULES

VI.

Mathematics for Production Scheduling*

Melvin Anshen, Charles C. Holt, Franco Modigliani, John F. Muth, and Herbert A. Simon †

Fluctuations in customers' orders create difficult problems for managers responsible for scheduling production and employment. Changes in shipments must be absorbed by some combination of the following actions:

Adjusting the amount of overtime work.
Adjusting the size of the work force.
Adjusting the finished goods inventory.
Adjusting the order backlog.

Since each of these courses of action has certain associated costs, one of the prime responsibilities of production management is to make decisions that represent minimum cost choices. Difficult enough when fluctuations in orders can be predicted, the decision-making assignment is even

* From the *Harvard Business Review*, Vol. 36, No. 2 (1958), 51–58. Reprinted by permission of the *Harvard Business Review*.

† Authors' note: The research for this article was a group study carried out by members of the Office of Naval Research Project on Planning and Control of Industrial Operations at the Carnegie Institute of Technology.

more complex in the common circumstance of unforeseen changes in demand. But the importance of the fundamental responsibility is clear. Better decisions within a company contribute directly to its profits. Even more broadly, better decisions in many companies can increase the efficiency with which the nation uses its resources—a fact of growing importance as our arms race with the Soviet Union intensifies.

This article reports some of the findings of a research team that has been studying the application of mathematical techniques to the scheduling of production and employment. As a result of this work, new methods have been developed for improving the quality of scheduling decisions and for helping managers to make substantially better decisions than they could make by using prevailing rule-of-thumb and judgment procedures. Once a general rule has been developed, the computations required to establish a monthly production schedule can be completed by a clerk in a few hours or on a computer in a few minutes.

In a paint manufacturing plant the new methods were applied with significant results:

A comparison of the actual performance of the factory under management's scheduling decisions with the performance that would have been realized if the new technique had been used indicated a cost advantage of at least 8.5% for the mathematical decision rule, with further gains to be derived from improved sales forecasting. The plant was not a large one; there were only 100 employees. Yet the annual saving amounted to $51,000, reflecting reductions in a number of cost items, including regular payroll, overtime, hiring, training, layoff, and inventory.

The *specific* decision method described in this article is applicable to other plants with similar production flows and cost structures. Moreover, the *general* mathematical method can be adapted to production scheduling in plants with different cost structures. Ultimately, the basic technique should be applicable in areas other than production scheduling.

PRODUCTION AND MATHEMATICS

To use mathematics as a tool, one must understand it as a language. Since it differs from the language of production, the essential first step in applying it to a plant problem is to translate the description of production from its familiar vocabulary into the language of mathematics.

Such a transformation calls for generalizing, quantifying, and identifying the goals and constraints (limitations or restrictions). Data drawn from financial and cost-accounting systems are useful for this purpose, but they are not ordinarily sufficient. They need to be supplemented by quantitative approximations of production functions that are seldom described numerically. This may call for simplification and aggregation. Fortunately, as the following comments demonstrate, the actual transformation is less formidable than these words may suggest.

ELEMENTS OF DECISION

At one end of the production process, orders (on hand or anticipated) generate production. At the other end of the process, shipments satisfy orders. Within these limits the process accumulates costs.

Total costs for a given time period are influenced by managerial scheduling decisions. These decisions commonly are taken with reference to selected goals. Certain costs, for example, are associated with the stability of the production schedule over time:

If there is steady employment of a group of workers, costs are lower than if the group fluctuates in size. Costs associated with hiring, training, layoff, and overtime are minimized, as well as the less tangible costs related to undertime operations.

If incoming orders are not stable, however, a level rate of production can be maintained only by accepting fluctuations in the order backlog or by making shipments as required from a buffer stock of finished goods.

A decision to absorb fluctuations through finished-goods inventory commits the firm to direct investment costs and to the expenses associated with storage, handling, spoilage, obsolescence, and adverse price changes. Similarly, a decision to absorb order fluctuations through a buffer backlog also has recognizable costs associated with it, although these are not measured by standard accounting techniques—the costs of customer dissatisfaction, loss of future business, and adverse price changes.

In most work settings, production decisions are further complicated by the movement of several products through common facilities and work groups. Another problem often encountered is the variable procurement costs for materials and parts, which are related to purchase lot size and stability of incoming deliveries.

Finally, decision strategy must consider the effect of errors in forecasting future orders and of the accumulation of scheduling decisions over successive time intervals. Both these considerations compel the adoption of a dynamic strategy that combines a judgment as to the impact of the orders-stock-production-shipment complex on the immediately upcoming time period with a judgment designed to compensate for prior errors in scheduling for preceding time periods.

GETTING OPTIMUM RESULTS

The best, or minimum-cost, decision in this complicated setting with its multitude of interrelated variables is far from obvious. There is no easy way out. One management may pursue a shifting strategy outlined by rule-of-thumb procedures; another management may adopt a stable strategy designed to realize a single objective, such as level employment or prompt delivery of customers' orders. However, little argument is needed to show that such strategies cannot, except in extraordinary circumstances, produce optimum results.

Since every fluctuation in incoming orders can be met only by a choice among alternatives, each of which carries an inescapable set of associated costs, the scheduler is confronted with a complex and dynamic situation in which optimum performance requires absorption of fluctuations through a carefully weighted allocation among all buffer elements. *Part* of the impact may be taken by inventory adjustments (in both order backlogs and finished goods), *part* by overtime and undertime scheduling of workers, and *part* by changes in the size of the work force.

The best *mix* of these elements clearly depends on the nature of the production process (for example, the feasibility of smooth rather than one-step-at-a-time adjustments in the scale of operations, the relation of setup costs to length of run, and so on), and the cost structure in an individual plant. Even for a specific plant, the optimum allocation will change with the frequency, amplitude, and predictability of fluctuations in orders.

DESCRIBING THE PROBLEM

The mathematical approach to any decision-making problem requires several distinct steps:

(1) Managers must agree on the objective of maximizing or minimizing a specific criterion. For the firm as a whole this criterion would be profits. For the production-scheduling manager who controls neither sales nor profits, the critical criterion would be minimizing the costs of operations.

(2) All costs must be described quantitatively in comparable units, including intangible costs and those not regularly identified by financial and cost-accounting systems.

(3) A reporting and planning period must be selected for the accumulation and analysis of information relevant to scheduling decisions. The selection of the decision period is itself a problem. The significant factors include the size of errors in forecasting incoming orders, the cost of making forecasts, the time required to gather new information to improve earlier forecasts, the cost of making and administering decisions, and the relative costs of making a large number of small scheduling changes and a small number of large ones.

The process of quantifying intangibles, such as the costs associated with maintaining a buffer backlog of accepted but unproduced orders, is a process of making numerically explicit certain values that are always present in management thinking but in an ill-defined and cloudy form. Actually, precision in doing this is neither possible nor necessary. But it is essential to assign numerical weights to all variables and to recognize that doing this is no more than translating from a language that permits the implicit to a language that compels the explicit.

Further, the general decision problem must be expressed in a mathematical form that is flexible enough to comprehend the full range of production costs and simple enough to permit relatively easy solution. If we consider the nature of the costs associated with production, as outlined above, we will find that a U-shaped curve is a useful general expression. For example:

High costs are incurred in holding both large inventories and inventories so small that out-of-stock conditions are common, with consequent delays in shipments, short production runs to fill back orders, and customer dissatisfaction.

Similarly, frequent scheduling of both overtime and undertime (a less than fully employed work force) is expensive. Such costs are often regarded as intangible and are not explicitly reported in accounting procedures; but they must be explicitly quantified for mathematical treatment. Somewhere between the extremes of overtime and undertime, labor costs are at a minimum.

These considerations indicate the feasibility of achieving a reasonable and workable approximation of the complex of production costs by the simplest mathematical expression that gives a U-shaped curve—a quadratic function.

ASSUMPTIONS AND ADVANTAGES

It should be observed that the mathematical view of the problem does *not* assume that the costs of hiring workers equal the costs of laying them off, or that changes in costs in either direction are symmetrical. It does *not* assume that the costs associated with adding to inventory holdings equal the costs of depleting inventory, or that changes in either direction are symmetrical.

One common misunderstanding about the language of mathematics is the belief that precise numerical expression requires equal precision in reporting "facts." Mathematics can be an effective decision-making tool even in circumstances in which the values assigned to costs represent no more than approximations.

In this sense, the mathematical approach is more precise and consistent, and therefore more rational, than judgment based on experience and informed hunch. It compels the scheduler to consider all criteria previously defined as essential, and it compels him to consider them consistently every time a scheduling decision is made. In fact, after the decision rule, expressed as a formula with explicit values for specified constant elements, has been framed, it does the considering for the scheduler as a routine of the mathematical process.

It follows that the ultimate judgment of the efficacy of a mathematical decision-making process in a production setting is not in terms of its ability to schedule for minimum *true* costs. After all, the truth about all costs probably can never be determined. But it can be demonstrated mathematically that the decisions arrived at by means of the rule are the optimum decisions for the assigned cost values.

The important test thereafter is showing that the decisions arrived at by means of the mathematical tool are better decisions, and that operations are scheduled at lower costs, than decisions arrived at by alternative methods. This can be demonstrated by matching the actual record under established scheduling procedures with the record that would have been made under the mathematical decision rule.

NEW METHODS APPLIED

To test the application of the general mathematical techniques described above, the research team studied the scheduling problem in a paint factory. To simplify the analysis, without changing its fundamental concept, scheduling decisions were assumed to be made monthly and costs were accumulated over the same period.

COST COMPONENTS

First the following kinds of cost components were identified:

Regular payroll, hiring, and layoff.
Overtime and undertime.
Inventory, back order, and machine setup.

These costs were developed as discrete components and then were combined in an expression of the complete cost function for the factory as a whole.

Payroll. With monthly adjustments in the size of the work force, regular payroll costs per month were a linear function of the size of the work force; that is, if they had been correlated on a graph, with payroll costs on the vertical axis and work-force size on the horizontal axis, the resultant diagonal line would have been fairly straight. Payroll dollars for regular work time also varied directly with the size of the work force measured in man-months.

In contrast, hiring and layoff costs were associated with the magnitude of *change* in the size of the force. Costs of hiring and training rise with the number of workers hired and trained; layoff costs are associated with the number of workers discharged. There is no necessary symmetry between hiring and layoff costs in their relation to the number of workers processed; and random factors, reflecting the tightness of the local labor market or reorganization of the work structure at certain levels of employment, may also be present sporadically. The representation of these costs by a U-shaped curve, therefore, was only an approximation of the average costs of changes of various magnitudes in the work force.

Overtime. Overtime operations in the factory involved wage payments at an hourly rate 50% higher than the regular time rate. Undertime costs, reported only indirectly through the accounting system, reflected waste of labor time measured by the difference between the actual monthly wage bill and the wage bill for the smaller work force that would have sufficed to accomplish the actual production. Actual overtime during any month is determined, of course, not only by a work load in excess of that which can be produced by the regular force in regular hours, but also by such random disturbances as emergency orders, machine breakdown, quality control problems, fluctuations in productivity, and so on.

In setting the production rate and the work force for a month, the scheduler must balance the risk of maintaining too large a work force against the risk of holding a smaller work force but being required to pay overtime compensation. As in the case of hiring and layoff costs, these considerations suggested a U-shaped, possibly unsymmetrical, cost curve.

Inventory. Absorbing order fluctuations through inventory and back-order buffers gives rise to new costs. Holding a good-size inventory incurs costs such as interest, obsolescence, handling, storage, and adverse price movements. On the other hand, a decision to reduce these costs by operating with a smaller inventory invites out-of-stock conditions with the associated costs of delayed shipments, lost sales, and added machine setups for special production runs to balance out stocks and to service mandatory shipments. The analysis pointed to the need for an optimum inventory level at which combined costs were at a minimum.

COST FUNCTION DEVELOPED

The complete cost function for production and employment scheduling was developed by adding the components reviewed above. (For its mathematical form see Appendix, Reference 1.) The mathematical generalization was then applied to the specific situation in the paint factory by inserting numerical values representing estimates of the various costs involved.

Some of the estimates were drawn directly from accounting data or obtained through statistical treatment of accounting data. Other estimates, such as those for the intangible costs of delayed shipments, were subjective.

Here it is important to note that the accuracy of the estimates was not a critical consideration. An analysis of the effect of errors as large as a factor of two—that is, overestimating specific cost elements by 100% or under-estimating them by 50%—indicated that use of the resultant decision rules would incur costs only 11% higher than with correct estimates of costs.

DECISION RULES

At this point the mathematical process led to the development of two monthly decision rules, one to set the aggregate rate of production and the other to establish the size of the work force. (For the mathematical derivation of these rules see Appendix, Reference 2.) The two rules are set forth in Exhibit I.

EXHIBIT I.   PRODUCTION AND EMPLOYMENT DECISION RULES FOR PAINT FACTORY

$$P_t = \begin{cases} +.463\ O_t \\ +.234\ O_{t+1} \\ +.111\ O_{t+2} \\ +.046\ O_{t+3} \\ +.013\ O_{t+4} \\ -.002\ O_{t+5} \\ -.008\ O_{t+6} \\ -.010\ O_{t+7} \\ -.009\ O_{t+8} \\ -.008\ O_{t+9} \\ -.007\ O_{t+10} \\ -.005\ O_{t+11} \end{cases} + .993\ W_{t-1} + 153. - .464\ I_{t-1}$$

$$W_t = .743\ W_{t-1} + 2.09 - .010\ I_{t-1} + \begin{cases} +.0101\ O_t \\ +.0088\ O_{t+1} \\ +.0071\ O_{t+2} \\ +.0054\ O_{t+3} \\ +.0042\ O_{t+4} \\ +.0031\ O_{t+5} \\ +.0023\ O_{t+6} \\ +.0016\ O_{t+7} \\ +.0012\ O_{t+8} \\ +.0009\ O_{t+9} \\ +.0006\ O_{t+10} \\ +.0005\ O_{t+11} \end{cases}$$

Where:

P_t is the number of units of product that should be produced during the forthcoming month, t.

W_{t-1} is the number of employees in the work force at the beginning of the month (end of the previous month).

I_{t-1} is the number of units of inventory minus the number of units on back order at the beginning of the month.

W_t is the number of employees that will be required for the current month, t. The number of employees that should be hired is therefore $W_t - W_{t-1}$.

O_t is the forecast of number of units of product that will be ordered for shipment during the current month, t.

O_{t+1} is the same for the next month, $t+1$; and so forth.

The production rule incorporates a weighted average of the forecasts of twelve months' future orders, which contributes to smoothing production. The weights assigned to future orders decline rapidly because it is not economical to produce for distant shipment in view of the cumulative cost of holding inventory. (This accounts for the negative numbers for the last seven months in the production rule in Exhibit I.) The employment rule also incorporates a weighted average of forecasts of future orders, with the weights projected further into the future before becoming negligible.

The second term of the production equation ($.993 W_{t-1}$) reflects the influence of the number of workers employed at the end of the preceding month. Because both large decreases in the payroll and large amounts of unused labor are costly, the level of scheduled production responds to the size of the work force at the start of the month.

The next two terms in the production decision rule ($513. - .464 I_{t-1}$) relate the inventory to production. If net inventory at the end of the preceding month is large, the negative term will exceed the positive term, with a resultant downward influence on scheduled production. A reverse relationship would contribute to establishing a higher level of production. This term also functions to take account of past forecast errors, since their effect is to raise the net inventory above, or push it below, the desired level.

The first term of the employment rule ($.743 W_{t-1}$) provides for a direct influence between the work force on hand at the beginning of a month and the scheduled employment during the month, reflecting the costs associated with changing the size of the work force. The next two terms ($2.09 - .010 I_{t-1}$) make provision for the effect of the net inventory position on the employment decision. A large net inventory will lead to a decrease in the scheduled work force, and a small net inventory will have the opposite effect.

The terms of the two rules make explicit the dynamic interaction of production and employment. For example, production during a month affects the inventory position at the end of the month. This affects the employment decision in the next month, which then influences the production decision in the third month. Again, the influence of net inventory on both production and employment decisions provides a self-correcting force which operates to return inventory to its optimum position regardless of the accuracy of sales forecasts.

It is most difficult, if not impossible, to account for this interaction without a mathematical decision rule. The manager who makes these decisions on the basis of intuition and experience may hit the right answer some of the time, but he will not do so consistently.

The weighting of the sales forecasts and the feedback factors determines the magnitude of production and employment responses to fluctuations in orders, thereby allocating the fluctuations among work force, overtime, inventory, and backlog in the interest of minimizing total costs. While the work force responds to rather long-run fluctuations in orders, the principal response of production is to near-term orders and to the inventory position. Thus, the rule provides for the absorption of short-run fluctuations in orders and errors of forecasting by scheduling overtime and undertime operations.

SUPERIORITY OF DECISION RULES

How much are decision rules of the kind described an improvement over the usual methods of scheduling production?

This question was answered for the paint factory by making a hypothetical application to scheduling in the plant and comparing the results with actual performance under established procedures. Production and employment decisions in the paint factory were analyzed for a six-year period. The production and employment decision rules were then applied to simulate the decisions that would have been made if they had been in use during the same six-year period.

Because the same data were used by the research team as by management, hindsight could be of no advantage except in one situation, and here measures were taken to counteract it. A necessary ingredient for the comparison was a monthly series of forecasts of future orders throughout the period under analysis. Because no such forecasts had actually been recorded, the comparison could not be made on the basis of forecasts identical to those implicitly in the minds of management when it made its scheduling decisions. As a substitute, two sets of forecasts were devised which bracketed the forecasts actually used by management:

The first set of forecasts consisted of actual orders received. This was, in other words, a "perfect" forecast, assuming the future to be known in the present; use of it established an upper limit for performance.

The second set of forecasts was derived by assuming that future orders would be predicted by a moving average of past orders. Specifically, orders for a year ahead were forecast as equal to those actually received in the preceding year. This annual forecast was then converted to a monthly forecast by applying a seasonal adjustment based on actual past performance.

A comparison of actual costs under management scheduling with hypothetical costs under the decision rules did not tell the whole story. The figures were not solid; problems of allocating costs between paint and the other products processed in the plant, as well as the absence of a firm accounting underpinning for certain intangible costs, gave a tentative quality to the data. The research team judged, however, that the comparison was a valid one for all practical purposes and that the cost differences shown in Exhibit II were highly significant. The figures cover two periods:

1. The longest period for which cost figures were available for a three-way comparison between actual performance and expected performance under the

new rules using both a perfect forecast and a moving-average forecast, 1949–1953.

2. The period in which company performance was matched against the decision rule using a moving-average forecast, 1952–1954.

Exhibit II shows that the general effect of the decision rules, with either moving-average or perfect forecasts, was to smooth the very sharp month-to-month fluctuations in both production and size of work force in actual factory performance. Overtime and inventory-holding costs were somewhat higher under the rules with the moving-average forcast (a "backward-looking" forecast) than the actual costs were, but this excess was more

---

EXHIBIT II.   ACTUAL PERFORMANCE VS. EXPECTED PERFORMANCE
             UNDER DECISION RULES
             (*In thousands of dollars*)

		Decision rule	
		---	---
Costs	Company performance	Moving-average forecast	Perfect forecast
A. Cost Comparisons for 1949–1953			
Regular payroll	$1,940	$1,834	$1,888
Overtime	196	296	167
Inventory	361	451	454
Back orders	1,566	616	400
Hiring and layoffs	22	25	20
Total cost	$4,085	$3,222	$2,929
	139%	110%	100%
B. Cost Comparisons for 1952–1954			
Regular payroll	$1,256	$1,149	
Overtime	82	95	
Inventory	273	298	
Back orders	326	246	
Hiring and layoffs	16	12	
Total cost	$1,953	$1,800	
	108.5%	100%	

---

than offset by the fact that back orders were consistently held at lower levels. It is worth observing that the costs associated with back orders are particularly difficult to include as significant factors in rule-of-thumb and judgment decisions.

The decision rule with the moving-average forecasts saved $173,000 annually against factory performance. For this stage in the history of this plant, greater savings could have been secured by making optimum use of crude forecasts than by improving forecasts. Note that the decision rule with perfect forecasts had lower costs than the same rule with the moving-average forecasts in the 1949–1953 period—by 10%, or an average of $59,000 annually. This difference, which is entirely attributable to better forecasting, is a sizable one but only about a third as large as the other saving.

In the 1952–1954 period actual factory costs exceeded costs under the decision rule by 8.5%, or $51,000 per year on the average. The economies of the decision rule were achieved by (a) reducing payroll costs more than overtime costs increased, (b) reducing back-order penalty costs more than inventory-holding costs increased, and (c) reducing hiring and layoff costs.

CONCLUSIONS

While further exploration of the problems involved in applying mathematical decision rules to production and scheduling decisions seems clearly desirable as a basis for definitive conclusions, the study reported in this article provides firm support for several preliminary judgments. Empirical experience with the rules in the paint factory corroborates the findings of the research team. The methods have been in actual and satisfactory operation in the factory for several years now, and their use is currently being extended to other factories operated by the same company. The same methods have also been adapted to several other production-scheduling situations in other companies and have satisfactorily passed "dry run" tests preliminary to actual installations in these situations. This report of findings is confined to the paint factory study because this is the only one for which the data are publicly available at the present time.

USE OF RULES

Decision rules supplement, rather than displace, management judgment in scheduling production and employment. As such they are of great value in helping management to:

1. Quantify and use the intangibles which are always present in the background of its thinking but which are incorporated only vaguely and sporadically in scheduling decisions.
2. Make routine the comprehensive consideration of all factors relevant to scheduling decisions, thereby inhibiting judgments based on incomplete, obvious, or easily handled criteria.
3. Fit each scheduling decision into its appropriate place in the historical series of decisions and, through the feedback mechanism incorporated in the decision rules, automatically correct for prior forecasting errors.
4. Free executives from routine decision-making activities, thereby giving them greater freedom and opportunity for dealing with extraordinary situations.

In the case of the paint factory, for example, use of the decision rules permits regular monthly scheduling of production and employment to become a clerical function. Management attention can now be directed to refining cost estimates and periodically adjusting estimates to reflect changes in costs resulting from modifications of work flow and production process.

Beyond this, management has more time to consider nonroutine factors and special situations that might provide reasons for modifying scheduling decisions computed from the mathematical rules. Anticipated changes in raw material availability, in the supply of workers with necessary skills, in customers' procurement requirements, or in the character of competitors' service offerings can get the attention they deserve from executives relieved of the burden of repetitive, complex scheduling decisions.

Management time is also free to develop ways and means of improving sales forecasting, with the knowledge that such gains can be fed directly into the decision rules and thus improve their efficiency.

But it would be shortsighted to think of the decision rules only in terms of the production setting of the paint factory. They can be modified to apply to other types of scheduling problems. The required changes are in the specific cost terms, not in the general structure of the rules. To be sure, the development of the rules in a different kind of plant requires careful study of the costs that are relevant to scheduling decisions, supported by explicit quantification of all cost elements. Subject to this limitation, however, the general technique is applicable to scheduling in any plant in which the relevant costs may be approximated by U-shaped curves.

Decision problems in areas outside production would also appear to be candidates for the application of mathematical decision rules of the type described. The scheduling of warehouse operations, of employment in retail stores, of certain classes of retail merchandise stocks, of working capital, and of some types of transportation operations—all appear to be fruitful areas for research. And with ingenuity management will undoubtedly discover still other applications in the future.

Appendix

The broad implications of this study should be of interest not only to those persons directly concerned with production management but also to a wide managerial group. A more detailed, technical presentation of this research can be found in the following references:

(1) C. C. HOLT, F. MODIGLIANI, AND H. A. SIMON, "A Linear Decision Rule for Production and Employment Scheduling," *Management Science,* October 1955, p. 1.

(2) C. C. HOLT, F. MODIGLIANI, AND J. F. MUTH, "Derivation of a Linear Decision Rule for Production and Employment," *Management Science,* January 1956, p. 159.

(3) H. A. SIMON, C. C. HOLT, AND F. MODIGLIANI, "Controlling Inventory and Production in the Face of Uncertain Sales," *National Convention Transactions,* American Society for Quality Control, 1956, p. 371.

(4) H. A. SIMON, "Dynamic Programming Under Uncertainty with a Quadratic Criterion Function," *Econometrica,* Volume 24, p. 74.

VII.

Linear Decision Rules and Freight Yard Operations*

Edwin Mansfield and Harold H. Wein†

The scheduling of output and employment is an important topic in Industrial Engineering and management science. Linear decision rules have recently been devised to deal with this problem, and in practice they have resulted in substantial savings.[1] In this paper we explore the usefulness of such rules in scheduling output and employment in freight yards. The results are tentative and subject to obvious limitations, but they seem to indicate that these rules could be useful there. If so, linear decision rules may provide at least a partial solution to an important railroad problem.

At the outset, we should note that the model used here is a first approximation. Many factors that may be important are given only brief attention and some aspects of our formulation of the problem are tentative. We mention these difficulties below, although we do not always take them up in great detail.

* From *The Journal of Industrial Engineering,* Vol. 9, No. 2 (1958), 93–98. Reprinted by permission of *The Journal of Industrial Engineering.*

† This report is based on research supported by a grant from the Westinghouse Air Brake Corporation to Carnegie Institute of Technology. It is part of a larger project concerning the railroad industry. We should like to acknowledge the valuable assistance of C. Link, R. Nadel, and E. Saunders of the cooperating railroad, and the comments of our colleague, J. Dreze on an earlier draft.

[1] These rules were proposed by C. Holt, F. Modigliani, and H. Simon (3) and C. Holt, F. Modigliani and J. Muth (4). For an earlier work, see C. Holt and H. Simon (5); and for the proof of a basic proposition involved, see H. A. Simon (12).

SCHEDULING OUTPUT AND EMPLOYMENT IN FREIGHT YARDS

We begin this section by briefly describing 1. a freight yard, and 2. the switching function. Then the scheduling problem is considered. Note at the outset the importance of freight yards to the firm as a whole. The operation of these yards may result in about one-third of a firm's total operating costs.

1. Freight yards differ with respect to size and layout, but they all contain sets of tracks. In large yards, the track layout usually consists of a receiving area where incoming cars are stored, a classification area where they are switched, and an outbound area where they are stored before being hauled away as a train.

2. Although it is not the only function of a yard, switching is certainly one of the most important functions. Cars arrive on incoming trains and they must be sorted out to form outgoing trains. This sorting operation is called switching. It is performed by a switch-engine that pulls a group of cars from a receiving track and shoves the cars in the group onto the appropriate classification tracks.[2] Freight yards differ greatly with regard to the number of cars switched per day. Some small yards switch fewer than 50 cars whereas a few very large yards may switch as many as 4000 cars.

In this paper, we are concerned chiefly with large yards, i.e., those that switch 1500 or more cars per day. At such yards, most engine crews are specialized; certain crews do practically nothing but switching and no other crews can engage in such work. We are interested in the scheduling of the switching output and the switch-engine crews. To fully understand this problem, it is necessary to consider the conditions under which the yard management makes decisions concerning output and employment and the costs that must be considered when a decision is made.

The general yardmaster in a freight yard usually makes these decisions. In doing so, he operates within a somewhat different framework than that typically found in manufacturing. 1. There is no possibility of producing for inventory. The railroads are a service industry and the yard can perform services only on demand. 2. He cannot reject "orders." Under normal circumstances, he must switch all cars that arrive. 3. The planning period is generally quite short. Each day, the yardmaster decides how many switch-engine crews will be used during the next twenty-four hours and how they will be allocated during the period.[3]

[2] For a more complete description of freight yard operations, see M. Beckmann, C. McGuire, and C. Winston (1).

[3] It is commonly possible for extra crews to be hired or laid off up to two hours before the beginning of a shift. Hence, the yardmaster can often change the number of crews during one shift for the next. In practice, however, it seems that he usually plans for the entire next day and that his plans are seldom altered appreciably. A brief discussion of the problem concerning the proper planning period is contained in a following section.

When he plans the switching output and the number of switch-engine crews for the next day, the yardmaster is uncertain about the number of cars that will arrive to be switched and the average productivity of the crews. He must forecast these variables as best he can. Crew productivity is generally treated as a constant unless climatic conditions are abnormal or congestion exists in the yard.[4] In forecasting the number of car arrivals, he often uses advance information concerning some types of traffic.[5] This information is helpful, but it by no means dispels the problem of forecasting.

Having made these forecasts, the yardmaster is ready to decide on the number of cars to be switched on the next day and the number of switch-engine crews to be used then.[6] The various strategies that are open to him, and the costs that must be considered are discussed in the following section.

ALTERNATIVE STRATEGIES AND RELEVANT COSTS

The yardmaster's decision on a given day is but one in a long sequence of such decisions. A useful way of viewing his problem is to consider how he should react to changes in the number of cars that arrive to be switched. There are, in fact, large day-to-day fluctutations in the number of car arrivals, and he may adopt many strategies to meet them. 1. He may try to vary the number of crews and the number of cars switched in accordance with variations in the forecasted number of car arrivals. 2. He may try to vary the number of cars switched in accordance with these variations; but

---

[4] The productivity of the crews is relatively low when it is very cold, icy, etc. When many unswitched cars accumulate in the yard, the latter becomes congested. Serious congestion also reduces productivity because a larger part of a crew's time must be devoted to "preparatory moves."

[5] He derives this information mainly from teletype "consists" of symbol trains and from conversations with the division chief dispatcher. The former provide him with information concerning the number of cars on some important trains that will arrive up to about 7 hours hence. The latter provide him with information concerning the time at which trains will arrive.

[6] A freight yard is a service installation, and the number of cars that the yardmaster switches during the next day is not wholly under his control. In particular, he cannot switch more cars than are available to be switched. In formulating the linear decision rules, we neglect this constraint on the switching output. This seems to be legitimate so long as the rules very seldom call for the constraint to be violated. In the freight yard studied, the output prescribed by the rules violated this constraint on the following percentage of days: perfect forecast—0%, naive forecast—6%, yardmaster's forecast—0%. On the basis of this evidence it appears that the prescribed output does not violate the constraint so long as the forecasts are at all adequate. Of course, this evidence pertains only to 61 days. Another problem here is the distribution of car arrivals over time. One may take this roughly into account by linking it up with crew productivity. Still another problem revolves about the output measure used here. The number of "cuts" switched might be used instead.

he may maintain a constant number of crews, and use overtime to do the necessary switching. 3. He may switch a constant number of cars, use a constant number of crews, and allow the backlog of unswitched cars to fluctuate freely. 4. He may use some mixture of the foregoing.[7]

His choice among these strategies will depend on the costs associated with them. Clearly, the costs that are relevant are straight-time crew costs, overtime costs for crews, backlog costs, and costs associated with changes in the number of crews. We shall proceed to describe these costs and to represent them as functions of the decision variables.[8]

The straight-time crew cost seems to be self-explanatory. On the ith day, it is proportional to the number of crews used then (K_i).

The overtime cost for crews needs no explanation. Given the number of crews (K_i) and their average productivity (P), this cost is probably close to proportional to $S_i - PK_i$ where S_i is the number of cars switched on the ith day. For $S_i < PK_i$, it is probably close to zero.

The backlog in a freight yard is the number of unswitched cars that are present in the yard.[9] *Backlog costs* are the costs associated with various backlogs. Two important costs that are included are the cost of car delay and the cost of productivity decreases due to congestion. Congestion occurs when many unswitched cars accumulate in the yard. As the congestion becomes more severe, the productivity of the crews is reduced and the costs of unsatisfactory service increase because more cars are delayed.

Three simplifications are made in treating backlog costs. 1. We make them depend only on the size of the backlog. No account is taken of the types of cars in the backlog. 2. We make them depend only on the backlog at the end of the day. Although the backlog varies during each day, it does not seen to depart very greatly from that at the end of the day. 3. We make all costs accrue to the day when the backlog was formed. The costs

---

[7] For a more detailed account of the ways in which a plant may adapt to fluctuations in demand, see (3, p. 3–5).

[8] The decision variables are, of course, the number of switch-engine crews and the number of cars switched. The costs that are discussed do not include all yard costs. Most of the excluded costs are essentially fixed or independent of the decision variables. Inspection, oiling and related costs can be included in the analysis but, for simplicity, they were omitted. The costs included here differ substantially from those included in our other papers.

[9] It is possible for a car to be switched more than once in a yard. In this case, there may be some ambiguity in our definition of backlog. For example, a car has been switched once but it must be switched again. Is it included in the backlog? We did not include it. But if it seems important to do so, the analysis may very easily be adapted accordingly.

may actually be spread over subsequent days, but it is more convenient to lump them together and charge them to the initial day.[10]

The cost of various backlogs is quite small for backlogs of intermediate size.[11] But outside this intermediate range, the costs rise steeply. The increase on the right is due to congestion. The increase on the left is due to the fact that a portion of the backlog arrived just before the end of the day. It would be very costly and sometimes impossible to switch these cars before the end of the day.[12]

Costs are also associated with *changes in the number of crews*. A substantial increase in the number of crews can often be effected only by the addition of less productive crews. A substantial decrease in the number of crews is often costly because union agreements prescribe penalities for laying off regular crews. The magnitude of these costs depends, of course, on the caliber of the extra crews and the nature of local labor agreements. At the freight yard studied below, these costs seem to be very small. But at other yards, they are likely to be much more important.[13]

LINEAR DECISION RULES

In planning the number of crews and the volume of switching for the next day, the yardmaster must consider the various costs described above. He must meet changes in traffic volume with a proper mixture of changes

---

[10] One may wonder why the backlog is not treated explicitly as a queue and why queueing theory is not used to determine the expected backlog and waiting time. It would seem more natural, and it might seem to avoid some of the crudeness in our handling of waiting-time costs and productivity. There are several reasons. One reason is that the relatively simple queueing models for which analytical solutions are available do not seem to fit the situation in freight yards very well (2). Monte Carlo methods would have to be used and it would be difficult to include the results in an analytical model resulting in simple scheduling rules. Moreover, if the analytical model were cast aside and if numerical methods were used throughout, it would be difficult to get any sort of general solution to the scheduling problem we consider.

[11] Some of the backlog costs are intangible, difficult to express in dollar terms and rather crudely handled. For example, waitingtime or delay costs for cars are part of the backlog costs. In the freight yard studied, a rough estimate by the yardmaster and other officials of the average relationship between waiting-time costs and backlog was used. (In simple queueing models, there are explicit relationships between expected queue length and expected waiting time (6); but they refer to the steady-state and the models do not seem to be very good aproximations here (2). In view of these difficulties, it fortunate that moderate errors in the cost parameters have little effect on the efficiency of the rules. See (3, p. 15).

[12] The number of such cars depends on the distribution over time of the train and car arrivals. In the freight yard studied below, we relied on historical data and the yardmaster's judgment in determining the average number of cars that arrived so late that they could not possibly be switched before midnight.

[13] These costs are approximated by a function of form: $a_6(K_i - K_{i-1})^2$.

in the number of crews, changes in overtime, and changes in backlog. By a proper mixture, we mean one that in some sense minimizes costs. The problem of finding such a mixture is clearly not an easy one.

If the costs can be approximated by quadratic functions, it is possible to determine linear decision rules to aid the yardmaster in his choice. Such rules we derived for one large freight yard in the Midwest. Cost data were gathered there, and the quadratic approximations seemed to provide a reasonably good fit to the actual cost functions over the normal range. The quadratic cost function that resulted was:

$$C_i = \sum_{i=1}^{N} C_i$$

$$= \sum_{i=1}^{N} 91K_i + .85S_i - 68K_i + .0064 \, (S_i - 80K_i)^2$$

$$+ .004(B_i - 400)^2 + (K_i - K_{i-1})^2, \qquad \text{Eq. 1.}$$

where C_i is the total cost for N days, C_i is the total cost on the ith day,[14] K_i is the number of crews used on the ith day, S_i is the number of cars switched on the ith day, and B_i is the backlog at the end of the ith day.

There are six terms on the right in Eq. 1. The first term represents the straight-time crew costs. The next three terms approximate the overtime costs. The fifth term represents the backlog costs. The last term approximates the costs associated with changes in the number of crews. By definition,

$$B_i = B_{i-1} + A_i - S_i \qquad \text{Eq. 2.}$$

where A_i is the number of cars that arrive to be switched on the ith day.

Holt, Modigliani, Simon, and Muth (5) (6) have shown that linear decision rules can be derived that will minimize the expected value of Eq. 1. under rather general conditions. These rules stipulate how K_i and S_i should be chosen. In the freight yard under consideration, these rules are:

$$K_i = .01091\hat{A}_i + .00118\hat{A}_{i+1} - .00017\hat{A}_{i+2} - .00006\hat{A}_{i+3}$$
$$+ .05171K_{i-1} + .01091B_{i-1} - 4.62984 \qquad \text{Eq. 3.}$$
$$S_i = .91245\hat{A}_i + .07937\hat{A}_{i+1} - .01728\hat{A}_{i+2} - .00487\hat{A}_{i+3}$$
$$+ 2.43193K_{i-1} + .91245B_{i-1} - 364.36 \qquad \text{Eq. 4.}$$

where $\hat{A}_i$ is the forecasted number of cars that will arrive on the ith day to be switched.

COST COMPARISONS: RULE VS. ACTUAL

Some evidence concerning the potential usefulness of the rules may be gathered by comparing the actual cost for some period with the hypothetical cost had the rules been used. By its very nature, this evidence can only be

[14] By total costs, we mean the sum of the straight-time, overtime, backlog, and crew-change costs.

tentative and suggestive rather than conclusive. Moreover, the evidence presented here refers only to the one yard where data were gathered.

At this yard, a comparison of the actual and hypothetical performance was made for a two-month period in 1955.[15] To make such a comparison, certain hypothetical or assumed forecasts had to be used.[16] *First,* we assumed that the yardmaster forecasted traffic perfectly. In this case, the rule would have smoothed the switching output somewhat, but the general movement over time would have been similar to the actual movement. There would have been greater changes from day to day in the number of crews, but fewer crews would have been employed on the average. The backlog would have varied less, and it would have hovered about the optimum level. The rule's performance in terms of cost would have been better than the actual performance. Average daily costs are shown in Table I. The overtime and backlog costs seem to be reduced sharply, and the decrease in straight-time crew costs is also substantial. Total costs are reduced by about 10 percent, the total saving amounting to about 100,000 dollars a year.

Second, we assumed that the yardmaster could not forecast traffic at all. We assume that he forecasted for each day the level of traffic that arrived one week previous to that day. In this case, the movement over time of the switching would not have been smoothed. Greater changes would have occurred from day to day in the number of crews, but fewer would have been employed. The backlog would have varied greatly.[17] Average daily costs are shown in Table I. Even on the basis of these naive forecasts, the rule's performance seems slightly superior to actual performance. But the estimated savings amount to only about .6 percent or $6,500 a year.

TABLE I. COMPARISON OF ACTUAL COSTS AND COSTS
UNDER THE RULES
(*Daily costs in dollars*)

| | | With Rules | | |
| | | Based on Perfect Forecast | Based on Naive Forecast | Based on Yardmaster's Forecast |
Cost Category	*Actual*			
Straight Time	$2313	$2232	$2248	$2216
Overtime	139	22	33	32
Backlog	72	2	207	208
Crew Change	4	7	25	32
Total	$2528	$2263	$2513	$2488

[15] For a discussion of the way in which these hypothetical costs are derived and their limitations, see (3). Note too that the costs considered here are only the costs at this one yard. Any secondary effect on other yards is ignored.

[16] No records were available concerning past forecasts made by the yardmaster.

[17] The interquartile range for the backlog would have been 280 cars. The actual performance of the yard was such that it equalled 220 cars.

These two comparisons suggest that the indicated savings vary considerably with the accuracy of the forecasts. Hence, a *third* comparison seems worthwhile. In this comparison, the yardmaster's actual forecasts are used. For fourteen days, we recorded his forecasts of the number of cars that would arrive to be switched during each of the next four days. His forecasting errors were computed, and hypothetical forecasts with the same error pattern were formulated for the original two-month period. Had the rules been used with these forecasts, average daily costs would apparently have been about 1.5 percent lower than actual costs. Although this saving may appear to be modest, it would amount to about $15,000 a year at this yard alone. If such a saving were realized at every large yard, the railroad we studied would gain well over $500,000 a year. (The relevant cost comparison appears in Table I.)

Finally, the costs with the rule and perfect forecasts differ greatly from the costs with the rule and the yardmaster's forecasts.[18] (The former are about 9 percent below the latter.) To the extent that this cost differential is a crude measure of the cost of forecasting errors, it appears that the installation of equipment and techniques to improve the yardmaster's forecasts might be worthwhile. As matters stand, his forecasts do not seem greatly superior to the naive forecasts. (The costs with the rule based on his forecasts are only 1 percent lower than the costs with the rule based on the naive forecasts.) The yardmaster could never forecast perfectly, but the 9 percent differential may be some indication of the maximum saving from improved forecasting

REACTION TO THE RULES

Though comparisons such as those shown in Table I are some evidence concerning the potential usefulness of the rules, it was felt that additional evidence might be obtained by getting the yardmaster's reaction to the output and employment schedule they prescribe and the problems he envisages in actually applying them. To gather this type of evidence, an output and employment schedule was computed from the rule for fourteen days.[19] Each day, the yardmaster was shown the number of crews and the switching output that were called for, and he was asked if he could see any difficulty or disadvantage in the plan. He cited two factors that in his opinion might constitute problems in using the rules.

---

[18] Note, however, that they are not the yardmaster's actual forecasts during the two-month period. They are based on his forecasts in a later period.

[19] Some of the cost coefficients on which this rule was based were not appropriate to this period, but they seemed to be sufficiently close to the new coefficients that no adjustment was made. The yardmaster's actual forecasts were used here in deriving the output and employment schedule.

First, he felt that fluctuations in productivity could be important and that they might limit the usefulness of the rules. Without detailed data on productivity changes, it is difficult to assess the importance of this factor. Productivity changes that can be represented as random variation about a productivity estimate should cause little difficulty (11, p. 11), and the changes arising from the heterogeneity of the output and the distribution of car arrivals can perhaps be represented in this way.[20] But the productivity changes that represent an appreciable shift in the "productivity probability-distribution" can cause considerable trouble. Hence if there are interseasonal differences in productivity, different rules should be used for each season.[21]

To understand the second problem he cited, one should note that the crew productivity is generally believed to be fairly constant (all other things equal[22]) so long as the number of crews falls in a certain wide interval. If it falls below this interval, the yard functions poorly; if it falls above this interval, productivity decreases because of interference.[23] On one day, the prescribed number of crews fell above this interval, and he cited this as a second problem. If it occurred frequently, this would indeed constitute a problem. But judging from the initial two-month period, it is an extremely rare occurrence.[24] In the very few instances where it occurs, a simple remedy may be to monitor the rule.[25]

---

[20] The productivity of the crews, like the productivity of service counters in queueing theory, is affected by the proportion of time they are idle. This proportion is clearly a function of the distribution of car arrivals over time. Cars are not homogeneous with regard to switching. Two groups of twenty cars may be switched, but because of differences in "cut size" and other factors, one group may take a longer time to switch than the other. Note that congestion-induced productivity changes are taken into account in the backlog costs.

[21] Interseasonal differences in productivity may occur because of climatic differences and differences in type of traffic. It might also be noted that crews are assigned to various places in the yard. The rules offer no guidance with respect to crew location, but the yardmaster seemed to think that this problem was relatively minor.

[22] Some of the "things" held constant are distribution of car arrivals, cut size, climate, degree of congestion in the yard, experience of crews, and amount of clean-up and other miscellaneous work.

[23] Essentially, interference occurs when the functioning of one crew prevents another from working effectively.

[24] With perfect forecasts, the number of crews never fell outside the interval; with the yardmaster's forecasts, it fell outside the interval once; with naive forecasts, it never fell outside the interval.

[25] The rule may be monitored by using the number of crews within the interval that is closest to the number prescribed by the rule. Note too that the rule would almost surely have to be abandoned during the few instances when a yard is seriously congested.

Finally, the yardmaster was questioned concerning the problem of the proper planning period. The day is used here as a planning period, but since some changes in the number of crews can be made during one shift for the next, each shift could be used as a planning period. Possible advantages in using shifts are that the yardmaster's forecasts may be more accurate and that the problem of allocating crews and overtime among shifts is met. His replies shed only a limited amount of light on this matter. He seemed to feel that a planning period of one day was satisfactory and that the problem of allocation among shifts was of a secondary order.

CONCLUSION

An attempt has been made here to explore the usefulness of linear decision rules in scheduling output and employment in freight yards. The results refer almost exclusively to one large freight yard where a relatively intensive investigation was conducted. A comparison of the actual performance of the yard with the performance the rules would have prescribed was fairly encouraging. With forecasts like the yardmaster's, a substantial saving was shown but it was small percentage-wise. The yardmaster seemed very interested in the rules. He cited two problems; in both cases, there was a good chance that they would be minor.

On the whole, these results seem fairly encouraging. But note three things. First, some factors that may be quite important received little attention in the model. For example, switching takes place in a time dimension that is only partially taken into account. Some cars may have to be switched by a certain time to make proper connections, and the switching rate may have to hit peaks during the day. Second, some aspects of the model may not be entirely satisfactory. For example, the treatment of switching output as strictly a decision variable and the handling of productivity and car-delay costs seem crude at best. Third, the estimates of the cost coefficients are sometimes subject to considerable error.

Of course, in any simple model, some factors must be given limited treatment and some aspects of the formulation seem crude. Discussions with railroad officials seem to indicate that our treatment of the problem is reasonably satisfactory to the extent they can judge. In the last analysis, the test must be the performance of the rules under operating conditions. Until such a test is conducted, no really informed judgment can be made. What is needed at this point is a combination of such tests with a refinement of the model at those places that seem most important in the light of the tests. The refinement that would be required would probably not be too difficult; the difficult thing now is to know if, and where, the refinement should occur.

To conclude, we feel that linear decision rules might be used effectively in freight yards and that they might in this way contribute to the solution of an important railroad problem. But until some operating tests are conducted, no final judgment can be made.

References

(1) BECKMANN, M., McGUIRE, C., AND WINSTON, C., *Studies in Economics of Transportation,* Yale University Press, New Haven, 1956.

(2) CRANE, R., BROWN, F., AND BLANCHARD, R., "An Analysis of a Railroad Classification Yard," *Operations Research,* August 1955.

(3) HOLT, C., MODIGLIANI, F., AND SIMON, H., "A Linear Decision Rule for Production and Employment Scheduling," *Management Science,* October 1955.

(4) HOLT, C., MODIGLIANI, G., AND MUTH, J., "Derivation of a Linear Decision Rule for Production and Employment," *Management Science,* January 1956.

(5) HOLT, C., AND SIMON, H., "Optimal Decision Rules for Production and Inventory Control," *Proceedings of the Conference on Operations Research in Production and Inventory Control,* Case Institute of Technology, January 1954.

(6) KENDALL, D. G., "Some Problems in the Theory of Queues," *Journal of the Royal Statistical Society,* XIII (1951).

(7) MANSFIELD, E., AND WEIN, H., "Notes on Railroad Productivity and Efficiency Measures," *Land Economics* (forthcoming).

(8) MANSFIELD, E., AND WEIN, H., "A Model for the Location of a Railroad Classification Yard, *Management Science* (forthcoming).

(9) MANSFIELD, E., AND WEIN, H., "A Regression Control Chart for Costs," *Applied Statistics* (forthcoming).

(10) MANSFIELD, E., AND WEIN, H., "A Study of Decision-Making within the Firm" (mimeographed).

(11) MUTH, J. F., "Master Scheduling in a Factory-Warehouse System," *ONR Memorandum 40,* Carnegie Institute of Technology.

(12) SIMON, H. A., "Dynamic Programming under Uncertainty with a Quadratic Criterion Function," *Econometrica,* January 1956.

Chapter 6

THE *PERT* SCHEDULING TECHNIQUE

VIII.

*Program Evaluation and Review Technique**

David G. Boulanger

Since the first management "principles" were introduced, most planning and control methods have been predicated on using historical data. Early shop practitioners sought the most efficient utilization of time by employing time-study and task-setting methods based on stopwatch measurement of "past" processes that were physical and finite in character. Few useful techniques have been offered facilitating forward planning of management activities for which empirical information was not available.

Current industrial activities, however, can be summarized as heavily oriented toward research and development. A "one best way" of planning and pursuing R & D projects in terms of most efficient use of time presents some intangibles that cannot conveniently be measured. This growing condition, particularly in defense industries, has prompted the development of a prognostic management planning control method called Program Evaluation and Review Technique, or PERT.[1] This article intends to briefly

---

* From *Advanced Management,* Vol. 26, No. 4 (1961) 8–12. Reprinted by permission of *Advanced Management.*

[1] Various acronyms are coined (*e.g.,* PEP, PET, *etc.*) to describe modifications from the PERT method described here.

present the idea of the PERT method in a manner permitting the reader to ascertain its potential usefulness. A bibliography provides source material containing more detailed intricacies of PERT.

The PERT technique was developed as a method of planning and controlling the complex Polaris Fleet Ballistic Missile Program for Special Projects Office (SP) of Bureau of Ordnance, U.S. Navy. The team consisted of members from SP, the contractor organization, and Booz, Allen and Hamilton, Chicago.[2] Over-all, PERT appears to be a manifestation of the program concept of management with emphasis on "management by exception," in that potentially troublesome areas in R & D programs can be spotted and action taken to prevent their occurrence.

PERT, as a dynamic program tool, uses linear programming and statistical probability concepts to plan and control series and parallel tasks which appear only remotely inter-related. Many tasks involve extensive research and development which itself is difficult to schedule, least of all to find a "one best way" of doing it. PERT's objective is to determine the optimum way by which to maximize the attainment, in time, of some predetermined objective that is preceded by a number of constraints—hence its linear programming feature. A measure of the degree of risk is predicted in probabilistic terms to foretell the reasonableness of accomplishment on scheduled time—hence its statistical probability feature.

PROGRAM NETWORK DEVELOPMENT

The bar chart, presumably derived from Gantt and still widely used, serves to plan the occurrence of entire phases of tasks in series and parallel groups over a time period.

An outgrowth of the simple bar chart, called a "milestone chart," indicates significant event accomplishments as illustrated in Figure 1.

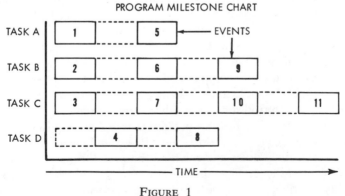

PROGRAM MILESTONE CHART

FIGURE 1

---

[2] See bibliography Item 5.

Neither technique ties together interdependencies between tasks and significant events. Series and parallel paths should indicate the inter-relationship constraints between events and tasks as shown by the arrows in Figure 2.

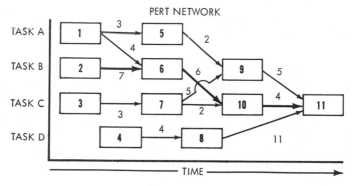

FIGURE 2

A network *event* describes a milestone, or checkpoint. An event does not symbolize the performance of work, but represents the point in time in which the event is accomplished. Each event is numbered for identification.

Arrows connecting events are *activities,* and represent performance of work necessary to accomplish an event. No event is considered accomplished until all work represented by arrows leading to it has been completed. Further, no work can commence on a succeeding event until the preceding event is completed.

If we include in Figure 2 the estimated weeks to accomplish each activity, *e.g.,* $\xrightarrow{3}$, the earliest time objective Event 11 above can be accomplished is the sum of the longest path leading to it. This is the *critical path,* and is identified by the heavy lines connecting Events 2, 6, 10, and 11 totaling 17 weeks. The critical path contains the most significant *and* limiting events retarding program completion in less than 17 weeks.

But the time required to complete a future task is more realistically stated in terms of a likelihood rather than a positive assurance. To apply this likelihood in a probabilistic sense, three time estimates are stated as a future *range of time* in which an activity may be accomplished. The three time estimates are called *optimistic, most likely,* and *pessimistic.* They serve as points on a distribution curve whose mode is the most likely, and the extremes (optimistic and pessimistic) whose spread corresponds to the probability distribution of time involved to perform the activity. It is assumed there would be relatively little chance (*e.g.,* 1 out of 100) the activity would be accomplished *outside* the optimistic or pessimistic time estimate range. Figure 3 illustrates the estimating time distribution for completing an activity some time in the future.

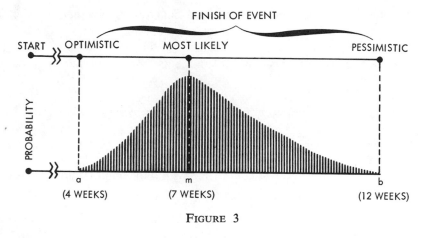

FIGURE 3

From the three time estimates (a, m, b above), a statistical elapsed time (t_e) can be derived by solving $t_e = \dfrac{a + 4(m) + b}{6}$ for each activity.[3] Following this, a statistical variance (σ^2) can be derived by solving $\sigma^2 = \left(\dfrac{b - a}{6}\right)^2$ for each activity.[4] Variance may be descriptive of uncertainty associated with the three time estimate interval. A large variance implies greater uncertainty in an event's accomplishment and *vice versa,* depending whether the optimistic and pessimistic estimates are wide or close together. This facilitates evaluating risks in a program network, and using trade-offs in time and resources to minimize risk and maximize more efficient use of "factors of production."

PROGRAM NETWORK ANALYSES

The analytical value derived from any **PERT** network depends on the configuration and content of the network. Every network should contain events which, to the program team's best knowledge, serve to significantly constrain the achievement of the end objective event. Next, events are

---

[3] The elapsed time formula is based on the assumption that the probability density of the beta distribution $f(t) = K(t\text{-}a)^\alpha (b\text{-}t)^\gamma$ is an adequate model of the distribution of an activity time.

[4] The statistical variance formula assumes the standard deviation as $\frac{1}{6}(b\text{-}a)$.

inter-connected with "activities" to illustrate their flow and interdepend-encies. After the network of events and activities is defined, three time estimates for each activity are made.

To illustrate network development and analyses, a hypothetical R & D program is assumed specifying contract completion 11 months (47 weeks) after order. Fixed resources are allocated to the program: *e.g.,* 40-hour work week, given personnel, budgeted money, *etc.* Management now is interested in:

1. What's the one best way of conducting effort toward completion?

2. What's the earliest expected time we can complete the program?

3. What are our chances of completing within the contract limitations of 47 weeks?

The network in Figure 4 is a simplified analogue of our plan to develop a "vehicle armament system." Events are described with a verb in the past tense to indicate their end accomplishment at a fixed point in time.

PERT NETWORK

VEHICLE ARMAMENT SYSTEM

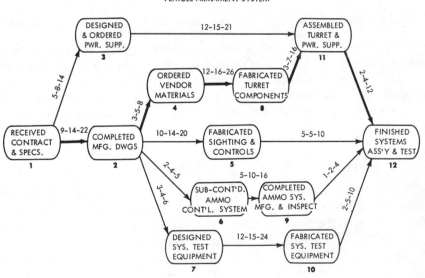

FIGURE 4

PERT ANALYSIS

A	B	C	D	E	F	G	H	I	J	K
Event	Pre. Ev.	t_e	σ^2	T_E	T_L	$T_L\text{-}T_E$	T_S	P_R	$T_L\text{-}T_E$	Event
12	11	5.0	2.78	49.5	49.5	0.0	47.0	.28	0.0	2
	5	5.8	.69						0.0	4
	9	2.2	.25						0.0	8
	10	5.3	1.78						0.0	11
11	8	7.8	4.70	44.5	44.5	0.0			0.0	12
	3	15.5	2.25							
8	4	17.0	5.44	36.7	36.7	0.0			9.5	7
4	2	5.2	.69	19.7	19.7	0.0			9.5	10
5	2	14.3	2.78	28.8	43.7	14.9			14.9	5
9	6	10.2	3.36	28.5	47.3	18.8			18.8	6
6	2	3.8	.25	18.3	37.1	18.8			18.8	9
10	7	16.0	4.00	34.7	44.2	9.5			20.5	3
7	2	4.2	.25	18.7	28.2	9.5				
3	1	8.5	2.25	8.5	29.0	20.5				
2	1	14.5	4.70	14.5	14.5	0.0				
1	—	—	—	—	—	—				

The analysis of the network is next performed and explained below.

Column A. Each event is listed beginning with objective event back to the start event.

Column B. The preceding event(s) is (are) listed beside each event. Hence, there is a succeeding and preceding event for each activity.

Column C. Statistical Elapsed Time (t_e) for each activity is found by substituting optimistic, most likely, pessimistic estimates for a, m, b and solving $t_e = \dfrac{a + 4(m) + b}{6}$

Column D. Variance (σ^2) for each activity is found by substituting optimistic and pessimistic estimates for a and b and solving $\sigma^2 = \left(\dfrac{b - a}{6}\right)^2$.

Column E. Earliest Expected Time (T_E) of accomplishment for each *event* is found by adding the elapsed time (t_e) of each activity to cumulative total elapsed times through the preceding event, staying within a single path working from "start to finish." When more than one activity leads to an event, that activity whose elapsed time (t_e) gives the greatest sum up to that event is chosen as the expected time for that event.

Column F. Latest Time (T_L) for each event is found by first fixing the earliest time of the objective event as its latest time. Next, the objective events corresponding elapsed time in Column C (*i.e.*, 5.0 weeks) is subtracted to find the latest time of the preceding event, staying within a single path working backward from finish to start. When more than one activity leads from an event (while working backwards to determine latest time), the activity which gives the *least* sum through that event is selected.

Some events may be accomplished later than expected time and have no effect on meeting the objective event. Knowledge of "slack" time in a network (*i.e.,* how much and where located) is of interest in determining program effects of "trade-offs" in resources from high-slack to low-slack areas.

Since linear programming theory says "negative slack" is not admissible (*i.e.,* not technically feasible at the objective event assuming fixed resources), we commence from an objective viewpoint to compute "positive" (or non-negative) slack. In spite of theory, a latest time derived from a fixed contractual date *less* than earliest expected time must be recognized to determine how much network "compression" is necessary to meet a scheduled date with reasonable assurance. The theory simply recognizes time is not reversible; therefore, to alleviate "negative" slack one must either extend contractual dates or employ added resources like overtime, more funds, personnel, *etc.* We assume in our analyses that resources are fixed at inception of program to maintain profit potentials.

Column G. Slack time for each event is found by subtracting Expected Time from Latest Time ($T_L - T_E$). The purpose is 1) to locate the critical path in the network designated here by events having zero slack and 2) to determine next-most-critical paths, as well as those events having substantial slack.

The critical path contains events most apt to be troublesome technically or administratively, and are danger points causing potential over-all schedule slippage. Next-most-critical path(s) is (are) found by substituting next higher slack event(s) into a second single path from start to finish. For example, the second-most-critical path is found by including Events 7 and 10 (whose slack of 9.5 weeks are the next-higher slack event over the critical path events) to give a new critical path described as Events 1, 2, 7, 10, 12. Next-most-critical paths should be observed because their criticalness may be nearly as severe as the original critical path.

By locating events having substantial slack time, it becomes possible to effect trade-offs in resources to those events having little or zero slack. For example, Events 6 and 9 each have 18.8 weeks slack, meaning their expected time of completion could be intentionally delayed 18.8 weeks without causing slippage in over-all program schedule. A point of optimization in network development is approached when the greatest possible number of events have the smallest possible range in slack from the lowest to highest slack value.

Column H. Schedule Time (T_S) is the contractual date of completion. A scheduled time may also exist for major events within a network, which later facilitates evaluating the range of risks throughout a program plan.

Column I. Probability (P_R) of meeting a scheduled time is calculated to determine feasibility of program accomplishment under the constraints in the network. Generally, probability values between .25 and .60 indicate an acceptable range to proceed with a program as depicted in the network. Probability values less than .25 assume the schedule time, T_S, cannot reasonably be met with the given resources. Values higher than .60 may indicate excess resources "built in" the network, and may warrant consideration for their use elsewhere. Probabilities need not be computed where schedule time —T_S and expected time —T_E are equal, as this assumes .5 or 50 percent probability of completing on schedule.

Probability of events are computed as follows:

(1) Solve for each event which has a schedule time (in our example, the objective event):

$$\frac{T_S - T_E}{\sigma_\Sigma \sigma^{2}*} = \frac{47.0 - 49.5}{\sqrt{18.31}} = \frac{-2.5}{4.279} = -.584$$

(2) Refer answer to Area Under the Normal Curve Table and compute probability P_R.

The value —.584 refers to —.584 standard deviations from the mean under a normal curve. Referring to a normal curve table, we find its corresponding percent of area under the normal curve to be about —.21904.

Thinking of area under the normal curve and probability as synonymous, we subtract —.21904 from .50000 (the mean of a normal curve) to derive a probability of .28906, or 28 percent. Explained, there is a 28 percent chance of meeting the schedule time of 47.0 weeks, and hence may be "acceptable" to proceed with the program under plans and resources factored in the network. Any standard of "acceptability" in probability terms should be flexible according to the importance of a program and the consequences if schedule time should not be met. Therefore, any probability value attached to a program plan should be viewed and used cautiously.

Columns J and K. Under Column J is the ascending order of slack, and under Column K their corresponding event numbers. This brings out the Critical Path as 0.0 slack events, next-most critical path(s), and those events or paths with high slack from which resources and time may be deployed to events having zero or low slack. This facilitates locating the "one best way" of reaching the objective event in relation to time.

---

* Read as "standard deviation of the sum of the variances." In our example, this is solved by: 1) finding the sum of the variances (σ^2) for the events in the Critical Path, that is $4.70 + .69 + 5.44 + 4.70 + 2.78 = 18.31$; 2) finding the square root of $18.31 = 4.279$. Probability for *any* event in a network can be computed if a T_S and T_E value is known, and by finding that event within a single network path.

RE-EVALUATION AND OPTIMIZATION

A potential value from PERT at inception of an R & D program is the opportunity it affords to introduce revised constraints into the plan and then simulate its outcome. If repeated, the optimum network can be sought, its troublesome areas located, and various tasks set under optimum conditions before time, cost, and performance were expended. Computer programs are available to expedite this, but manual methods are economical for networks up to 200 events depending on complexity of event inter-relationships. Various schedules and performance reporting formats can be developed from the analyses for team use and management analysis.

Two advantages from PERT are 1) the exacting communications it offers to participants in a program and 2) its use as a planning foundation to support bid proposals. Each participant can see his relative position and understand the timing and relationship of his responsibilities to other participants on the program team. Often the intangibles and assumptions that plague accurate bid proposals are brought out when supported with a PERT network and analysis.

USING PERT FOR RESOURCES PLANNING, COST ANALYSIS*

Considerable study is reported with PERT applied to resources (manpower and facilities) planning. Introducing a second variable to create a simultaneous two dimensional model whose objective functions are to be optimized—while their preceding constraints are being manipulated (at the same time satisfying various restrictions placed on potential solution)—will be more difficult to perform, and probably involve more elaborate procedures.

Some work is reported with PERT applied to cost analysis of a program (presumably assuming a three or N-dimensional model with variables of time, resources, cost, *et al*). It appears the object would be something analogous to predetermining that point on an average total cost curve where marginal cost intersects marginal revenue—hence, maximization of profits. Some suggestions have been offered relative to the "assumed" linearity between time and cost, in the duration of a program, but this needs clarifying before concrete methods of planning costs by PERT can be formulated.

---

* Notes from American Management Association Meeting, Saranac Lake, N.Y. March 27–29, 1961.

Bibliography

FAZAR, WILLARD, "Progress Reporting in the Special Projects Office," *Navy Management Review;* IV, No. 4 (Apr. 1959).

HAMLIN, FRED, "How PERT Predicts for the Navy," *Armed Forces Management* (July 1959).

KLASS, PHILIP J., "PERT/PEP Management Tool Use Grows," *Aviation Week;* Vol. 73, No. 22 (Nov. 28, 1960), pp. 85–91.

KLASS, PHILIP J., "PERT Plan Eases Management Problems," *Aviation Week;* Vol. 74, No. 15 (Apr. 10, 1961), pp. 80–81.

MALCOLM, D. G., J. H. ROSEBOOM, C. E. CLARK, AND W. FAZAR, "Application of a Technique for Research and Development Program Evaluation," *Journal of Operations Research;* Vol. 7, No. 5 (Sept.–Oct. 1959), pp. 646–669.

PERT Data Processing Lesson Plan Handbook for Technicians, Department of the Navy, Bureau of Naval Weapons, Special Projects Office; GPO Catalog No. D217.14: P94, Washington: Government Printing Office, 1960.

PERT Instruction Manual and Systems and Procedures for the Program Evaluation System. Department of the Navy, Bureau of Naval Weapons, Special Projects Office; GPO Catalog No. D217.14: P94/2, Washington: Government Printing Office, 1960.

PERT Summary Report, Phase I, Department of the Navy, Bureau of Naval Weapons, Special Projects Office; GPO Catalog No. D217.2: P94/958, Washington: Government Printing Office, 1960.

PERT Summary Report, Phase II, Department of the Navy, Bureau of Naval Weapons, Special Projects Office; GPO Catalog No. D217.2: P94/958-2, Washington: Government Printing Office, 1961.

Polaris Management, Department of the Navy, Special Projects Office; GPO Catalog No. D217.2: P75, Washington: Government Printing Office, 1961.

Proceedings of the PERT Co-ordination Task Group Meeting (17–18 March 1960 and 16–17 August 1960), Department of the Navy, Bureau of Naval Weapons, Special Projects Office; GPO Catalog No. D217.2: P94/4/960, Washington: Government Printing Office, 1960.

Summary Minutes for Meeting of Contractor PERT Reporting Personnel (8–9 June 1960 and 14–15 July 1960), Department of the Navy, Bureau of Naval Weapons, Special Projects Office; GPO Catalog No. D217.2: P94/5/960, Washington, Government Printing Office, 1960.

Summary Minutes for Meeting of Contractor PERT Reporting Personnel (15–16 November 1960, held at U.S. Naval Weapons Laboratory, Dahlgren, Virginia); GPO Catalog No. D217.2: P94/5/960-2, Washington: Government Printing Office, 1961.

IX.

How to Plan and Control with PERT*

Robert W. Miller

The last three years have seen the explosive growth of a new family of planning and control techniques adapted to the Space Age. Much of the development work has been done in the defense industry, but the construction, chemical, and other industries have played an important part in the story, too.

In this article we shall consider what is perhaps the best known of all of the new techniques, Program Evaluation Review Technique. In particular, we shall look at:

PERT's basic requirements, such as the presentation of tasks, events, and activities on a network in sequential form with time estimates.

Its advantages, including greatly improved control over complex development and production programs, and the capacity to distill large amounts of data in brief, orderly fashion.

Its limitations, as in situations where there is little interconnection between the different activities pursued.

Solutions for certain difficulties, e.g., the problem of relating time needed and job costs in the planning stage of a project.

Policies that top management might do well to adopt, such as taking steps to train, experiment with, and put into effect the new controls.

LEADING FEATURES

The new techniques have several distinguishing characteristics:

(1) They give management the ability to plan the best possible use of resources to achieve a given goal, within over-all time and cost limitations.

---

* From the *Harvard Business Review,* Vol. 40, No. 2 (1962), 93–104. Reprinted by permission of the *Harvard Business Review.*

(2) They enable executives to manage "one-of-a-kind" programs, as opposed to repetitive production situations. The importance of this kind of program in the national and world economy has become increasingly clear.

Many observers have noted that the techniques of Frederick W. Taylor and Henry L. Gantt, introduced during the early part of the century for large-scale production operations, are inapplicable for a major share of the industrial effort of the 1960's—an era aptly characterized by Paul O. Gaddis as the "Age of Massive Engineering."[1]

(3) They help management to handle the uncertainties involved in programs where no standard cost and time data of the Taylor-Gantt variety are available.

(4) They utilize what is called "time network analysis" as a basic method of approach and as a foundation for determining manpower, material, and capital requirements.

CURRENT EFFORTS AND PROGRESS

A few examples may serve to indicate for top management the current status of the new techniques:

The Special Projects Office of the U.S. Navy, concerned with performance trends in the execution of large military development programs, introduced PERT on its Polaris Weapon Systems in 1958. Since that time, PERT has spread rapidly throughout the U.S. defense and space industry. Currently, almost every major government and military agency concerned with Space Age programs is utilizing the technique, as are large industrial contractors in the field. Small businesses wishing to participate in national defense programs will find it increasingly necessary to develop a PERT capability if they wish to be competitive in this field.

At about the same time the Navy was developing PERT, the DuPont company, concerned with the increasing costs and time required to bring new products from research to production, initiated a study which resulted in a similar technique known as CPM (Critical Path Method). The use of the Critical Path Method has spread quite widely, and is particularly concentrated in the construction industry.

A very considerable amount of research now is taking place on the "extensions" of PERT and CPM time-network analysis, into the areas of manpower, cost, and capital requirements. As an ultimate objective, "trade-off" relationships between time, cost, and product or equipment performance objectives are

[1] See "Thinking Ahead: The Age of Massive Engineering," HBR January–February 1961, p. 138.

being sought. This research is being sponsored in two ways—directly by the military and privately by large companies. Anyone familiar with the current scene will be impressed by the amount of activity taking place in this field. For example, at least 40 different code names or acronyms representing variations of the new management controls have come to my attention.

Applications of the new techniques, beyond the original engineering-oriented programs for which they were developed, are increasing every day. The PERT approach is usefully introduced in such diverse situations as planning the economy of an underdeveloped nation or establishing the sequence and timing of actions to effect a complex merger.

WHAT IS PERT?

Now let us turn to PERT in particular. What are its special characteristics and requirements?

The term is presently restricted to the area of time and, as promulgated by the Navy, has the following basic requirements:

(1) All of the individual tasks to complete a given program must be visualized in a clear enough manner to be put down in a *network,* which is comprised of *events* and *activities.* An event represents a specified program accomplishment at a particular instant in time. An activity represents the time and resources which are necessary to progress from one event to the next. Emphasis is placed on defining events and activities with sufficient precision so that there is no difficulty in monitoring actual accomplishment as the program proceeds.

(2) Events and activities must be sequenced on the network under a highly logical set of ground rules which allow the determination of important critical and subcritical paths. These ground rules include the fact that no successor event can be considered completed until all of its predecessor events have been completed, and no "looping" is allowed, i.e., no successor event can have an activity dependency which leads back to a predecessor event.

(3) Time estimates are made for each activity of the network on a three-way basis, i.e., optimistic, most likely, and pessimistic elapsed-time figures are estimated by the person or persons most familiar with the activity involved. The three time estimates are required as a gauge of the "measure of uncertainty" of the activity, and represent full recognition of the probabilistic nature of many of the tasks in development-oriented and non-standard programs. It is important to note, however, that, for the purposes of computation and reporting, the three time estimates are reduced to a

single expected time (t$_e$) and a statistical variance (σ^2).

(4) Depending on the size and complexity of the network, computer routines are available to calculate the critical path through it. Computers can also calculate the amount of slack (viz., extra time available) for all events and activities not on the critical path. A negative slack condition can prevail when a calculated end date does not achieve a program date objective which has been established on a prior—and often arbitrary—basis.

TIME ESTIMATES

Interpretation of the concepts of optimistic, most likely, and pessimistic elapsed times has varied over the past few years. The definitions which, in my opinion, represent a useful consensus are as follows:

• *Optimistic*—An estimate of the *minimum* time an activity will take, a result which can be obtained only if unusual good luck is experienced and everything "goes right the first time."

• *Most likely*—An estimate of the *normal* time an activity will take, a result which would occur most often if the activity could be repeated a number of times under similar circumstances.

• *Pessimistic*—An estimate of the *maximum* time an activity will take, a result which can occur only if unusually bad luck is experienced. It should reflect the possibility of initial failure and fresh start, but should not be influenced by such factors as "catastrophic events"—strikes, fires, power failures, and so on—unless these hazards are inherent risks in the activity.

The averaging formulas by which the three time estimates are reduced to a single expected time (t$_e$), variance (σ^2) and standard deviation (σ) are shown in Appendix A. The approximations involved in these formulas are subject to some question, but they have been widely used and seem appropriate enough in view of the inherent lack of precision of estimating data. The variance data for an entire network make possible the determination of the *probability of meeting an established schedule date,* as shown in Appendix B.

CRITICAL PATH

In actual practice, the most important results of the calculations involved in PERT are the determination of the critical path and slack times for the network. Exhibit I contains data on the critical path and slack times for a sample problem (they are based on the method of calculation given in

EXHIBIT I.   SLACK ORDER REPORT

PERT SYSTEM   Airborne Computer — Slack Order Report

Date 7/12/61   Week 0.0   Time in Weeks   Page 1

Event	T_E	T_L	T_L-T_E	T_s	P_r	
001	0.0	0.0	0			T_E = Expected event date
010	7.2	7.2	0			
011	12.2	12.2	0			T_L = Latest allowable event date
008	14.5	14.5	0			T_L-T_E = Event slack
009	19.5	19.5	0			T_s = Scheduled event date
013	21.5	21.5	0			
014	23.5	23.5	0	23.5	.50	P_r = Probability of achieving T_s date
020	20.6	21.5	+ .9			
019	15.6	16.5	+ .9			
012	14.4	15.3	+ .9			
018	9.4	10.3	+ .9			
007	18.2	20.3	+2.1			
006	16.0	18.1	+2.1			
005	13.2	14.3	+2.1			
003	14.2	19.5	+5.3			

Appendix C). The data are shown in the form of a *slack order report* (lowest to highest slack), which is perhaps one of the most important output reports of PERT.

Other output reports, such as event order and calendar time order reports, are also available in the PERT system.

The actual utilization of PERT involves review and action by responsible managers, generally on a biweekly basis. Because time prediction and performance data are available from PERT in a "highly ordered" fashion (such as the slack order report), managers are given the opportunity to concentrate on the important critical path activities. The manager must determine valid means of shortening lead times along the critical path by applying new resources or additional funds, which are obtained from those activities that can "afford" it because of their slack condition. Alternatively, he can re-evaluate the sequencing of activities along the critical path. If necessary, those activities which were formerly connected in a series can be organized on a parallel or concurrent basis, with the associated trade-off risks involved. As a final, if rarely used, alternative, the manager may choose to change the scope of work of critical path activities in order to achieve a given schedule objective.

It should be pointed out that the PERT system requires constant updating and reanalysis; that is, the manager must recognize that the outlook for the completion of activities in a complex program is in a constant state of flux, and he must be continually concerned with problems of re-evaluation and reprograming. A highly systematized method of handling this aspect of PERT has been developed. An example of the input transaction document involved is given in Exhibit II.

BENEFITS GAINED

Perhaps the major advantage of PERT is that the kind of planning required to create a valid network represents a major contribution to the definition and ultimate successful control of a complex program. It may surprise some that network development and critical path analysis do, in fact, reveal interdependencies and problem areas which are either not obvious or not well defined by conventional planning methods. The creation of the network is a fairly demanding task, and is a sure-fire indicator of an organization's ability to visualize the number, kind, and sequence of activities needed to execute a complex program.

Another advantage of PERT, especially where there is a significant amount of uncertainty, is the three-way estimate. While introducing a complicating feature, this characteristic does give recognition to those realities of life which cause difficulties in most efforts at planning the future.

The three-way estimate should result in a greater degree of honesty and accuracy in time forecasting; and, as a minimum, it allows the decision maker a better opportunity to evaluate the degree of uncertainty involved in a schedule—particularly along the critical path. If he is statistically sophisticated, he may even wish to examine the standard deviation and probability of accomplishment data, which were mentioned previously as features of PERT. (If there is a minimum of uncertainty in the minds of personnel estimating individual activity times, the single-time approach may, of course, be used, while retaining all the advantages of network analysis.)

And, finally, the common language feature of PERT allows a large amount of data to be presented in a highly ordered fashion. It can be said that PERT represents the advent of the management-by-exception principle in an area of planning and control where this principle had not existed with any real degree of validity. An additional benefit of the common language feature of PERT is the fact that many individuals in different locations or organizations can easily determine the specific relationship of their efforts to the total task requirements of a large program.

This particular benefit of PERT can represent a significant gain in the modern world of large-scale undertakings and complex organizational relationships.

COPING WITH PROBLEMS

A new and important development like PERT naturally is attended by a certain amount of confusion and doubt. PERT does indeed have its problems. However, they are not always what businessmen think they are, and often there is an effective way of coping with the restrictions. In any event, it is time to compare the situations in which PERT works best with situations in which real (or imagined) troubles occur.

UNCERTAIN ESTIMATES

One key question concerns the unknowns of time and resources that management frequently must contend with.

In PERT methodology an available set of resources including manpower and facilities is either known or must be assumed when making the time estimates. For example, it is good practice to make special notations directly on the network when some special condition (e.g., a 48-hour rather than a 40-hour week) is assumed. Experience has shown that when a well-thought-through network is developed in sufficient detail, the first activity time estimates made are as accurate as any, and these should not be changed unless a new application of resources or a trade-off in goals is specifically determined. A further caution is that the first time estimates should not be biased by some arbitrarily established schedule objective, or by the assumption that a particular activity does not appear to be on a critical path. Schedule biasing of this kind, while it obviously cannot be prevented, clearly atrophies some of the main benefits of the technique— although it is more quickly "discovered" with PERT than with any other method.

Because of the necessity for assumptions on manpower and resources, it is easiest to apply PERT in *project-structured* organizations, where the level of resources and available facilities are known to the estimator. PERT does not itself *explicitly* resolve the problem of multiprogram planning and control. But there is general recognition of this problem, and considerable effort is being devoted to a more complete approach to it. Meanwhile, in the case of common resource centers, it is generally necessary to undertake

EXHIBIT II. INPUT TRANSACTION DOCUMENT

PERT
REPORT OF TIME INTERVAL ESTIMATES & PROGRESS

CLASSIFICATION:

Revision No. 2
13 February 1959

Flow Chart No.   Report Period

From: (Name & Location of Contractor)   To:

Contract No.   From:
     To:

For office use only				Activity Identification		Time Interval Estimates			Completion Date	Remarks
				Beginning Event No.	Ending Event No.	Optimistic (weeks) *	Most Likely (weeks) *	Pessimistic (weeks) *		
(1)	(A)(2) (3)	(4)		(B)	(C)	(D)	(E)	(F)	(G)	(H)
12	13 — 16	17		18 — 26	34 — 42	44 — 47	48 — 51	52 — 55	60 — 65	
									Mo. Day Yr.	
1				010	003	5.0	6.0	7.0	— — —	New Activity
1				003	007	0	0	0	— — —	New Activity
1										
										Re-estimated Activity
2				010	018	1.0	1.0	2.0	— — —	(Change)
2				018	019	5.0	6.0	8.0	— — —	(Change)

Signature of Responsible Official: Date Signed: CLASSIFICATION:

* Columns D, E, and F. These estimates should be given for the full activity even though the activity has already started.

a loading analysis, making priority assumptions and using the resulting data on either a three-time or single-time basis for those portions of the network which are affected. It should be pointed out, however, that in terms of actual experience with PERT, the process of network development forces more problems of resource constraint or loading analysis into the open for resolution than do other planning methods.

Although PERT has been characterized as a new management control approach for R & D effort, it has perhaps been most usefully applied in those situations where there is a great deal of interconnection between the activities of a network, or where there are interface connections between different networks. Certainly, network development and critical path analysis are *not* too appropriate for the pure research project, where the capabilities of small numbers of individuals with highly specialized talents are being utilized at a "constant rate" and where their activities have no significant dependence on other elements of the organization.

JUSTIFYING THE COST

One of the most frequently raised objections to PERT is the cost of its implementation. A fundamental point to examine here is whether or not a currently established planning system is giving value commensurate with its cost—or perhaps more basic still, whether the system is used at all effectively to pinpoint and control problem areas. It is quite true that, by the very nature of its logical requirements for networking, the PERT approach calls for a higher degree of planning skill and a greater amount of detail than is the case with conventional methods. In addition, the degree of detail —or the "level of indenture," as it is called—is a function of:

1. What is meaningful to the person or persons who will actually execute the work.
2. The depth of analysis that is required to determine the valid critical path or paths.

It is perhaps more appropriate to view the implementation of PERT as costing *initially* something in the order of twice that of a conventional planning system. This figure will vary significantly with such factors as:

The degree of planning capability already available.
The present effectiveness and homogeneity of the organization.
The amount and quality of PERT indoctrination given.

The advocates of PERT are quick to point out that the savings achieved through better utilization of resources far outweigh the system's initial implementation costs. This better utilization of resources is achieved through concentration on critical path activities—for example, limiting overtime effort to these key activities as opposed to across-the-board use of overtime. Even more important are the "downstream" savings which are achieved by earlier and more positive action on the part of management to resolve critical problems.

USE OF STANDARD NETWORKS

Because of the considerable impact of PERT on many organizations where detailed planning has not had major emphasis, a trend has recently developed which can be characterized as "model or standard networking." This has to do with efforts to use the typical or established pattern of carrying out a new program in a particular industry. Model networking has many advantages (particularly in handling the large amounts of data involved in PERT), but it may also compromise one of the real objectives of PERT— i.e., *obtaining a valid network which is meaningful to the person or persons who will actually execute the work.* In the area in which PERT is used most effectively, no two programs are ever exactly the same, and no two individuals will have exactly the same approach to the development of a network. Therefore, model networks should be introduced with this caution: management should always allow for the possibility of modifications which will match the realities of the program.

In addition, the introduction of so-called "master plan networks" and the top-down structuring of networks for large programs involving many different firms, while very necessary from the point of view of long-range planning and the ultimate management of such programs, should be handled with a philosophy of flexibility. The cardinal principle is that a management control structure is no better than the adequacy and accuracy of the data at its base. In the future, the top-down structuring approach—which is already evident on some major defense and space programs—will probably increase; but internal objectives, at least, will be subject to reconfirmation or realignment at the level of industry, depending upon the development of actual operating networks. The top-down structuring approach is necessary, however, in order to preserve the mechanics of *network integration;* it is important that the data from lower level networks be properly and meaningfully summarized into higher level management data.

APPLICATION TO PRODUCTION

A final problem, and one that is often viewed as a disadvantage of the PERT technique, is the system's lack of applicability to all of the manufacturing effort. As has been stated, PERT deals in the time domain only and does not contain the quantity information required by most manufacturing operations. Nevertheless, PERT can be, and has been, used very effectively through the preliminary manufacturing phases of production prototype or pilot model construction, and in the assembly and test of final production equipments which are still "high on the learning curve." After these phases, established production control techniques which bring in the quantity factor are generally more applicable.

Note, however, that many programs of the Space Age never leave the preliminary manufacturing stage, or at least never enter into mass production. Therefore, a considerable effort is going forward at this time to integrate the techniques of PERT within some of the established methods of production control, such as line-of-balance or similar techniques that bring in the quantity factor.

COMPUTER OR NO COMPUTER

As a result of the Navy's successful application of PERT on the Polaris program, and other similar applications, there is a common impression that the technique is only applicable when large-scale data-processing equipment is available. This is certainly true for large networks, or aggregations of networks, where critical path and slack computations are involved for several hundred or more events. It is as desirable to have a computer handle a PERT problem when a large volume of data is involved as it is to use a computer in any extensive data-processing assignment.

Probably equally significant is the fact that several ingenious manual methods have been developed in industry by those organizations which have become convinced of PERT's usefulness. These manual methods range from simple inspection on small networks to more organized but clerically oriented routines for determination of critical path, subcritical path, and slack times on networks ranging from fifty to several hundred events.

This is sufficient proof that PERT can be applied successfully to smaller programs wherever the degree of interconnection and problems of uncertainty warrant it. For those organizations practiced in the technique, both the creation of small networks and the formation of time estimates and their reduction to critical path and slack analyses can be done in a matter of hours. Exhibit I shows the network for a relatively small electronics program. Developed in less than a day, the whole network required only two hours for manual computation.

It seems clear that the small business organization which wishes to participate in national defense and space programs, or to improve its own internal schedule planning and control, should not hesitate to adopt PERT merely because it does not possess large-scale data-processing equipment.

PERT EXTENSIONS

Variations of PERT to accommodate multi-project and manufacturing situations have already been mentioned, and these are merely representative of a basic movement to *extend* the approach into the areas of manpower, cost, and the equipment performance variable. The ultimate objective of these efforts is to quantify the trade-off relationships which constantly come up in development programs but are rarely acted on with explicit data in hand.

Though none of these extensions have as yet attained as much maturity and acceptance as PERT, anyone familiar with the current scene will be impressed by the amount of effort being given to them throughout the country in both the military and industry. One healthy offset to this particular trend is the fact that the U.S. Air Force has withdrawn its code name PEP (Program Evaluation Procedure), which was an equivalent for PERT. There remains, however, a great need for government agencies to standardize input and output requirements of basic PERT time before uniformly effective extensions can be made into the area of PERT cost.

COST OF PERT

Much of the research effort on the new management controls which has taken place throughout the country is concentrated on the problem of manpower and cost. This is probably a reflection of certain facts well known to most managers of complex development programs:

The job-costing structures generally found in industry on such programs need a great deal of interpretation to relate *actual costs* to *actual progress*. They are rarely, if ever, related in any explicit manner to the details of the scheduling plan.

Cost constraints, either in the form of manpower shortages or funding restrictions, have a great deal to do with the success with which a program of this type can be managed.

It seems clear that both of these problems must be solved in any valid PERT cost approach.

SOLUTIONS REQUIRED

The first problem means that an explicit relationship must be established between the time network and the job-cost structure, either on a one-to-one basis for each network activity, or for a designated chain of activities. As a minimum, it seems clear that more detailed job-cost structures are required than are currently in general use, although this requirement should present no serious limitation for organizations which possess modern data-processing methods and equipment.

With regard to the development of actual cost figures *from the time network,* an estimate of manpower requirements, segregated by classification, is usually considered the easiest place to start, since these requirements were presumably known at the time the network was established. In fact, however, the actual summation of such data often reveals a manpower or funding restriction problem, and forces a replanning cycle if no alternatives are available. (The summation may also reveal inefficiencies in personnel loading which can be removed by proper use of slack activities.)

Two other problems that should be mentioned are:

Handling of nonlabor items—The costs for these items are often aggregated in a manner quite different from that which would result from analysis of a time network. For example, there is a tendency to buy common materials on one purchase order for a number of different prototypes, each one of which represents a distinct phase of progress in the program. A refined allocation procedure may be needed to handle this problem.

Coordination and control efforts (e.g., those carried out by project or systems engineering[2])—These are often not indicated on time networks unless they result in specific outputs. For PERT costing, the network in all cases must be complete, i.e., it must include all effort which is charged to the program. This is one of the areas of deficiency in many present-day networks, and one which must be overcome before an effective PERT cost application can be made.

Each of the foregoing problems can be handled if the underlying network analysis is sound and subject to a minimum of change. As a result, a number of different approaches are being attempted in the development of costed networks which have as their objective the association of at least one cost estimate with a known activity or chain of activities on the network.

The ultimate objective of all this is not only improvement in planning and control, but also the opportunity to assess possibilities for "trading off" time and cost, i.e., adding or subtracting from one at the expense of the other. It is generally assumed that the fundamental relationships between time and cost are as portrayed in Exhibit III. Curve A represents *total direct costs* versus time, and the "U" shape of the curve results from the assumption that there is an "optimum" time-cost point for any activity or job. It is assumed that total costs will increase with any effort to accelerate or delay the job away from this point.

Some companies in the construction industry are already using such a time-cost relationship, although in a rather specialized manner:

---

[2] See Clinton J. Chamberlain, "Coming Era in Engineering Management," HBR September–October 1961, p. 87.

EXHIBIT III. ASSUMED TIME-COST RELATIONSHIPS FOR A JOB

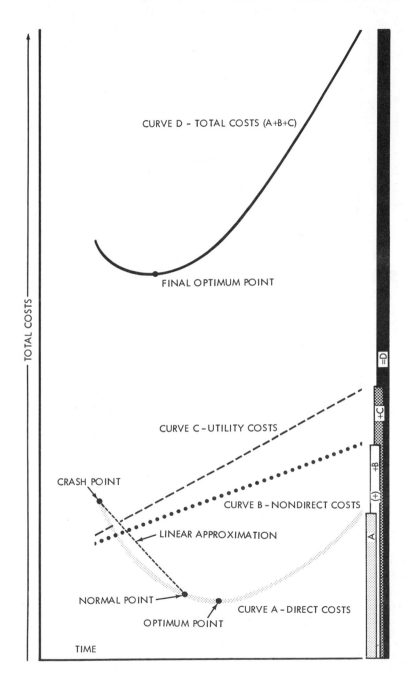

In one application, an assumption is made that there is a *normal* job time (which might or might not coincide with the theoretical optimum), and that from this normal time, costs increase linearly to a *crash* time, as indicated in Exhibit IV. This crash time represents the maximum acceleration the job can stand. On the basis of these assumptions, a complete mathematical approach and computer program have been developed which show how to accelerate progress on a job as much as possible for the lowest possible cost. The process involves shortening the critical path or paths by operating on those activities which have the lowest time-cost slopes.

CHALLENGE OF COST DATA

Making time-cost data available for each activity in usable form is one of the fundamental problems in using PERT in development programs. At the planning stage, in particular, it is often difficult to determine time-cost relationships in an explicit manner, either for individual activities or for aggregates of activities. (There are often good arguments for characterizing time-cost relationships at this stage as nonlinear, flat, decreasing, or, more likely, as a range of cost possibilities.) If alternative equipment or program objectives are added as a variable, the problem is further compounded. While posing the problem, it should be pointed out that solutions for the technical handling of such data, in whatever form they are obtained, have recently been developed.

Curve B of Exhibit III indicates *total non-direct costs,* which are assumed to increase linearly with time. Clearly, accounting practices will have to be reviewed to provide careful (and probably new) segregations of direct from non-direct costs for use in making valid time-cost trade-off evaluations.

Curve C is a representation of a *utility cost curve,* which is needed to complete the picture for *total time-cost* optimization (indicated as the final optimum point on Curve D). The utility cost curve represents a quantification of the penalty for *not accomplishing the job at the earliest possible time,* and is also shown as a linear function increasing with time.

The difficulties of determining such a curve for many programs, either in terms of its shape or dollar value, should be obvious. But it is significant to note that in certain industrial applications such utility cost data have already been developed, typically in the form of "outage" costs or loss-of-profit opportunities, and used as the basis for improved decision making. Further, in the military area, utility cost is the converse of the *benefit* concept in the *benefit-cost* ratio of a weapon system; this factor varies with the time of availability of a weapon system, even though judgments of benefit are made difficult by rapidly changing circumstances in the external world.

CONCLUSION

It is clear that there are difficulties yet to be overcome in advancing the new management controls—particularly in the new areas into which PERT is being extended. Yet it is equally clear that significant progress has been made during the last few years. Assuming that developments continue at the rate at which they have taken place up to this time, what position should top management adopt *today* with regard to its own internal policies on the new management controls? Here are the most important steps:

(1) Management should review its present planning and scheduling methods and compare their effectiveness with that of the PERT system. (I refer here to time networks only—not time-and-cost networks.) If the company has no direct experience with PERT, it will certainly want to consider training and experimentation programs to acquaint the organization with the technique. Management may even decide to install PERT on all of its development programs (as some companies have done), even though it has no contractual requirement to do so.

(2) Management may wish to enter directly into research efforts on the new management controls or, if such efforts are already underway in the organization, place them on a higher priority basis. As a minimum, it will probably want to assign someone in the organization to follow the numerous developments that are taking place in the field.

(3) Executives should consider carefully the problem of organization to make the most effective use of the new management controls. They should consider the responsibilities of the level of management that actually uses PERT data in its working form, and the responsibilities of the levels of management that review PERT in its various summary forms. Clearly, the usefulness of the new management controls is no greater than the ability of management actually to act on the information revealed. It should be realized that problems of "re-centralization" will probably accompany the advent of the new tools, particularly when applied to the planning and control of large projects throughout an entire organization.

(4) Finally, management may wish to assess the longer range implications of the new management controls, both for itself and for the entire industrial community, since the forces calling for centralization of planning and control within the firm can apply equally well outside it. In the Age of Massive Engineering, the new controls will be utilized to an increasing extent in the nation's defense and space programs, which are in turn increasing in size and complexity. It seems clear that the inevitably closer relationships between government and industry will require the establishment of new guidelines for procurement and incentive contracting where these management control techniques are used.

APPENDIXES

Readers interested in applying PERT may find it helpful to have a more precise formulation of certain calculations mentioned earlier in this article. The mathematics involved is basically simple, as the following material demonstrates.

Appendix A

EXPECTED TIME ESTIMATE

In analyzing the three time estimates, it is clear that the optimistic and the pessimistic time should occur least often, and that the most likely time should occur most often. Thus, it is assumed that the most likely time represents the peak or modal value of a probability distribution; however, it can move between the two extremes. These characteristics are best described by the Beta distribution, which is shown in two different conditions in the figures that follow.

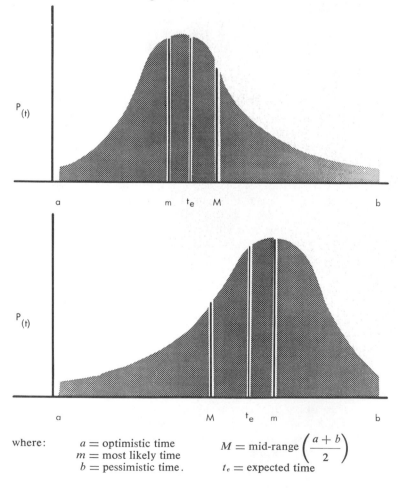

where: a = optimistic time M = mid-range $\left(\dfrac{a+b}{2}\right)$
          m = most likely time
          b = pessimistic time. t_e = expected time

As a result of analyzing the characteristics of the Beta distribution,[*] the final approximations to expected time (t_e), variance (σ^2), and standard deviation (σ) were written as follows for a given activity:

1. $t_e = \dfrac{1}{3} \ (2m + M)$

$\qquad = \dfrac{1}{3} \left(2m + \dfrac{a+b}{2} \right)$

$\qquad = \dfrac{a + 4m + b}{6}$

2. $\sigma^2 = \left(\dfrac{b-a}{6} \right)^2$

3. $\sigma = \dfrac{b-a}{6}$

The first equation indicates that t_e should be interpreted as the weighted mean of m (most likely) and M (mid-range) estimates, with weights of 2 and 1, respectively. In other words, t_e is located one third of the way from the modal to the mid-range values, and represents the 50% probability point of the distribution, i.e., it divides the area under the curve into two equal portions.

Appendix B

PROBABILITY OF MEETING SCHEDULE TIMES

On the basis of the Central Limit Theorem, one can conclude that the probability distribution of times for accomplishing a job consisting of a number of activities may be approximated by the normal distribution, and that this approximation approaches exactness as the number of activities becomes great (for example, more than 10 activities along a given path). Thus, we may define a curve which represents the probability of a meeting on established schedule-end date, T_S:

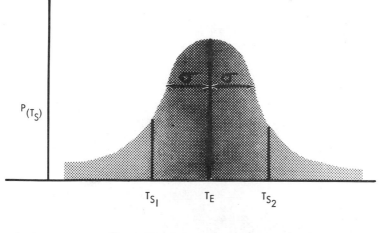

where:

$$T_E = \Sigma t_{e_1} + t_{e_2} + \cdots t_{e_n}$$
$$\sigma^2(T_E) = \Sigma \sigma^2(t_{e_1}) + \sigma^2(t_{e_2}) + \ldots \sigma^2(t_{e_n})$$
$$T_{S_1} = \text{Scheduled Time (earlier than } T_E)$$
$$T_{S_2} = \text{Scheduled Time (later than } T_E)$$

---

[*] NOTE: The Beta distribution is analyzed in the PERT Summary Report, Phase I (Special Projects Office, Department of the Navy, Washington, D.C., July 1958).

The probability of meeting the T_S date when given T_E and σ^2 for a chain of activities is defined as the ratio of (1) the area under the curve to the left of T_S to (2) the area under the entire curve. The difference between T_S and T_E, expressed in units of σ, is:

$$\frac{T_S - T_E}{\sigma}$$

This will yield a value for the probability of accomplishing T_S by use of the normal probability distribution table. Thus:

$$\frac{T_{S_1} - T_E}{\sigma} = -1.2\sigma, \ Pr \ (\text{accomplishment of } T_{S_1}) = .12$$

$$\frac{T_{S_2} - T_E}{\sigma} = +1.2\sigma, \ Pr \ (\text{accomplishment of } T_{S_2}) = .88$$

Appendix C

DETERMINING CRITICAL PATH AND SLACK TIMES

The computation steps required to determine the critical path and slack times for the network shown in EXHIBIT I are as follows:

Step 1. Determine t_e for every activity on the network in accordance with the equation:

$$t_e = \frac{a + 4m + b}{6}$$

Step 2. Starting with Event No. 001, determine T_E (or cumulative T_E) for all succeeding events by summing small t_e's for each activity leading up to the event, *but choosing the largest value for the final T_E figure in those cases where there is more than one activity leading into an event.*

Step 3. The process covered in Step 2 is now reversed. Starting with the final event, we determine the *latest allowable time,* T_L, for each event so as not to affect critical path event times. For example, Event No. 007, with a T_E of 18.2 weeks, can be delayed up to a T_L of 20.3 weeks, before it will affect critical path Event No. 013.

Step 4. The difference between T_L and T_E, known as slack, is next computed for each event. These computations are shown in EXHIBIT I in the form of a slack order report, i.e., in order of lowest to highest values of *positive* slack. Note that along the critical path there is zero slack at every event, since by definition there is no possibility of slippage along the critical path without affecting the final event date. In this example, if the end schedule date of Event No. 014 were set at 23.0 weeks rather than at 23.5 weeks, there would be 0.5 weeks of *negative* slack indicated for every event along the critical path.

Step 5. The computation of variance and of standard deviation for this network is optional and involves adding the variances for each activity along the critical path, which are obtained from the formula:

$$\sigma^2 = \left(\frac{b - a}{6}\right)^2$$

The interested reader may verify that the variance for final Event No. 014, with a T_E of 23.5 weeks, is 1.46 weeks.

Chapter 7

HEURISTICS IN PRODUCTION SCHEDULING

X.

*A Heuristic Method of Assembly Line Balancing**

Maurice D. Kilbridge and Leon Wester

The principle of the division of labor when applied to the mass assembly of manufactured items takes the form of the progressive assembly line. The work is divided into individual tasks and assigned to consecutive operators on the line. As the product moves down the line each operator adds to it his share of the work. The process of apportioning the assembly work among the operators is known as "line balancing."

Although progressive assembly has been practiced for fifty years[1] in American industry, some of the basic problems associated with it have not received adequate attention. Among these is the line balancing problem which, until recently, was not formulated analytically. Trial and error and enumeration techniques have been relied upon, with the result that industry wastes an estimated four to ten percent of operators' time on assembly lines through unequal work assignments.

* From *The Journal of Industrial Engineering,* Vol. 12, No. 4 (1961), 292–98. Reprinted by permission of *The Journal of Industrial Engineering.*

[1] The first progressive assembly line was started at the Ford Highland Park Plant in 1913, and Henry Ford is properly credited with its invention. He combined the long known principles of the division of labor, the fabrication of interchangeable parts, and the movement of product past fixed work stations into the concept of assembly as a continuous process.

In the past five years several analytical studies of line balancing have appeared in the literature (1), (2), (3), (4), (5), (6), (7), (8), (9). The systems proposed in these studies range from rigorous mathematical techniques to approximation routines written for digital computers. Those presenting computer programs are based on arbitrarily zoned assembly lines. Although all the proposed methods have merits, none has the advantage of simplicity. Either the method requires a computer, or only a person of considerable mathematical competence can cope with it.

The problem is approached here with emphasis on the applicability of the method to existing conditions in manufacturing plants where computers and mathematicians are not always available. An algorithmic solution is desirable, but, as frequently happens in combinatorial problems, an algorithm becomes intractable as the problem size increases. Therefore a heuristic method of line balancing was devised which requires logical analysis of problem data. It is presented here with emphasis on procedure rather than on computational details.

ASSEMBLY LINE TERMINOLOGY

A *work station* is an assigned location where a given amount of work is performed. Assembly line work stations are generally manned by one operator. However, on short runs an operator may man more than one station, and on lines of large products (aircraft, for example) work stations are frequently manned by several operators.

A *minimum rational work element* is an indivisible element of work or natural minimum unit beyond which assembly work cannot be divided rationally. For example, a minimum rational element may include the following motion pattern: reach to a tool, grasp it, move it into position, perform a single task, return the tool. In practice such work elements are considered indivisible since they cannot be split between two operators without creating unnecessary work in the form of extra handling.

The *total work content* is the aggregate amount of work of the total assembly. The total work content time is the time required to perform the total work content. The *station work content* time is the time required to perform the work content of the given station. This time is also known as the operation time.

The *cycle time* is the time the product spends at each work station on the line when the line is moving at standard pace, or 100 percent efficiency. Stated in other words, the cycle time is the amount of time elapsing between successive units as they move down the line at standard pace. Extending this definition, the cycle time is the maximum operation time. The cycle time, and the pace at which the line operates, together determine the rate at which products flow from the line.

Balance delay time is the amount of idle time on the line due to the imperfect division of work between stations. Since it seems to be seldom possible to divide the work evenly between all operators on the line, those operators having shorter assignments will have some idle time. This idle time is a measure of the imbalance of the line.

In practice those operators having shorter work assignments will not actually stand idle at the end of each cycle, but will work continuously at a slower pace. The effect, measured in terms of labor cost, however, is the same as if they were idle part of the time and working at a faster pace the rest of the time.

If all of the station work content times were equal, there would be no imbalance. The degree or percent of imbalance, simply called "balance delay," is the ratio between the average idle time at the stations and the maximum operation time. Stated otherwise, balance delay is the ratio between the total idle time and the total time spent by the product in moving from the beginning to the end of the line.

Balancing restrictions are constraints imposed on the order or time sequence in which work elements can be performed. They are of three types:

1. Technological restrictions on the order of assembly of components or piece parts.
2. Restrictions imposed by fixed facilities or machines on the line.
3. Restrictions of position, where position refers to the operator or operators.

THEORETICAL ANALYSIS OF BALANCE DELAY

Balance delay in percent is defined in mathematical terms as the ratio

$$d = 100 \frac{c - \bar{c}}{c}$$

where c is the maximum operation time or cycle time, and $\bar{c}$ is the average operation time. If the assembly line is manned by n operators (one at each of n work stations), then d can also be written as

$$d = 100 \frac{nc - n\bar{c}}{nc} = 100 \frac{nc - \Sigma_i t_i}{nc}, \quad (nc - \Sigma_i t_i \geq 0),$$

where t_i $(i = 1, 2, \ldots, k)$, is the duration of the ith work element in the distribution and $\Sigma_i t_i$ is the total work content time.

It is important to note that for a given cycle time, c, and a given total work content time, $\Sigma_i t_i$, there exists a minimum number of operators, n_{min}. The minimum balance delay in percent is defined as

$$d_{min} = 100 \frac{n_{min}c - \Sigma_i t_i}{n_{min}c}$$

and is a function of cycle time, c. This function, called the balance delay function, can be plotted on a graph. Since the definition of d_{min} is unequivocal, the subscript can be dropped, and

$$d = 100 \frac{nc - \Sigma_i t_i}{nc}$$

will have the connotation of d_{min}.

The range of possible cycle times, c, is

$$t_{max} \leqq c \leqq \Sigma_i t_i.$$

That is, the cycle time, c, must equal or exceed the maximum element, t_{max}, in the work element distribution, but cannot exceed the total work content time, $\Sigma_i t_i$. The lower bound of c follows from the definition of cycle time. The upper bound is based on practical considerations. There is no sense in allowing the cycle time to increase beyond the total work content time. For computational convenience it will be assumed that the durations of work elements t_i, are expressed in integers, so that $\Sigma_i t_i$ is also an integer.

A simple but useful theorem in line balancing theory can now be stated as follows: A necessary but not sufficient condition for perfect balance (or zero delay) is that

$$nc - \Sigma_i t_i = 0,$$

where n (the number of work stations) is an integer. This implies that $\Sigma_i t_i$ must be divisible by c, for otherwise $n = \Sigma_i t_i/c$ is not an integer.

The condition is necessary, because if balance delay is zero, then $nc - \Sigma_i t_i = 0$, and $\Sigma_i t_i/c = n$ is an integer (by assumption).

It is not sufficient because situations exist for which, although $\Sigma_i t_i/c$ is an integer, it is not possible to assign the given elements to the n work stations.

In order to find all possible zero points of the balance delay function, $\Sigma_i t_i$ must be divided by all the c's, $(t_{max} \leqq c \leqq \Sigma_i t_i)$, respectively, for which the quotient $\Sigma_i t_i/c$ is an integer, n. Then if, for a given cycle time, c, all the work elements in the distribution can be fitted into the n work stations or intervals of duration c each, while heeding sequential restrictions, perfect balance has been attained for that particular case. Otherwise, the number, n, of work stations must be increased by the least integer rquired to achieve balance, and then the balance is not perfect $(d > 0)$. For all other cycle times, it is known a priori that the balance delay is not zero. To find the corresponding balance delay value, the number of work stations is chosen as an integer exceeding $\Sigma_i t_i/c$ by the minimum amount required to fit the elements into the n intervals.

Since the work element times are expressed in integers, the cycle times are integers also, and the balance delay function, $d = f(c)$, is a discrete function. However, it will be convenient to plot its graph by connecting consecutive points of the function with straight lines. The graph will thus have the appearance of continuity and will emphasize features and trends which might otherwise be overlooked.

In general, the balance delay function thus derived has the shape of a zigzag line reaching the cycle time axis wherever a zero point occurs. Figure 1 shows a portion of a balance delay curve for an assembly line. The curve is drawn for cycle times of from 0.80 minutes to 1.20 minutes. The figure shows that within this range, zero balance delay is attainable at

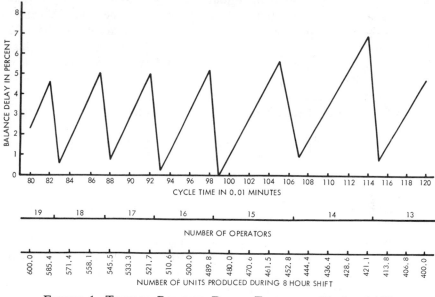

FIGURE 1. TYPICAL BALANCE DELAY FUNCTION, $80 \leqq c \leqq 120$

a cycle time of 0.99 minute. The cycle time actually in use on this line was 0.94 minute, which, according to Figure 1 would entail a minimum balance delay of about 1.25 percent. The balance delay actually experienced on the line was 5.0 percent.

The balance delay function tells what cycle time to select for a given distribution of work elements and a given number of operators. Since balance delay is to be minimized, a cycle time should be chosen which, in conjunction with the given number of operators, insures the least balance delay. These points may be found for all values of n at the local minima of the balance delay function.

Another question that can be answered from a glance at the balance delay function is how many units, N, can be produced most economically on the assembly line in a given time interval, say, during an eight-hour shift, with n operators, or conversely, what cycle time should be used in order to produce N units with n operators.

Since there is a one-to-one correspondence between the cycle time, c, and the number of units produced, N, during a given time of duration T $(N = \frac{T}{c})$, a horizontal scale indicative of N can be added to the graph of the balance delay function. For example, Figure 1 indicates that about 461 units can be produced in eight hours with 15 operators at a cycle time of 1.04 minutes with a minimum balance delay of 4.75 percent. The figure also shows that 15 operators can produce in eight hours 485 units at a cycle time of 0.99 minute with zero balance delay. This implies that production of 461 units will cost as much as that of 485 units. Thus management has the two least cost alternatives of choosing a production rate of 485 units per 8 hour shift at a cycle time of 0.99 minute, or of producing 461 units at this same cycle time in about a 7½ hour shift.

THE LINE BALANCING METHOD

To describe the heuristic method of line balancing an illustration is given which is not drawn from industry. Other examples are available; however, they involve technological complexities which have no direct bearing on the method. The illustration is that first suggested by Salveson (6) of dressing in the morning, that is, of assembling one's clothes. The example has essentially the same properties as many industrial jobs, and therefore is not trivial. The work can be divided into a given number of operators of equal duration while heeding necessary sequential restrictions. Each operation consists of one or more irreducible work elements combined in such a way as to equalize the time required for each operation.

The elements and their time durations are shown in Table I. Thus, element 1 of duration 9 must precede element 3 of duration 10, and element 7 of duration 13. Element 3 must precede element 5 of duration 17 and element 7 must precede element 14 of duration 22, and so forth.

The precedence diagram is drawn so that the assembly progresses from left to right, each element being as far left as possible at the start of the procedure. Precedence diagrams are constructed as described by Jackson (4). First, in column I of the diagram are listed all work elements which

TABLE I. WORK ELEMENTS IN "ASSEMBLING CLOTHES"

Element No.	Description	Time (in 0.01 min.)
1.	Pick up and put on left sock	9
2.	Pick up and put on right sock	9
3.	Pick up and put on left shoe	10
4.	Pick up and put on right shoe	10
5.	Tie left shoe lace	17
6.	Tie right shoe lace	17
7.	Pick up, put on, and attach left garter	13
8.	Pick up, put on, and attach right garter	13
9.	Pick up, put on left spat	20
10.	Pick up, put on right spat	20
11.	Pick up and put on undershorts	10
12.	Pick up and put on undershirt	11
13.	Tuck in undershirt	6
14.	Pick up and put on trousers	22
15.	Pick up and put on shirt	11
16.	Button 5 buttons	19
17.	Tuck in shirt	12
18.	Button shirt neck button	4
19.	Turn up collar	3
20.	Pick up and put on tie, turn down collar	7
21.	Tie tie	55
22.	Pick up and put on tie clip	14
23.	Fold back left cuff—pick up and put on left cuff link	27
24.	Fold back right cuff—pick up and put on right cuff link	29
25.	Pick up and put on belt	26
26.	Buckle belt	6
27.	Pick up and put on vest	5
28.	Button vest (6 buttons)	24
29.	Pick up and place handkerchief	4
30.	Pick up and place wallet	5
31.	Pick up and place small change	7
32.	Pick up and place keys	4
33.	Pick up and put on suit jacket	15
34.	Button suit jacket	7
35.	Pick up and place pocket handkerchief	7
36.	Pick up and place fountain pen	9
37.	Pick up and place glasses	4
38.	Pick up and place glass case	3
39.	Pick up and put on wrist watch	5
40.	Pick up and put on scarf	4
41.	Pick up and put on top coat	21
42.	Button top coat	12
43.	Pick up and put on hat	6
44.	Pick up and put on left glove	5
45.	Pick up and put on right glove	5
	Total work content ($\Sigma_i t_i$)	552

need not follow any work elements. Then, in column K $(K \geq \mathrm{II})$ are entered all those work elements which must follow work elements already on the diagram. Finally, arrows are drawn from work elements in column $K - 1$ to work elements in column K which must follow them. This procedure is repeated, replacing column $K - 1$ by columns $K - 2, \ldots, 1$, successively, except that no arrow is drawn from one work element to another if it is possible to follow arrows already drawn from the first work element to the second.

The problem of line balancing is to achieve the least possible balance delay for given conditions. Thus, for a specified distribution of elements and restrictions on their ordering, and a given cycle time, c, one may be required to find the minimum number, n, of operators to perform the task; or, for a given number, n, of operators, one may wish to determine the shortest cycle time, c. If neither c nor n is given, it is necessary to determine the value, or values, of c and n for which balance delay is zero. This is the procedure followed below.

To determine the cycle times for which $\Sigma_i t_i / c$ is an integer, it is convenient to write $\Sigma_i t_i$ as a product of prime numbers, i.e.,

$$\Sigma_i t_i = 552 = 2 \times 2 \times 2 \times 3 \times 23.$$

Since $55 \leq c \leq 552$, it is easily seen that the quotient $\Sigma_i t_i / c$ is an integer for

$$
\begin{aligned}
c_1 &= 2 \times 2 \times 2 \times 3 \times 23 = 552 \\
c_2 &= 2 \times 2 \times 3 \times 23 &= 276 \\
c_3 &= 2 \times 2 \times 2 \times 23 &= 184 \\
c_4 &= 2 \times 3 \times 23 &= 138 \\
c_5 &= 2 \times 2 \times 23 &= 92 \\
c_6 &= 3 \times 23 &= 69
\end{aligned}
$$

Hence, perfect balance can possibly be achieved with

$$n_1 = \frac{\Sigma_i t_i}{c_1} = \frac{552}{552} = 1 \text{ station (trivial case)}$$

$$n_2 = \frac{\Sigma_i t_i}{c_2} = \frac{552}{276} = 2 \text{ stations}$$

$$n_3 = \frac{\Sigma_i t_i}{c_3} = \frac{552}{184} = 3 \text{ stations}$$

$$n_4 = \frac{\Sigma_i t_i}{c_4} = \frac{552}{138} = 4 \text{ stations}$$

$$n_5 = \frac{\Sigma_i t_i}{c_5} = \frac{552}{92} = 6 \text{ stations}$$

$$n_6 = \frac{\Sigma_i t_i}{c_6} = \frac{552}{69} = 8 \text{ stations}$$

The question now is whether perfect balance is actually attainable for the above six cycle times.

Elements which are mutually independent can be permuted among themselves in any work sequence without violating restrictions on precedence relations. Furthermore it can be seen that many elements can be moved without disturbing the precedence restrictions. The flexibility depends on the number of restrictions, but in most industrial cases this number is moderate, affecting the flexibility only slightly.

The above two properties of elements in the precedence diagram—permutability and lateral transferability—are exploited in the attempt to achieve optimum balance. Other properties which offer additional opportunities will not be discussed here since in most cases they are of minor interest.

Next in the line balancing procedure is the construction of a table containing detailed information about each element taken from successive columns of the precedence diagram. Thus column A of Table II shows the column number, and column B indicates the element identification number.

Column C is reserved for remarks concerning the transferability of elements.

For instance, it is indicated under "Remarks" that element No. 39 can be moved from column I to columns II, III, . . . , up to column XI. It is also stated that element No. 4 can be moved from columns II to columns III, IV, . . . , up to column IX provided elements Nos. 6 and 10 are displaced accordingly, and so forth. Column D gives the time duration for each element, column E, the sum of time durations for each column in the diagram, and column F the cumulative time sums.

Although perfect line balance was achieved for all six values of c (552, 276, 184, 138, 92, 69), the heuristic method will be demonstrated only for $c_3 = 184$.

TABLE II. TABULAR REPRESENTATION OF PRECEDENCE
DIAGRAM FOR WORK ELEMENTS IN "ASSEMBLING CLOTHES"

(A) Column Number of Diagram	(B) Element Identification Number	(C) Remarks	(D) Element Time Duration t_i	(E) Sum of Time Durations	(F) Cumulative Time Sums
I 1			9		
2			9		
11			10		
12			11		
39		→ II, ..., XI	5	44	44
II 3	(w. 5, 9)	→ III, ..., IX	10		
7			13		
4	(w. 6, 10)	→ III, ..., IX	10		
8			13		
13			6		
37	(w. 43)	→ III, ..., XIII	4	56	100
III 5	(w. 9)	→ IV, ..., X	17		
6	(w. 10)	→ IV, ..., X	17		
14			22		
15			11		
43		→ IV, ..., XIV	6	73	173
IV 9		→ V, ..., XI	20		
10		→ V, ..., XI	20		
29		→ V, ..., XI	4		
30		→ V, ..., XI	5		
31		→ V, ..., XI	7		
32		→ V, ..., XI	4		
25		→ V +	26		
16			19		
19			3		
23		→ V, VI	27		
24		→ V, VI	29	164	337
V 17			12		
20			7	19	356
VI 26			6		
27			5		
18		→ VII, ..., IX	4	15	371
VII 21			55		
33	(w. 35, 36, 38)	→VIII	15	70	441
VIII 22			14		
35		→ IX, X	7		
36		→ IX	9		
38		→ IX	3	33	474
IX 28			24	24	498
X 34			7	7	505
XI 40			4	4	509
XII 41			21	21	530
XIII 42			12	12	542
XIV 44			5		
45			5	10	552

Example for $c_3 = 184$.

If the work can be balanced perfectly for $c_3 = 184$, then the number of stations is

$$n_3 = \frac{\Sigma_i t_i}{c_3} = \frac{552}{184} = 3.$$

Column F of Table II indicates that if time elements can be arranged in a proper sequence, the cumulative sum will add to 184 within column IV. Is it possible to permute the elements in column IV, so that this number (184) is actually obtained? A cursory examination shows that if elements Nos. 31 and 32 are moved to the top of column IV, the cumulative sum of time durations up to and including element No. 32 is exactly equal to 184. Hence, one assigns work elements Nos. 1, 2, . . . , 39, 3, . . . , 37, 5, . . . , 43, 31, 32, in that order, to the first station (see Table III).

The work sequence for station one is thus: 1. pick up and put on left sock; 2. pick up and put on right sock; 11. pick up and put on undershorts; 12. pick up and put on undershirt; 39. pick up and put on wrist watch; 3. pick up and put on left shoe; 7. pick up, put on and attach left garter; 4. pick up and put on right shoe; 8. pick up, put on and attach right garter; 13. tuck in undershirt; 37. pick up and place glasses; 5. tie left shoe lace; 6. tie right shoe lace; 14. pick up and put on trousers; 15. pick up and put on shirt; 43. pick up and put on hat; 31. pick up and place small change; 32. pick up and place keys. Although this may seem to be a curious dressing sequence, it is obviously possible, in that it does not contradict any of the sequencing restrictions.

Referring to column F of Table III, it is evident that the cumulative sum of 368 (i.e. $184 + 184$) will occur within column VI of the diagram, if the elements can be ordered suitably. However, it is not possible to simply permute the elements in that column to arrive at the total of 368, and it is now necessary to resort to another stratagem. By moving elements in the diagram from their respective columns to positions in succeeding columns, the desired result is achieved.

Thus it is convenient to make the following changes:

Move element No. 9 from column   IV to column VIII,
Move element No. 10 from column   IV to column VIII,
Move element No. 25 from column   IV to column VIII,
Move element No. 33 from column VII to column VIII,
Move element No. 26 from column   VI to column   IX,
Move element No. 35 from column VIII to column   IX,
Move element No. 36 from column VIII to column   IX,
Move element No. 38 from column VIII to column   IX.

TABLE III. MODIFIED TABLE II AFTER ASSIGNMENT OF
WORK ELEMENTS TO STATION 1 ONLY ($t_3 = 184$)

(A) Column Number of Diagram		(B) Element Identification Number	(C) Remarks	(D) Element Time Duration, t_i	(E) Sum of Time Durations	(F) Cumulative Time Sums	
I	1			9			
	2			9			
	11			10			
	12			11			
	39			5			
II	3			10			
	7			13			
	4			10			
	8			13			
	13			6			Station 1
	37			4			
III	5			17			
	6			17			
	14			22			
	15			11			
	43			6			
IV	31			7			
	32			4	184	184	
	9		→ V, ..., XI	20			
	10		→ V, ..., XI	20			
	29		→ V, ..., XI	4			
	30		→ V, ..., XI	5			
	25	(w. 26)	→ V +	26			
	16			19			
	19			3			
	23		→ V, VI	27			
	24		→ V, VI	29	153	337	
V	17			12			
	20			7	19	356	
VI	26		→ VII, ..., IX	6			
	27			5			
	18			4	15	371	
VII	21			55			Unassigned Work
	33	(w. 35, 36, 38)	→ VIII	15	70	441	
VIII	22			14			
	35		→ IX, X	7			
	36		→ IX	9			
	38		→ IX	3	33	474	
IX	28			24	24	498	
X	34			7	7	505	
XI	40			4	4	509	
XII	41			21	21	530	
XIII	42			12	12	542	
XIV	44			5			
	45			5	10	552	

TABLE IV. MODIFIED TABLE III AFTER ASSIGNMENT OF
WORK ELEMENT TO ALL THREE STATIONS ($c_3 = 184$)

(A) Column Number of Diagram	(B) Element Identification Number	(C) Remarks	(D) Element Time Duration, t_i	(E) Sum of Time Durations	(F) Cumulative Time Sums	
I	1		9			
	2		9			
	11		10			
	12		11			
	39		5			
II	3		10			
	7		13			
	4		10			
	8		13			Station 1
	13		6			
	37		4			
III	5		17			
	6		17			
	14		22			
	15		11			
	43		6			
IV	31		7			
	32		4	184	184	
	29		4			
	30		5			
	16		19			
	19		3			
	23		27			
	24		29			
V	17		12			Station 2
	20		7			
VI	27		5			
	18		4			
VII	21		55			
VIII	22		14	184	368	
	9		20			
	10		20			
	25		26			
	33		15			
IX	28		24			
	26		6			
	35		7			
	36		9			
	38		3			Station 3
X	34		7			
XI	40		4			
XII	41		21			
XIII	42		12			
XIV	44		5			
	45		5	184	552	

After the modification of Table III, the cumulative sum of time durations equaling 368 falls into column VIII. Thus, elements Nos. 29, . . . , 24, 17, 20, 27, 28, 21, 22, in that order, are assigned to the second station, and the remaining elements Nos. 9 through 45, as indicated in Table IV, are assigned to the third station. It is thus demonstrated that perfect balance can be achieved with a cycle time $c_3 = 184$.

The heuristic method of line balancing was demonstrated for a cycle time with promise of potential zero balance delay. This was done because perfect balancing cases are the most difficult to solve. This is true because it is easier to pack the work elements into cycle times when it is not required that the time intervals be completely filled. For all cycle times other than the six values derived, it is known a priori that perfect balance is unattainable. To find the resulting balance delay the number of stations, n, is chosen as an integer exceeding $\Sigma_i t_i / c$ by the minimum amount required to pack the elements into these n stations. If balance can be attained with n being the smallest integer larger than $\Sigma_i t_i / c$, optimality is assured. Otherwise care and judgment must be exercised before the solution can be labeled "optimum."

GENERAL OBSERVATIONS REGARDING THE HEURISTIC METHOD

The following generalizations and suggestions may prove helpful in applying the heuristic method.

1. Permutability within columns is used to facilitate the selection of elements of the length desired for optimum packing of the work stations. Lateral transferability helps to deploy the work elements along the stations of the assembly line so they can be used where they best serve the packing solution.

2. Generally the solutions are not unique. Elements assigned to a station, which belong after the assignment is made in one column of the precedence diagram, can generally be permuted within the column. This allows the line supervisor some leeway to alter the sequence of work elements without disturbing optimum balance.

3. Long time elements are best disposed of first, if possible. Thus, if there is a choice between the assignment of an element of duration, say, 20, and the assignment of two elements of duration, say, 10 each, assign the larger element first. Small elements are saved for ease of manipulation at the end of the line.

The situation is analogous to that of a paymaster dispensing the week's earnings in cash. He will count out the largest bills first. Thus, if the amount to be paid a worker is $77, the paymaster will give three $20 bills first, then one $10 bill, one $5 bill, and two $1 bills, in that order.

4. When moving elements laterally, the move is best made only as far to the right as necessary to allow a sufficient choice of elements for the work station being considered.

CONCLUSIONS

The proposed method of assembly line balancing is not a mere mechanical procedure, since judgment and intuition must be used to derive a meaningful solution. However, the procedure is simple and can be used by production engineers without difficulty. Optimality is usually assured when the ordering restrictions on the work elements are of a technological nature only. In a few industrial cases where the sequential restrictions governing the elements are stringent, caution must be used in labeling the solution "optimum." If, in addition to technological restrictions, the constraints are positional or involve fixed plant facilities, such as overhead cranes, testing booths or other immovable installations, the work elements must be grouped into subdistributions. The consideration of these cases is beyond the scope of this presentation.

The heuristic method is an improvement over the trial and error methods traditionally used in assembly line balancing. Changes in model or in production processes can be made without creating difficult rebalancing work. The heuristic method generally provides a solution which is not unique, thus permitting the line supervisor to choose that solution which minimizes balance delay and also satisfies secondary objectives.

The method can be applied in any industry using progressive assembly techniques. It has been used successfully in the electronics and home appliance industries.

References

(1) BRYTON, B., "Balancing of a Continuous Production Line," unpublished M.S. Thesis, Northwestern University, 1954.

(2) BURGESON, J. W., AND DAUM, T. E., *Production Line Balancing,* File Number 10.3.002, International Business Machines Corporation, Akron, Ohio, 1958, 62 pp.

(3) HOFFMAN, T. R., "Permutations and Precedence Matrices with Automatic Computer Applications to Industrial Problems," unpublished Ph.D. Thesis, University of Wisconsin, 1959.

(4) JACKSON, J. R., "A Computing Procedure for a Line Balancing Problem," *Management Science,* 3 (1956), pp. 261–271.

(5) MITCHELL, J., "A Computational Procedure for Balancing Zoned Assembly Lines," *Research Report No.* 6-94801-1-R3, Westinghouse Research Laboratories, Pittsburgh, 1957, 11 pp.

(6) SALVESON, M. E., "The Assembly Line Balancing Problem," *The Journal of Industrial Engineering*, 3 (1955), pp. 18–25.

(7) TONGE, F. M., "Summary of a Heuristic Line Balancing Procedure," *The RAND Corporation*, T-1799, September 1959.

(8) TONGE, F. M., "A Heuristic Program of Assembly Line Balancing," *The RAND Corporation*, p. 193, May 1960.

(9) TONGE, F. M., "Summary of a Heuristic Line Balancing Procedure," *Management Science*, October 1960, pp. 21–39.

PART II

Inventory Control

Chapter 8

INTRODUCTION TO PART II

Inventory control has been, and no doubt will continue to be, one of the most important areas for operational analysis. It is important because a very sizable portion of the assets of any typical manufacturing or distribution enterprise is tied up in inventories. General Electric's investment in inventories was over $655 million in 1960. This figure represented 25 percent of G.E.'s total assets. With this kind of investment in inventory, which again is very typical in manufacturing firms, the need for planning good inventory control systems is apparent.

The first three chapters in this section present an outline of the important considerations for efficient inventory policy. Originally printed as a series in the *Harvard Business Review*, these articles have stimulated considerable interest in inventory control in both academic and industrial circles.

Chapter 9 begins with a discussion of the functions of inventories, some problems of inventory management, and the nature of inventory costs. The remainder of the article is devoted to the important question of determining the economic lot size.

The concept of an inventory system is developed in Chapter 10. The tie-in between production scheduling and inventory control is discussed and an excellent case example of the development of an efficient inventory control system is presented.

Chapter 11 brings the areas of production planning and control into the inventory picture. Methods for meeting various demand patterns are discussed and integrated with over-all inventory policy. This series does an excellent job of presenting a comprehensive view of inventory control, and is a good starting point for students interested in obtaining a background in this area.[1]

---

[1] The material presented in this series has been expanded by Mr. Magee and is now available in book form: John F. Magee, *Production Planning and Inventory Control*, McGraw-Hill Book Co., Inc., 1958.

Quite often inventory problems are difficult to handle simply because of their size. Companies with large distribution operations involving thousands of products distributed through several warehouses must often set an extremely large number of inventory levels. Chapter 13 concerns the use of simulation to determine inventory levels in the warehouses of a distribution company. This article presents a good example of the newer techniques that are increasingly being brought to bear on inventory problems.

Chapter 12 could well be included in Part Three on Facilities Planning, since it deals with a new method for evaluating alternative procedures for producing a given product. The method is actually a combination of break-even analysis and the economic lot size model, however, and is therefore more closely related to inventory control strategy.

Although break-even analysis and the economic lot size model may appear at first to be a strange combination, either technique, used individually, may lead to some significant errors. Break-even analysis does not account for the possibility of producing over several cycles and neglects inventory carrying cost. The economic lot size model, on the other hand, ignores the possibility of alternative manufacturing methods and accompanying differences in cost. The combined model developed in Chapter 12 is an interesting application of some of the considerations discussed in Chapters 9 through 11 and provides potentially useful techniques for evaluating production alternatives.

Finally, in Chapter 14, statistical methods are applied to problems of inventory control. Thus, the material in Part Two first surveys the inventory control area and then develops extensions of modern analytical methods to large-scale inventory systems and to dynamic relationships of lot-size and production alternatives.

Chapter 9
BASIC FUNCTIONS

XI.

Guides to Inventory Policy
*I. Functions and Lot Sizes**

John F. Magee

"Why are we always out of stock?" So goes the complaint of great numbers of businessmen faced with the dilemmas and frustrations of attempting simultaneously to maintain stable production operations, provide customers with adequate service, and keep investment in stocks and equipment at reasonable levels.

But this is only one of the characteristic problems business managers face in dealing with production planning, scheduling, keeping inventories in hand, and expediting. Other questions—just as perplexing and baffling when managers approach them on the basis of intuition and pencil work alone—are: How often should we reorder, or how should we adjust production, when sales are uncertain? What capacity levels should we set for job-shop operations? How do we plan production and procurement for seasonal sales? And so on, and so on.

In this series of articles, I will describe some of the technical developments which aim at giving the business manager better control over inventory and scheduling policy. While these techniques sometimes employ con-

---

* From the *Harvard Business Review*, Vol. 34, No. 1 (1956), 49–60. Reprinted by permission of the *Harvard Business Review*.

cepts and language foreign to the line executive, they are far from being either academic exercises or mere clerical devices. They are designed to help the business manager make better policy decisions and get his people to follow policy more closely.

As such, these techniques are worth some time and thought, commensurate with the central importance of production planning and inventory policy in business operations. Indeed, many companies have found that analysis of the functions of inventories, measurement of the proper level of stocks, and development of inventory and production control systems based on the sorts of techniques described in this and following sections can be very profitable. For example:

Johnson & Johnson has used these techniques for studying inventory requirements for products with seasonally changing demand, and also to set economical inventory goals balancing investment requirements against additional training and overtime costs.

The American Thread Company, as a supplier to the fashion goods industry, plagued with large in-process inventories, day-to-day imbalances among production departments, labor turnover, and customer service difficulties, found these methods the key to improved scheduling and control procedures. Now these improved procedures help keep an inventory of tens of thousands of items in balance and smooth out production operations even in the face of demand showing extremely erratic fluctuations due to fashion changes.

The Lamp Division of the General Electric Company has reported using these methods to survey its finished inventory functions and stock requirements in view of operating conditions and costs. This survey indicated how an improved warehouse reorder system would yield inventory cuts at both factories and warehouses, and pointed to the reorder system characteristics that were needed; it led to the installation of a new reorder and stock control system offering substantial opportunities for stock reduction. The analytic approach can also be used to show clearly what the cost in inventory investment and schedule changes is to achieve a given level of customer service.

An industrial equipment manufacturer used these methods to investigate inventory and scheduling practices and to clear up policy ambiguities in this area, as a prelude to installing an electronic computer system to handle inventory control, scheduling, and purchase requisitions. In general, the analytic approach has proved a valuable help in bringing disagreements over inventory policy into the open, helping each side to recognize its own and the others' hidden assumptions, and to reach a common agreement more quickly.

The Procter & Gamble Company recently described how analysis of its factory inventory functions and requirements, using these methods, has pointed out means for improved scheduling and more efficient use of finished stock. The analysis indicated how the company could take advantage of certain particular characteristics of its factories to cut stocks needed to meet sales fluctuations while still maintaining its long-standing policy of guaranteed annual employment.

These are only a few instances of applications. Numerous others could be drawn from the experience of companies ranging from moderate to large size, selling consumer goods or industrial products, with thousands of items or only a few, and distribution in highly stable, predictable markets or in erratically changing and unpredictable circumstances.

In the present article major attention will be devoted to (a) the conceptual framework of the analytic approach, including the definition of inventory function and the measurement of operational costs; and (b) the problem of optimum lot size, with a detailed case illustration showing how the techniques are applied.

This case reveals that the appropriate order quantity and the average inventory maintained do not vary directly with sales, and that a good answer to the lot size question can be obtained with fairly crude cost data, provided that a sound analytical approach is used. The case also shows that the businessman does not need calculus to solve many inventory problems (although use has to be made of it when certain complications arise).

INVENTORY PROBLEMS

The question before management is: How big should inventories be? The answer to this is obvious—they should be just big enough. But what is big enough?

This question is made more difficult by the fact that generally each individual within a management group tends to answer the question from his own point of view. He fails to recognize costs outside his usual framework. He tends to think of inventories in isolation from other operations. The sales manager commonly says that the company must never make a customer wait; the production manager says there must be long manufacturing runs for lower costs and steady employment; the treasurer says that large inventories are draining off cash which could be used to make a profit.

Such a situation occurs all the time. The task of all production planning, scheduling, or control functions, in fact, is typically to balance conflicting objectives such as those of minimum purchase or production cost, minimum inventory investment, minimum storage and distribution cost, and maximum service to customers.

PRODUCTION VS. TIME

Often businessmen blame their inventory and scheduling difficulties on small orders and product diversity: "You can't keep track of 100,000 items. Forecasts mean nothing. We're just a job shop." Many businessmen seem to feel that their problems in this respect are unusual, whereas actually the problems faced by a moderate-size manufacturer with a widely diversified product line are almost typical of business today.

The fact is, simply, that under present methods of organization the costs of paper work, setup, and control, in view of the diversity of products sold, represent an extremely heavy drain on many a company's profit and a severe cost to its customers. The superficial variety of output has often blinded management to the opportunities for more systematic production flow and for the elimination of many of the curses of job-shop operation by better organization and planning.

The problem of planning and scheduling production or inventories pervades all operations concerned with the matter of production versus time—i.e., the interaction between production, distribution, and the location and size of physical stocks. It occurs at almost every step in the production process: purchasing, production of in-process materials, finished production, distribution of finished product, and service to customers. In multiplant operations, the problem becomes compounded because decisions must be made with reference to the amount of each item to be produced in each factory; management must also specify how the warehouses should be served by the plants.

ACTION VS. ANALYSIS

The questions businessmen raise in connection with management and control of inventories are basically aimed at action, not at arriving at answers. The questions are stated, unsurprisingly, in the characteristic terms of decisions to be made: "Where shall we maintain how much stock?" "Who will be responsible for it?" "What shall we do to control balances or set proper schedules?" A manager necessarily thinks of problems in production planning in terms of centers of responsibility.

However, action questions are not enough by themselves. In order to get at the answers to these questions as a basis for taking action, it is necessary to back off and ask some rather different kinds of questions: "Why do we have inventories?" "What affects the inventory balances we maintain?" "How do these effects take place?" From these questions, a picture of the inventory problem can be built up which shows the influence on inventories and costs of the various alternative decisions which the management may ultimately want to consider.

This type of analytic or functional question has been answered intuitively by businessmen with considerable success in the past. Consequently, most of the effort toward improved inventory management has been spent in other directions; it has been aimed at better means for recording, filing, or displaying information and at better ways of doing the necessary clerical work. This is all to the good, for efficient data-handling helps. However, it does not lessen the need for a more systematic approach to inventory problems that can take the place of, or at least supplement, intuition.

As business has grown, it has become more complex, and as business executives have become more and more specialized in their jobs or farther removed from direct operations, the task of achieving an economical balance intuitively has become increasingly difficult. That is why more businessmen are finding the concepts and mathematics of the growing field of inventory theory to be of direct practical help.

One of the principal difficulties in the intuitive approach is that the types and definitions of cost which influence appropriate inventory policy are not those characteristically found on the books of a company. Many costs such as setup or purchasing costs are hidden in the accounting records. Others such as inventory capital costs may never appear at all. Each cost may be clear to the operating head primarily responsible for its control; since it is a "hidden" cost, however, its importance may not be clear at all to other operating executives concerned. The resulting confusion may make it difficult to arrive at anything like a consistent policy.

In the last five years in particular, operations research teams have succeeded in using techniques of research scientists to develop a practical analytic approach to inventory questions, despite growing business size, complexity, and division of management responsibility.

INVENTORY FUNCTIONS

To understand the principles of the analytic approach, we must have some idea of the basic functions of inventories.

Fundamentally, inventories serve to uncouple successive operations in the process of making a product and getting it to consumers. For example, inventories make it possible to process a product at a distance from customers or from raw material supplies, or to do two operations at a distance from one another (perhaps only across the plant). Inventories make it unnecessary to gear production directly to consumption or, alternatively, to force consumption to adapt to the necessities of production. In these and similar ways, inventories free one stage in the production-distribution process from the next, permitting each to operate more economically.

The essential question is: At what point does the uncoupling function of inventory stop earning enough advantage to justify the investment required? To arrive at a satisfactory answer we must first distinguish between (a) inventories necessary because it takes time to complete an operation and to move the product from one stage to another; and (b) inventories employed for organizational reasons, i.e., to let one unit schedule its operations more or less independently of another.

MOVEMENT INVENTORIES

Inventory balances needed because of the time required to move stocks from one place to another are often not recognized, or are confused with inventories resulting from other needs—e.g., economical shipping quantities (to be discussed in a later section).

The average amount of movement inventory can be determined from the mathematical expression $I = S \times T$ in which S represents the average sales rate, T the transit time from one stage to the next, and I the movement inventory needed. For example, if it takes two weeks to move materials from the plant to a warehouse, and the warehouse sells 100 units per week, the average inventory in movement is 100 units per week times 2 weeks, or 200 units. From a different point of view, when a unit is manufactured and ready for use at the plant, it must sit idle for two weeks while being moved to the next station (the warehouse); so, on the average, stocks equal to two weeks' sales will be in movement.

Movement inventories are usually thought of in connection with movement between distant points—plant to warehouse. However, any plant may contain substantial stocks in movement from one operation to another—for example, the product moving along an assembly line. Movement stock is one component of the "float" or in-process inventory in a manufacturing operation.

The amount of movement stock changes only when sales or the time in transit is changed. Time in transit is largely a result of method of transportation, although improvements in loading or dispatching practices may cut transit time by eliminating unnecessary delays. Other somewhat more subtle influences of time in transit on total inventories will be described in connection with safety stocks.

ORGANIZATION INVENTORIES

Management's most difficult problems are with the inventories that "buy" organization in the sense that the more of them management carries between stages in the manufacturing-distribution process, the less coordination is required to keep the process running smoothly. Contrariwise, if inventories are already being used efficiently, they can be cut only at the expense of greater organization effort—e.g., greater scheduling effort to keep successive stages in balance, and greater expediting effort to work out of the difficulties which unforeseen disruptions at one point or another may cause in the whole process.

Despite superficial differences among businesses in the nature and characteristics of the organization inventory they maintain, the following three functions are basic:

(1) *Lot size inventories* are probably the most common in business. They are maintained wherever the user makes or purchases material in larger lots than are needed for his immediate purposes. For example, it is common prac-.tice to buy raw materials in relatively large quantities in order to obtain quantity price discounts, keep shipping costs in balance, and hold down clerical costs connected with making out requisitions, checking receipts, and handling accounts payable. Similar reasons lead to long production runs on equipment calling for expensive setup, or to sizable replenishment orders placed on factories by field warehouses.

(2) *Fluctuation stocks,* also very common in business, are held to cushion the shocks arising basically from unpredictable fluctuations in consumer demand. For example, warehouses and retail outlets maintain stocks to be able to supply consumers on demand, even when the rate of consumer demand may show quite irregular and unpredictable fluctuations. In turn, factories maintain stocks to be in a position to replenish retail and field warehouse stocks in line with customer demands.

Short-term fluctuations in the mix of orders on a plant often make it necessary to carry stocks of parts of subassemblies, in order to give assembly operations flexibility in meeting orders as they arise while freeing earlier operations (e.g., machining) from the need to make momentary adjustments in schedules to meet assembly requirements. Fluctuation stocks may also be carried in semifinished form in order to balance out the load among manufacturing departments when orders received during the current day, week, or month may put a load on individual departments which is out of balance with long-run requirements.

In most cases, anticipating all fluctuations is uneconomical, if not impossible. But a business cannot get along without some fluctuation stocks unless it is willing and able always to make its customers wait until the material needed can be purchased conveniently or until their orders can be scheduled into production conveniently. Fluctuation stocks are part of the price we pay for our general business philosophy of serving the consumers' wants (and whims!) rather than having them take what they can get. The queues before Russian retail stores illustrate a different point of view.

(3) *Anticipation stocks* are needed where goods or materials are consumed on a predictable but changing pattern through the year, and where it is desirable to absorb some of these changes by building and depleting inventories rather than by changing production rates with attendant fluctuations in employment and additional capital capacity requirements. For example, inventories may be built up in anticipation of a special sale or to fill needs during a plant shutdown.

The need for seasonal stocks may also arise where materials (e.g., agricultural products) are *produced* at seasonally fluctuating rates but where consumption is reasonably uniform; here the problems connected with producing and storing tomato catsup are a prime example.[1]

STRIKING A BALANCE

The joker is that the gains which these organization inventories achieve in the way of less need for coordination and planning, less clerical effort to handle orders, and greater economies in manufacturing and shipping are not in direct proportion to the size of inventory. Even if the additional stocks are kept well balanced and properly located, the gains become smaller, while at the same time the warehouse, obsolescence, and capital costs associated with maintaining inventories rise in proportion to, or perhaps even at a faster rate than, the inventories themselves. To illustrate:

Suppose a plant needs 2,000 units of a specially machined part in a year. If these are made in runs of 100 units each, then 20 runs with attendant setup costs will be required each year.

If the production quantity were increased from 100 to 200 units, only 10 runs would be required—a 50% reduction in setup costs, but a 100% increase in the size of a run and in the resulting inventory balance carried.

If the runs were further increased in length to 400 units each, only 5 production runs during the year would be required—only 25% more reduction in setup costs, but 200% more increase in run length and inventory balances.

The basic problem of inventory policy connected with the three types of inventories which "buy" organization is to strike a balance between the increasing costs and the declining return earned from additional stocks. It is because striking this balance is easier to say than to do, and because it is a problem that defies solution through an intuitive understanding alone, that the new analytical concepts are necessary.

INVENTORY COSTS

This brings us face to face with the question of the costs that influence inventory policy, and the fact, noted earlier, that they are characteristically not those recorded, at least not in directly available form, in the usual industrial accounting system. Accounting costs are derived under principles developed over many years and strongly influenced by tradition. The specific methods and degree of skill and refinement may be better in particular companies, but in all of them the basic objective of accounting procedures is to provide a fair, consistent, and conservative valuation of assets and a picture of the flow of values in the business.

In contrast to the principles and search for consistency underlying ac-

---

[1] See Alexander Henderson and Robert Schlaifer, "Mathematical Programming: Better Information for Better Decision-Making," reprinted here on p. 53.

counting costs, the definition of costs for production and inventory control will vary from time to time—even in the same company—according to the circumstances and the length of the period being planned for. The following criteria apply:

(1) *The costs shall represent "out-of-pocket" expenditures, i.e., cash actually paid out or opportunities for profit foregone.* Overtime premium payments are out-of-pocket; depreciation on equipment on hand is not. To the extent that storage space is available and cannot be used for other productive purposes, no out-of-pocket cost of space is incurred; but to the extent that storage space is rented (out-of-pocket) or could be used for other productive purposes (foregone opportunity), a suitable charge is justified. The charge for investment is based on the out-of-pocket investment in inventories or added facilities, not on the "book" or accounting value of the investment.

The rate of interest charged on out-of-pocket investment may be based either on the rate paid banks (out-of-pocket) or on the rate of profit that might reasonably be earned by alternative uses of investment (foregone opportunity), depending on the financial policies of the business. In some cases, a bank rate may be used on short-term seasonal inventories and an internal rate for long-term, minimum requirements.

Obviously, much depends on the time scale in classifying a given item. In the short run, few costs are controllable out-of-pocket costs; in the long run, all are.

(2) *The costs shall represent only those out-of-pocket expenditures or foregone opportunities for profit whose magnitude is affected by the schedule or plan.* Many overhead costs, such as supervision costs, are out-of-pocket, but neither the timing nor the size is affected by the schedule. Normal material and direct labor costs are unaffected in total and so are not considered directly; however, these as well as some components of overhead cost do represent out-of-pocket investments, and accordingly enter the picture indirectly through any charge for capital.

DIRECT INFLUENCE

Among the costs which directly influence inventory policy are (a) costs depending on the amount ordered, (b) production costs, and (c) costs of storing and handling inventory.

Costs that depend on the amount ordered—These include, for example, quantity discounts offered by vendors; setup costs in internal manufacturing operations and clerical costs of making out a purchase order; and, when capacity is pressed, the profit on production lost during downtime for setup. Shipping costs represent another factor to the extent that they influence the quantity of raw materials purchased and resulting raw stock levels, the size of intraplant or plant-warehouse shipments, or the size and the frequency of shipments to customers.

Production costs—Beyond setup or change-over costs, which are included in the preceding category, there are the abnormal or nonroutine costs of production whose size may be affected by the policies or control methods used. (Normal or standard raw material and direct labor costs are not significant in inventory control; these relate to the total quantity sold rather than to the amount stocked.) Overtime, shakedown, hiring, and training represent costs that have a direct bearing on inventory policy.

To illustrate, shakedown or learning costs show up wherever output during the early part of a new run is below standard in quantity or quality.[2] A cost of undercapacity operation may also be encountered—for example, where a basic labor force must be maintained regardless of volume (although sometimes this can be looked on as part of the fixed facility cost, despite the fact that it is accounted for as a directly variable labor cost).

Costs of handling and storing inventory—In this group of costs affected by control methods and inventory policies are expenses of handling products in and out of stock, storage costs such as rent and heat, insurance and taxes, obsolescence and spoilage costs, and capital costs (which will receive detailed examination in the next section).

Inventory obsolescence and spoilage costs may take several forms, including (1) outright spoilage after a more or less fixed period; (2) risk that a particular unit in stock or a particular product number will (a) become technologically unsalable, except perhaps at a discount or as spare parts, (b) go out of style, or (c) spoil.

Certain food and drug products, for example, have specified maximum shelf lives and must either be used within a fixed period of time or be dumped. Some kinds of style goods, such as many lines of toys, Christmas novelties, or women's clothes, may effectively "spoil" at the end of a season, with only reclaim or dump value. Some kinds of technical equipment undergo almost constant engineering change during their production life; thus component stocks may suddenly and unexpectedly be made obsolete.

CAPITAL INVESTMENT

Evaluating the effect of inventory and scheduling policy upon capital investment and the worth of capital tied up in inventories is one of the most difficult problems in resolving inventory policy questions.

Think for a moment of the amount of capital invested in inventory. This is the out-of-pocket, or avoidable, cash cost for material, labor, and overhead of goods in inventory (as distinguished from the "book" or accounting value of inventory). For example, raw materials are normally purchased in accordance with production schedules; and if the production of an item can be postponed, buying and paying for raw materials can likewise be put off.

---

[2] See Frank J. Andress, "The Learning Curve as a Production Tool," HBR January–February 1954, p. 87.

Usually, then, the raw material cost component represents a part of the out-of-pocket inventory investment in finished goods. However, if raw materials must be purchased when available (e.g., agricultural crops) regardless of the production schedule, the raw material component of finished product cost does not represent avoidable investment and therefore should be struck from the computation of inventory value for planning purposes.

As for maintenance and similar factory overhead items, they are usually paid for the year round, regardless of the timing of production scheduled; therefore these elements of burden should not be counted as part of the product investment for planning purposes. (One exception: if, as sometimes happens, the maintenance costs actually vary directly with the production rate as, for example, in the case of supplies, they should of course be included.)

Again, supervision, at least general supervision, is usually a fixed monthly cost which the schedule will not influence, and hence should not be included. Depreciation is another type of burden item representing a charge for equipment and facilities already bought and paid for; the timing of the production schedule cannot influence these past investments and, while they represent a legitimate cost for accounting purposes, they should not be counted as part of the inventory investment for inventory and production planning purposes.

In sum, the rule is this: for production planning and inventory management purposes, the investment value of goods in inventory should be taken as the cash outlay made at the time of production that could have been delayed if the goods were not made then but at a later time, closer to the time of sale.

Cost of Capital Invested. This item is the product of three factors: (a) the capital value of a unit of inventory, (b) the time a unit of product is in inventory, and (c) the charge or imputed interest rate placed against a dollar of invested cash. The first factor was mentioned above. As for the second, it is fixed by management's inventory policy decisions. But these decisions can be made economically only in view of the third factor. This factor depends directly on the financial policy of the business.

Sometimes businessmen make the mistake of thinking that cash tied up in inventories costs nothing, especially if the cash to finance inventory is generated internally through profits and depreciation. However, this implies that the cash in inventories would otherwise sit idle. In fact, the cash could, at least, be invested in government bonds if not in inventories. And if it were really idle, the cash very likely should be released to stockholders for profitable investment elsewhere.

Moreover, it is dangerous to assume that, as a "short-term" investment, inventory is relatively liquid and riskless. Businessmen say, "After all, we turn our inventory investment over six times a year." But, in reality, inventory investment may or may not be short-term and riskless, depending on circumstances. No broad generalization is possible, and each case must be decided on its own merits. For example:

A great deal of inventory carried in business is as much a part of the permanent investment as the machinery and buildings. The inventory must be maintained to make operations possible as long as the business is a going concern. The cash investment released by the sale of one item from stock must be promptly reinvested in new stock, and the inventory can be liquidated only when the company is closed. How much more riskless is this than other fixed manufacturing assets?

To take an extreme case, inventory in fashion lines or other types of products having high obsolescence carries a definite risk. Its value depends wholly on the company's ability to sell it. If sales are insufficient to liquidate the inventory built up, considerable losses may result.

At the other extreme, inventory in stable product lines built up to absorb short-term seasonal fluctuations might be thought of as bearing the least risk, since this type of investment is characteristically short-term. But even in these cases there can be losses. Suppose, for instance, that peak seasonal sales do not reach anticipated levels and substantially increased costs of storage and obsolescence have to be incurred before the excess inventory can be liquidated.

Finally, it might be pointed out that the cost of the dollars invested in inventory may be underestimated if bank interest rate is used as the basis, ignoring the risk-bearing or entrepreneur's compensation. How many businessmen are actually satisfied with uses of their companies' capital funds which do not earn more than a lender's rate of return? In choosing a truly appropriate rate—a matter of financial policy—the executive must answer some questions:

1. Where is the cash coming from—inside earnings or outside financing?
2. What else could we do with the funds, and what could we earn?
3. When can we get the investment back out, if ever?
4. How much risk of sales disappointment and obsolescence is really connected with this inventory?
5. How much of a return do we want, in view of what we could earn elsewhere or in view of the cost of money to us and the risk the inventory investment entails?

Investment in Facilities. Valuation of investment in facilities is generally important only in long-run planning problems—as, for example, when increases in productive or warehouse capacity are being considered. (Where facilities already exist and are not usable for other purposes, and where planning or scheduling do not contemplate changing these existing facilities, investment is not affected.)

Facilities investment may also be important where productive capacity is taxed, and where the form of the plan or schedule will determine the amount of added capacity which must be installed, either to meet the plan itself or for alternative uses. In such cases, considerable care is necessary in defining the facilities investment in order to be consistent with the principles noted above: i.e., that facilities investment should represent out-of-pocket investment, or, alternatively, foregone opportunities to make out-of-pocket investment elsewhere.

CUSTOMER SERVICE

An important objective in most production planning and inventory control systems is maintenance of reasonable customer service. An evaluation of the worth of customer service, or the loss suffered through poor service, is an important part of the problem of arriving at a reasonable inventory policy. This cost is typically very difficult to arrive at, including as it does the paper work costs of rehandling back orders and, usually much more important, the effect that dissatisfaction of customers may have on future profits.

In some cases it may be possible to limit consideration to the cost of producing the needed material on overtime or of purchasing it from the outside and losing the contribution to profit which it would have made. On the other hand, sometimes the possible loss of customers and their sales over a substantial time may outweigh the cost of direct loss in immediate business, and it may be necessary to arrive at a statement of a "reasonable" level of customer service—i.e., the degree of risk of running out of stock, or perhaps the number of times a year the management is willing to run out of an item. In other cases, it may be possible to arrive at a reasonable maximum level of sales which the company is prepared to meet with 100% reliability, being reconciled to have service suffer if sales exceed this level.

One of the uses of the analytic techniques described below and in following parts of this series is to help management arrive at a realistic view of the cost of poor service, or of the value of building high service, by laying out clearly what the cost in inventory investment and schedule changes is to achieve this degree of customer service. Sometimes when these costs are clearly brought home, even a 100% service-minded management is willing to settle for a more realistic, "excellent" service at moderate cost, instead of striving for "perfect" service entailing extreme cost.

OPTIMUM LOT SIZE

Now, with this background, let us examine in some detail one of the inventory problems which plague businessmen the most—that of the optimum size of lot to purchase or produce for stock. This happens also to be one of the oldest problems discussed in the industrial engineering texts— but this does not lessen the fact that it is one of the most profitable for a great many companies to attack today with new analytic techniques.

COMMON PRACTICES

This problem arises, as mentioned earlier, because of the need to purchase or produce in quantities greater than will be used or sold. Thus, specifically, businessmen buy raw materials in sizable quantities—carloads, or even trainloads—in order to reduce the costs connected with purchasing and control, to obtain a favorable price, and to minimize handling and transportation costs. They replenish factory in-process stocks of parts in sizable quantities to avoid, where possible, the costs of equipment setups and clerical routines. Likewise, finished stocks maintained in warehouses usually come in shipments substantially greater than the typical amount sold at once, the motive again being, in part, to avoid equipment setup and paperwork costs and, in the case of field warehouses, to minimize shipping costs.

Where the same equipment is used for a variety of items, the equipment will be devoted first to one item and then to another in sequence, with the length of the run in any individual item to be chosen, as far as is economically possible, to minimize change-over cost from one item to another and to reduce the production time lost because of clean-out requirements during change-overs. Blocked operations of this sort are seen frequently, for example, in the petroleum industry, on packaging lines, or on assembly lines where change-over from one model to another may require adjustment in feed speeds and settings and change of components.

In all these cases, the practice of replenishing stocks in sizable quantities compared with the typical usage quantity means that inventory has to be carried; it makes it possible to spread fixed costs (e.g., setup and clerical costs) over many units and thus to reduce the unit cost. However, one can carry this principle only so far, for if the replenishment orders become too large, the resulting inventories get out of line, and the capital and handling costs of carrying these inventories more than offset the possible savings in production, transportation, and clerical costs. Here is the matter, again, of striking a balance between these conflicting considerations.

Even though formulas for selecting the optimum lot size are presented in many industrial engineering texts,[3] few companies make any attempt to arrive at an explicit quantitative balance of inventory and change-over or setup costs. Why?

For one thing, the cost elements which enter into an explicit solution frequently are very difficult to measure, or are only very hazily defined. For example, it may be possible to get a fairly accurate measure of the cost of setting up a particular machine, but it may be almost impossible to derive a precise measure of the cost of making out a new production order. Again, warehouse costs may be accumulated separately on the accounting records, but these rarely show what the cost of housing an *additional* unit of material may be. In my experience the capital cost, or imputed interest cost, connected with inventory investment never appears on the company's accounting records.

Furthermore, the inventory is traditionally valued in such a way that the true incremental investment is difficult to measure for scheduling purposes. Often, companies therefore attempt to strike only a qualitative balance of these costs to arrive at something like an optimum or minimum-cost reorder quantity.

Despite the difficulty in measuring costs—and indeed because of such difficulty—it is eminently worthwhile to look at the lot size problem explicitly formulated. The value of an analytic solution does not rest solely on one's ability to plug in precise cost data to get an answer. An analytic solution often helps clarify questions of principle, even with only crude data available for use. Moreover, it appears that many companies today still have not accepted the philosophy of optimum reorder quantities from the over-all company standpoint; instead, decisions are dominated from the standpoint of some particular interest such as production or traffic and transportation. Here too the analytic solution can be of help, even when the cost data are incomplete or imperfect.

CASE EXAMPLE

To illustrate how the lot size problem can be attacked analytically—and what some of the problems and advantages of such an attack are—let us take a fictitious example. The situation is greatly oversimplified on purpose to get quickly to the heart of the analytic approach.

Elements of the Problem. Brown and Brown, Inc., an automotive parts

---

[3] See, for example, Raymond E. Fairfield, *Quantity and Economy in Manufacture* (New York, D. Van Nostrand Company, Inc., 1931).

supplier, produces a simple patented electric switch on long-term contracts. The covering is purchased on the outside at $0.01 each, and 1,000 are used regularly each day, 250 days per year.

The casings are made in a nearby plant, and B. and B. sends its own truck to pick them up. The cost of truck operation, maintenance, and the driver amounts to $10 per trip.

The company can send the truck once a day to bring back 1,000 casings for that day's requirements, but this makes the cost of a casing rather high. The truck can go less frequently, but this means that it has to bring back more than the company needs for its immediate day-to-day purposes.

The characteristic "saw-tooth" inventory pattern which will result is shown in Exhibit I, where 1,000 Q casings are picked up each trip (Q being whatever number of days' supply is obtained per replenishment trip). These are used up over a period of Q days. When the inventory is depleted again, another trip is made to pick up Q days' supply or 1,000 Q casings once more, and so on.

EXHIBIT I. PATTERN OF INVENTORY BALANCE
(1,000 Q casings obtained per replenishment trip; 1,000 casings used per day)

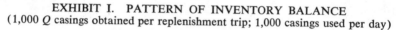

Inventory of casings

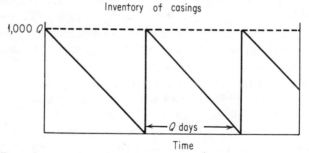

Time

B. and B. estimates that the cost of storing casings under properly controlled humidity conditions is $1 per 1,000 casings per year. The company wants to obtain a 10% return on its inventory investment of $10 (1,000 times $0.01), which means that it should properly charge an additional $1 (10% of $10), making a total inventory cost of $2 per 1,000 casings per year.

(Note that, in order to avoid undue complications, the inventory investment charge is made here only against the purchase price of the casings and not against the total delivery cost including transportation. Where transportation is a major component of total cost, it is of course possible and desirable to include it in the base for the inventory charge.)

Graphic Solution. Brown and Brown, Inc., can find what it should do by means of a graph (see Exhibit II) showing the annual cost of buying, moving, and storing casings:

The broken line shows total trucking costs versus the size of the individual purchase quantity:

EXHIBIT II. ANNUAL COST OF BUYING, MOVING, AND STORING
         CASINGS COMPARED WITH REORDER QUANTITY

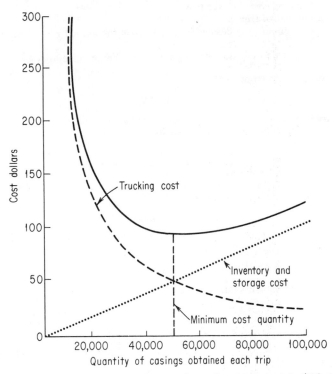

If 1,000 casings are purchased at a time, the total cost is $10 times 250 trips, or $2,500 per year.

If 10,000 casings are purchased at one time, only 25 trips need be made, for a total cost of $250 per year.

If 100,000 casings are purchased, only 2½ trips, on the average, have to be taken each year, for a total cost of $25.

The dotted line shows the inventory cost compared with the size of the purchased quantity:

If 10,000 casings are purchased at one time, the inventory at purchase will contain 10,000, and it will gradually be depleted until none are on hand, when a new purchase will be made. The average inventory on hand thus will be 5,000 casings. The cost per year will be $2 times 5,000 casings, or $10.

EXHIBIT III. EXAMPLE OF ALGEBRAIC SOLUTION OF SAME INVENTORY PROBLEM AS EXHIBIT II

The total annual cost of supplying casings is equal to the sum of the direct cost of the casings, plus the trucking cost, plus the inventory and storage cost.

Let:

T = total annual cost
b = unit purchase price, $10 per 1,000 casings
s = annual usage, 250,000 casings
A = trucking cost, $10 per trip
N = number of trips per year
i = cost of carrying casings in inventory at the annual rate of $2 per 1,000, or $0.002 per casing
x = size of an individual purchase ($x/2$ = average inventory)

Then the basic equation will be:

$$T = bs + AN + ix/2$$

The problem is to choose the minimum-cost value of x (or, if desired, N). Since x is the same as s/N, N can be expressed as s/x. Substituting s/x for N in the above equation, we get:

$$T = bs + As/x + ix/2$$

From this point on we shall use differential calculus. The derivative of total cost, T, with respect to x will be expressed as:

$$dT/dx = -As/x^2 + i/2$$

And the minimum-cost value of x is that for which the derivative of total cost with respect to x equals zero. This is true when:

$$x = \sqrt{2As/i}$$

Substituting the known values for A, s, and i:

$$x = \sqrt{2 \cdot 10 \cdot 250,000/.002} = 50,000 \text{ casings}$$

Similarly, if 100,000 casings are purchased at one time, the average inventory will be 50,000 casings, and the total inventory and storage cost will be $100.

The solid line is the total cost, including both trucking and inventory and storage costs. The total cost is at a minimum when 50,000 casings are purchased on each trip and 5 trips are made each year, for at this point the total trucking cost and the total inventory and storage cost are equal.

The solution to B. and B.'s problem can be reached algebraically as well as graphically. Exhibit III shows how the approach works in this very simple case.

SIMILAR CASES

The problem of Brown and Brown, Inc., though artificial, is not too far from the questions many businesses face in fixing reorder quantities.

Despite the simplifications introduced—for example, the assumption that usage is known in advance—the method of solution has been found widely useful in industries ranging from mail order merchandising (replenishing staple lines), through electrical equipment manufacturing (ordering machined parts to replenish stockrooms), to shoe manufacturing (ordering findings and other purchased supplies). In particular, the approach has been found helpful in controlling stocks made up of many low-value items used regularly in large quantities.

EXHIBIT IV. INFLUENCE OF PRODUCTION AND SALES RATE ON
PRODUCTION CYCLE INVENTORY

A number of realistic complications might have been introduced into the Brown and Brown, Inc., problem. For example:

In determining the size of a manufacturing run, it sometimes is important to acccount explicitly for the production and sales rate. In this case, the inventory balance pattern looks like Exhibit IV instead of the saw-tooth design in Exhibit I. The maximum inventory point is not equal to the amount produced in an individual run, but to that quantity less the amount sold during the course of the run. The maximum inventory equals $Q(1 - S/P)$, where Q is the amount produced in a single run, and S and P are the daily sales and production rates respectively.

This refinement can be important, particularly if the sales rate is fairly large compared with the production rate. Thus, if the sales rate is half the production rate, then the maximum inventory is only half the quantity made in one run, and the average inventory equals only one-fourth the individual run quantity. This means that substantially more inventory can be carried—in fact, about 40% more.

When a number of products are made on a regular cycle, one after another, with the sequence in the cycle established by economy in change-over cost, the total cycle length can be obtained in the same way as described above. Of course, it sometimes happens that there is a periodic breach in the cycle, either to make an occasional run of a product with very low sales or to allow for planned maintenance of equipment; the very simple run-length formulas can be adjusted to allow for this.

Other kinds of costs can also be included, such as different sorts of handling costs. Or the inventory cost can be defined in such a way as to include transportation, obsolescence, or even capital and storage cost as part of the unit value of the product against which a charge for capital is made. When a charge for capital is included as part of the base value in computing the cost of capital, this is equivalent to requiring that capital earnings be compounded; this can have an important bearing on decisions connected with very low volume items which might be purchased in relatively large, long-lasting quantities.

Complications such as the foregoing, while important in practice, represent changes in arithmetic rather than in basic concept.

SIGNIFICANT CONCLUSIONS

When the analytic approach is applied to Brown and Brown's problem and similar cases, it reveals certain relationships which are significant and useful to executives concerned with inventory management:

(1) *The appropriate order quantity and the average inventory maintained do not vary directly with sales.* In fact, both of these quantities vary with the square root of sales. This means that with the same ordering and setup cost characteristics, the larger the volume of sales of an item, the less inventory per unit of sales is required. One of the sources of inefficiency in many inventory control systems is the rigid adoption of a rule for ordering or carrying inventory equivalent to, say, one month's sales.

(2) *The total cost in the neighborhood of the optimum order quantity is relatively insensitive to moderately small changes in the amount ordered.* Exhibit II illustrates this proposition. Thus, all that is needed is just to get in the "right ball park," and a good answer can be obtained even with fairly crude cost data. For example, suppose the company had estimated that its total cost of holding 1,000 casings in inventory for a year was $1 when it actually was $2 (as in our illustration). Working through the same arithmetic, the company would have arrived at an optimum order quantity of 70,000 casings instead of 50,000. Even so, the total cost would have been (using the correct $2 annual carrying cost):

3.6 trips per year @ $10	=	$36
35,000 casings average inventory @ $0.002	=	70
Total annual cost	=	$106

Thus, an error of a factor of 2 in one cost results in only a 6% difference in total cost.

In summary, Brown and Brown's problem, despite its oversimplification, provides an introduction to the analytic approach to inventory problems.

In particular, it illustrates the first essential in such an approach—i.e., defining an inventory function. In this case the function is to permit purchase or manufacture in economical order quantities or run lengths; in other cases it may be different. The important point is that this basic function can be identified wherever it may be found—in manufacturing, purchasing, or warehouse operation.

The only way to cut inventories is to organize operations so that they are tied more closely together. For example, a company can cut its raw materials inventory by buying in smaller quantities closer to needs, but it does so at a cost; this cost results from the increased clerical operations needed to tie the purchasing function more closely to manufacturing and to keep it more fully informed of manufacturing's plans and operations. The right inventory level is reached when the cost of maintaining any additional inventory custion offsets the saving that the additional inventory earns by permitting the plant to operate in a somewhat less fully organized fashion.

B. and B.'s problem also illustrates problems and questions connected with defining and making costs explicit. The inventory capital cost is usually not found on a company's books, but it is implied in some of the disagreements over inventory policy. Here, again, bringing the matter into the open may help each side in a discussion to recognize its own and the others' hidden assumptions, and thus more quickly to reach a common agreement.

Chapter 10

UNCERTAINTY PROBLEMS IN INVENTORY CONTROL

XII.

Guides to Inventory Policy
II. Problems of Uncertainty*

John F. Magee

Marketing and production executives alike have an immediate, vital interest in safety stocks. In these days of strong but often unpredictable sales, safety stocks afford, for the factory as well as for the sales office, a method of buying short-term protection against the uncertainties of customer demand. They are the additional inventory on hand which can be drawn upon in case of emergency during the period between placement of an order by the customer and receipt of the material to fill the order. However, in practice their potentials are often needlessly lost.

One reason for the failure is a very practical one. Because safety stocks are designed to cope with the uncertainties of sales, they must be controlled by flexible rules so that conditions can be met as they develop. But sometimes the need for flexibility is used as an excuse for indefiniteness: "We can't count on a thing; we have to play the situation by ear." And, in any

---

* From the *Harvard Business Review,* Vol. 34, No. 2 (1956), 103–116. Reprinted by permission of the *Harvard Business Review.*

sizable organization, when people at the factory level start "playing it by ear," one can be almost sure that management policy will not be regularly translated into practice.

Our studies have shown that the methods used by existing systems in industry often violate sound control concepts. The economy of the company is maintained, in the face of instability and inefficiency in the inventory control system, only because of constant attention, exercise of overriding common sense, and use of expediting and other emergency measures outside the routine of the system.

Actually, it is possible to have inventory controls which are not only flexible but also carefully designed and explicit. But the task needs special analytical tools; in a complicated business it defies common-sense judgment and simple arithmetic. Methods must be employed to take direct account of uncertainty and to measure the response characteristics of the system and relate them to costs. Such methods are the distinctive mark of a really modern, progressive inventory control system.

Here are some of the points which I shall discuss in this article:

Basically, there are two different types of inventory replenishment systems designed to handle uncertainty about sales—*fixed order,* commonly used in stockrooms and factories, as in bins of parts or other materials; and *periodic reordering,* frequently used in warehouses for inventories involving a large number of items under clerical control. While the two are basically similar in concept, they have somewhat different effects on safety stocks, and choice of one or the other, or some related variety, requires careful consideration. Certain factors which should be taken into account in the choice between them will be outlined.

The fundamental problem of setting safety stocks under either system is balancing a series of types of costs which are not found in the ordinary accounting records of the company—costs of customer service failure, of varying production rates (including hiring and training expenses), of space capacity, and others. Often specialists can find the optimum balance with relatively simple techniques once the cost data are made explicit. However, part of the needed data can come *only from top management.* For example, the tolerable risk of service failure is generally a policy decision.

The specific problem of inventory control, including production scheduling, varies widely from company to company. Where finished items can be stocked, the important cost factors to weigh may be storage, clerical procedures, setup, supervision, etc. But where finished items cannot be stocked, the problem is one of setting capacity levels large enough to handle fluctuating loads without undue delay, which involves the cost of unused labor and machines. Despite the great variety of situations that are possible, specific mathematical approaches and theories are available for use in solving almost any type of company problem.

Both to illustrate the various techniques and by way of summary, a hypothetical case will be set forth where a company moved through a series of stages of inventory control. Significantly, the final step brought a large reduction in stocks needed for efficient service and also a great reduction in production fluctuations. Out of the range of this company's experience, other managements should be able to get some guidance as to what is appropriate for their own situations.

BASIC SYSTEMS

Like transit stocks and lot-size stocks (discussed specifically in the preceding article in this series) and also anticipation stocks (to be taken up in the subsequent article), safety stocks "decouple" one stage in production and distribution from the next, reducing the amount of over-all organization and control needed.

But the economies of safety inventories are not fairly certain and immediate. The objective is to arrive at a reasonable balance between the costs of the stock and the protection obtained against inventory exhaustion. Since exhaustion becomes less likely as the safety inventory increases, each additional amount of safety inventory characteristically buys relatively less protection. The return from increasing inventory balances therefore diminishes rapidly. So the question is: How much additional inventory as safety stock can be economically justified?

To answer this question we need to look at the two basic systems of inventory replenishment to handle uncertainty about sales and see how they produce different results.

FIXED ORDER

Under any fixed order system—the old-fashioned "two-bin" system or one of its modern varieties—the same *quantity* of material is always ordered (a binful in the primitive system), but the *time* an order is placed is allowed to vary with fluctuations in usage (when the bottom of one bin is reached). The objective is to place an order whenever the amount on hand is just sufficient to meet a "reasonable" maximum demand over the course of the lead time which must be allowed between placement of the replenishment order and receipt of the material.

Where the replenishment lead time is long (e.g., three months) compared with the amount purchased at each order (e.g., a one-month supply), there are presumably some purchase orders outstanding all the time which, on being filled, will help replenish the existing inventory on hand. In such cases, of course, the safety stocks and reorder points should be based upon both amount on hand and on order. Where, on the other hand, the lead time is short compared with the quantity ordered, as in most factory two-bin systems, the amount on hand and the total on hand and on order are in fact equivalent at the time of reordering.

The key to setting the safety stock is the "reasonable" maximum usage during the lead time. What is "reasonable" depends partly, of course, on the nature of short-term fluctuations in the rate of sale. It also depends— and here is where the top executive comes foremost into the picture— on the risk that management is prepared to face in running out of stock. What is the level of sales or usage beyond which management is prepared to face the shortages? For example:

In Exhibit I, continuing the hypothetical case of Brown and Brown, Inc., discussed in the first article of this series, the curve shows the number of weeks in which the demand for casings may be expected to equal or exceed any specified level. (Such a curve could be roughly plotted according to actual experience modified by such expectations or projections as seem warranted; refinement can be added by the use of mathematical analysis when such precision seems desirable.)

EXHIBIT I.   BROWN AND BROWN'S SAFETY STOCK

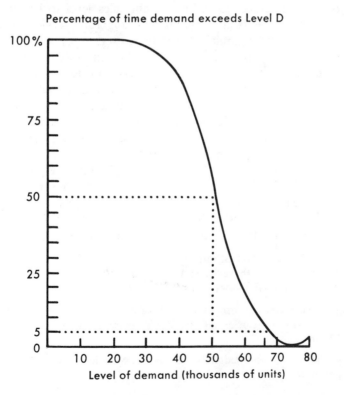

Percentage of time demand exceeds Level D

Level of demand (thousands of units)

Now, if it takes B. and B. a week to replenish its stocks and the management wishes to keep the risk of running out of stock at a point where it will
be out of stock only once every 20 weeks, or 5% of the time, then it will have
to schedule the stock replenishment when the inventory of casings on hand
drops to 66,000 units. Since the expected or average weekly usage is 50,000
units, the safety stock to be maintained is 16,000 (making a total stock of
66,000).

This example, of course, assumes a single rather arbitrary definition of
what is meant by risk or minimum acceptable level of customer service.
There are a number of ways of defining the level of service, each appropriate to particular circumstances. One might be the total volume of
material or orders delayed; another, the number of customers delayed
(perhaps only in the case of customers with orders exceeding a certain
size level), still another the length of the delays. All of these definitions
are closely related to the "probability distribution" of sales—i.e., to the
expected pattern of sales in relation to the average.

Costs of Service Failure. It is easy enough to understand the principle
that setting a safety stock implies some kind of a management decision
or judgment with respect to the maximum sales level to be allowed for,
or the cost of service failure. But here is the rub: service failure cost,
though real, is far from explicit. It rarely, if ever, appears on the accounting records of the company except as it is hidden in extra sales or manufacturing costs, and it is characteristically very hard to define. What is new
in inventory control is not an accounting technique for measuring service
cost but a method of self-examination by management of the intuitive assumptions it is making. The progressive company looks at what it is in
fact assuming as a service-failure cost in order to determine whether the
assumed figure is anywhere near realistic.

For example, characteristically one hears the policy flatly stated: "Back
orders are intolerable." What needs to be done is to convert this absolute,
qualitative statement into a quantitative one of the type shown in Exhibit
II. Here we see the facts which might be displayed for the management of
a hypothetical company to help it decide on a customer service policy:

To get a 90% level of customer service (i.e., to fill 90% of the orders immediately), a little over three weeks' stock must be carried—an investment of
$64,000 with an annual carrying cost of $12,800.

Filling another 5% of orders immediately, thereby increasing the service
level to 95%, would mean about one week's more stock, with an extra annual
cost of $3,800.

Filling another 4% immediately (a 99% service level) would cost an extra
$7,400 per year.

EXHIBIT II.   RELATION BETWEEN SAFETY STOCKS
AND ORDER DELAY

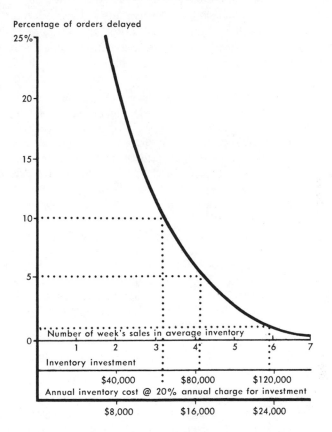

At each point the management can decide whether the extra cost is justified by the improved service. Thus, the chart becomes a device for comparing policies on service and inventories for consistency and rationality.

PERIODIC REORDERING

The periodic reordering system of inventory replenishment—the other basic approach to handling uncertainty about demand—is very popular, particularly where some type of book inventory control is employed and where it is convenient to examine inventory stocks on a definite schedule. The idea underlying all varieties of this system is to look at stocks at fixed *time* intervals, and to vary the order *amount* according to the usage since the last review.

The problem is that many seemingly similar ways of handling a cyclical ordering system may have hidden traps. A typical difficulty is instability in reordering habits and inventory levels caused by "overcompensation"; that is, by attempting to outguess the market and assuming that high or low sales at one point, actually due to random causes, indicate an established trend which must be anticipated. For example:

An industrial abrasives manufacturer found himself in a characteristic state of either being out of stock or having too much stock, even though his inventory control procedures were, at least judging by appearances, logically conceived. The procedures worked as follows: Each week the production scheduling clerk examined the ledger card on each item, and each month he placed a replenishment order on the factory based on (a) the existing finished stock on hand in the warehouse, (b) a replenishment lead time of six weeks, and (c) a projection for the coming two-month period of the rate of sales during the past two-month period.

The manufacturer blamed the instability of his market and the perversity of his customers for the difficulties he faced in controlling inventory, when in fact the seemingly logical reorder rule he had developed made his business behave in the same erratic fashion as a highly excitable and nervous driver in busy downtown traffic. The effects of sales fluctuations tended to be multiplied and passed on to the factory. *No use was made of inventories—especially safety stock—to absorb sales fluctuations.*

The most efficient and stable reorder scheme or rule has a very simple form:

A forecast or estimate of the amount to be used in the future is made for a period equal to the delivery lead time plus one reorder cycle. Then an order is placed to bring the total inventory on hand and on order up to the total of the amount forecast for the delivery lead and cycle times, plus a standard allowance for safety stock. Under such a scheme, the average inventory expected to be on hand will be the safety balance plus one-half the expected usage during a reorder cycle.

Note the contrast between this scheme and that used by the abrasives manufacturer. Here inventories are used to "decouple" production and sales. An upward fluctuation in sales is "absorbed" at the warehouse; it is not passed on to the plant until later (if at all). Many companies subscribe to this plan wholeheartedly in principle but only halfheartedly in practice. A common tendency, for instance, is to make the forecast but then, if sales increase, to revise it upward and transmit the increase back to the plant. The whole value of a safety stock based on a balancing of the costs of running out and the costs of rush orders to production is thus lost.

Readers may recognize the application here of servo theory, the body of concepts (including feedback, lags or reaction times, type of control, and the notion of stability) developed originally by electrical engineers in designing automatic or remotely controlled systems.[1] An inventory system, though not a mechanical device, is a control system and as a consequence is subject to the same kinds of effects as mechanical control systems and can be analyzed using the same basic concepts.

CHOICE OF SYSTEM

Each system of reordering inventories has it own advantages. Here are the conditions under which the fixed order system is advantageous:

Where some type of continuous monitoring of the inventory is possible, either because the physical stock is seen and readily checked when an item is used or because a perpetual inventory record of some type is maintained.

Where the inventory consists of items of low unit value purchased infrequently in large quantities compared with usage rates; or where otherwise there is less need for tight control.

Where the stock is purchased from an outside supplier and represents a minor part of the supplier's total output, or is otherwise obtained from a source whose schedule is not tightly linked to the particular item or inventory in question; and where irregular orders for the item from the supplier will not cause production difficulties.

For example, the fixed order system is suitable for floor stocks at the factory, where a large supply of inexpensive parts (e.g., nuts and bolts) can be put out for production workers to draw on without requisitions, and where a replenishment is purchased whenever the floor indicates the supply on hand has hit the reorder point.

By contrast, the periodic reordering system is useful under these conditions:

Where tighter and more frequent control is needed because of the value of the items.

Where a large number of items are to be ordered jointly, as in the case of a warehouse ordering many items from one factory. (Individual items may be shipped in smaller lots, but the freight advantages on large total shipments can still be obtained.)

Where items representing an important portion of the supplying plant's output are regularly reordered.

In general, since safety stocks needed vary directly with the length of the period between orders, the periodic system is less well suited where

---

[1] See H. J. Vassian, "Application of Discrete Variable Servo Theory to Inventory Control," *Journal of the Operations Research Society of America,* August 1955, p. 272.

the cost of ordering and the low unit value of the item mean infrequent large orders.

It should be noted that modifications of the simplest fixed order system or intermediates between the fixed order system and the periodic reordering system are also possible and very often useful; they can combine the better control and cost features of each of the "pure" schemes. For example:

One type of scheme often useful—the "base stock" system—is to review inventory stocks on a periodic basis but to replenish these stocks only when stocks on hand and on order have fallen to or below some specified level. When this happens, an order is placed to bring the amount on hand and on order up to a specified maximum level.

The choice of frequency of review and the minimum and maximum inventory points can be determined by analysis similar to that used for the other systems, but precautions must be taken—such as that stocks on order must always be counted when reorder quantities are figured—in order to avoid problems of instability and oscillation which can easily creep into rules that are apparently sound and sensible.

Interaction Among Factors. As mathematical analysis will indicate, the safety stock, reorder quantity, and reorder level are not entirely independent under either the fixed order or the periodic reordering system (or any combination thereof):

Where the order amount is fixed, the safety stock is protection against uncertainty over the replenishment time (measured by the reorder level). But it is the size of the order amount that determines the frequency of exposure to risk. With a given safety level, the bigger the order placed, the less frequently will the inventory be exposed to the possibility of run-out and the higher will be the level of service.

Where inventories are reordered on a periodic time cycle, the uncertainty against which safety stocks protect extends over the *total* of the reorder period and replenishment time. But here it is the length of the reordering cycle that determines the risk. The shorter the period and the closer together the reorders, the less will be the chance of large inventory fluctuations and, as a consequence, the less will be the size of safety stock required in order to maintain a given level of service.

The interaction among the frequency of reorder, the size of reorder, and safety stocks is often ignored as being unimportant, even in setting up fairly sophisticated inventory control schemes (although the same companies readily consider the *lot-size* problem in relation to the other factors). In many cases this many be justifiable for the purpose of simplifying inventory control, particularly methods for adjusting reorder quantities and safety stocks to changing costs and sales. On the other hand, cases do arise from time to time where explicit account must be taken of such interactions so that an efficient system may be developed.

Note, too, that the factors governing the choice of any reorder scheme are always changing. Therefore, management should provide for routine review of the costs of the system being used, once a year or oftener, so that trends can be quickly identified. Also, control chart procedures, like simple quality control methods, should be used to spot "significant" shifts in usage rates and in the characteristics of customer demand (fluctuations, order size, frequency of order, etc.). Schemes for checking such matters each time a reorder point is crossed are easily incorporated in the programs of automatic data-handling systems used for inventory control; they can also be applied to manual systems, but less easily and hence with some temptation to oversimplify them dangerously.

PRODUCTION SCHEDULING

Now let us turn to the important relationships between safety stocks and production. The safety stock affects, and is affected by, production run cycles, production "reaction times," and manufacturing capacity levels.

SETTING CYCLE LENGTHS

In production cycling problems, as in periodic reordering, the longer the run on each product, the longer one must wait for a rerun of that product; therefore, a larger safety stock must be maintained as protection. Shorter, more frequent runs give greater flexibility and shorter waiting periods between runs, and thus lower safety inventory requirements. Also, again the interaction between factors must be taken into account. For example:

A chemical company arrived at production run cycles for a set of five products going through the same equipment on the basis of only setup costs and cycle inventories (e.g., lot-size inventories), ignoring the interaction between cycle length and safety stocks. It found that on this basis an over-all product cycle of approximately 20 days, or one production month, appeared optimum, allowing 4 days per product on the average. However, when the problem was later re-examined, it was discovered that the uncertainty introduced by long lead times was so great that the over-all product cycle could in fact be economically cut back to less than 10 days. Doubling setup costs would be more than offset by savings in inventory and storage costs resulting from a reduction in the needed safety stocks.

Exhibit III illustrates the cost characteristics found to exist. The three *dashed* lines show separately the annual costs of changeovers, carrying cycle inventories, and carrying safety stocks, compared with the length of the individual production cycle. Adding together only the first two costs leads to the lower of the *solid* lines. This is at a minimum when the production cycle is 20 days long, indicating an apparent annual cost of $40,000. However, if *all* costs are included (the *solid* line at the top), the total annual cost on a 20-day cycle is $95,000. On this basis total costs are at a minimum when the cycle is 10 days long—only $70,000. This means a saving of $25,000 annually on the products in question.

EXHIBIT III.   INFLUENCE OF SAFETY STOCKS ON CHOICE
OF AN OPTIMUM PRODUCTION CYCLE

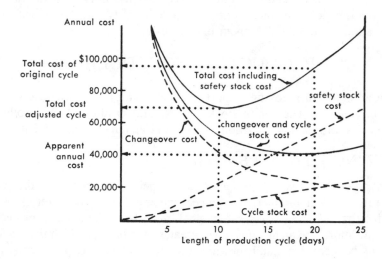

SETTING PRODUCTION LEVELS

Safety stocks give only short-term protection against sales uncertainty. If stocks are being replenished from production, the effectiveness of over-all control depends also on the ability to restore them in case of depletion.

If total demand varies, the ability to restore stocks depends, in turn, on the ability of the production facilities to react to chance fluctuations. In order to get low inventories, the process must have fast reactions properly controlled or (equivalently) in some cases large "capacity." If reactions are slow or limited, inventories must be large, and the inventory in effect serves another type of protective function, namely, protection of production rate or capacity from the stresses of demand fluctuation. To illustrate the kind of situation where this may be true:

Changes in the throughput rate of chemical processing equipment may be slow and difficult or expensive.

The output level of an assembly line operation may depend on the number of stations that are manned, or the number of shifts working. Some time may be required to change the production rate by changing the number of stations manned at each point along the line.

The production output of a job-shop operation may be influenced by the rate at which new workers can be hired and trained, or the cost of making changes in the manning level by bringing in new untrained workers or laying off people.

How fast should production operations respond to sales fluctuations, and to what extent should these fluctuations be absorbed by means of inventory? The costs of warehousing and cash investment in inventory need to be balanced against the costs of changing production rates or building excess capacity into the production system.

The actual cost of making out schedules, which depends on the frequency with which they are made and the degree of precision required, also should be considered, as well as the speed of reaction of production which is physically possible (e.g., the employee training time). When these costs are made explicit, management may find itself having to balance conflicting objectives. To illustrate:

A metal fabricator making a wide line of products to order attempted to provide immediate service to customers. He found that on the average his departments needed a substantial excess of labor over the normal requirements of the jobs flowing through, and this excess was essentially idle time. On the other hand, when he attempted to cut the excess too thin, backlogs began to build up. He had to weigh his desire to get the lead time down against the costs of excess unused labor.

Ordinarily we want to avoid passing back the full period-to-period sales fluctuation by making corresponding changes in the size of orders placed on production because it is uneconomical. What we can do instead is to:

1. Set the production level in each period equal to anticipated needs over the lead time plus the scheduling period not already scheduled, plus or minus *some fraction* of the difference between desired and actual inventory on hand.

2. Alternatively, change the existing production level or rate by *some fraction* of the difference between the existing rate and the rate suggested by the simple reorder rule (i.e., that an order be placed in each period equal to the anticipated requirements over the lead time plus the scheduling period, plus or minus the difference between desired and actual inventory on hand and on order).

Each of these alternatives is useful in certain types of plants, depending on whether the cost of production fluctuations comes primarily from, say, overtime and undertime (work guarantee) costs or from hiring, training, and layoff costs. Each in appropriate circumstances will lead to smoother production, at the expense of extra inventory to maintain the desired level of service.

When the different costs involved are identified and measured, mathematical techniques can be used to show the effect that varying the numbers in the rule (in particular, the size of the *fraction* used) has on inventory and production expense and to arrive at an economical balance between the needs of marketing and manufacturing. These two rules are expressions of servo theory, like that referred to earlier in connection with inventory. Here it may be worthwhile to see in some working detail how the theory can be applied mathematically:

The first rule can be stated as follows:

$$P_i = \sum_{k=0}^{T} F_{i+k} - \sum_{k=1}^{T} P_{i-k} + k(I_o - I_i); k \leq 1$$

P_i is the amount scheduled for production in period i, F_i is the forecast requirements for period i, I_o is the desired inventory, I_i is the actual opening inventory on hand in period i, and k is the response number which indicates what fraction of the inventory error or production rate departure is to be accounted for each period.

The fluctuations in inventory resulting from a choice of k in the first rule can be expressed as a function of the fluctuations in sales about the forecast, as follows (if fluctuations from month to month are not correlated):

$$\sigma_I = \sqrt{\frac{T(2k - k^2) + 1}{2k - k^2}} \; \sigma_F$$

where σ_I is the standard deviation of inventory levels, and σ_F is the standard deviation of actual sales about forecast sales each period. Similarly, the production rate variations resulting from any choice of k can be expressed as:

$$\sigma_P = \sqrt{\frac{k}{2 - k}} \; \sigma_F$$

The influence of the choice of a response number, k, on the standard deviation of inventories and on the standard deviation of production rates under the first type of rule is shown in Exhibit IV. Frequently the costs of production fluctuations are more or less directly proportional to the standard deviation of fluctuations in the production rate, a measure of the amount of change in production level which can be expected to occur. On the other hand, the normal inventory level, the average level expected, must be set large enough so that even with expected inventory fluctuations, service failures will not occur excessively. This means that the larger the standard deviation in inventory levels, the larger must be the normal level, generally in proportion. Therefore, one can "buy" production flexibility with larger inventories, and vice versa, with the particular costs in the process concerned determining the economical balance.[2]

The second rule can be worked through similarly. Here P^* is the changed amount scheduled for production, and the rule can be stated as follows:

$$P_i^* = P_{i-1}^* + k(P_i - P_{i-1}^*); k \leq 1 = (1 - k) P_{i-1}^* + kP_i$$

where

$$P_i = \sum_{k=0}^{T} F_{i+k} - \sum_{k=1}^{T} P_{i-k}^* + (I_o - I_i)$$

EXHIBIT IV.   EFFECT OF RESPONSE NUMBER K ON VARIATIONS
IN INVENTORY AND PRODUCTION RATE

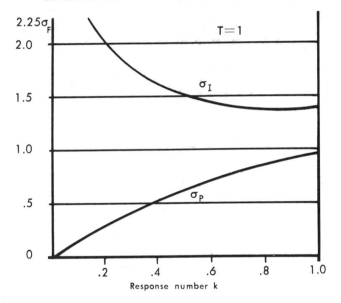

SETTING CAPACITY LEVELS

In some cases—particularly where output cannot be stocked easily—the problem of controlling the production level is not so much one of adjusting the level to respond to fluctuations in demand, as of setting the capacity of the plant or operation at a high enough level to permit demand fluctuations to be absorbed without excessive delay. If the capacity is set

---

[2] See H. J. Vassian, op. cit. See also Charles C. Holt, Franco Modigliani, and Herbert A. Simon, "A Linear Decision Rule for Production and Employment Scheduling," *Management Science,* October 1955, for another approach to this problem under different cost conditions.

equal only to the desired average rate, fluctuations in demand about this desired rate must either be absorbed by inventories or by orders piling up in a backlog. To illustrate:

The telephone companies have recognized for many years that telephone exchanges must be built with greater capacity than is required to handle the average load, in order to keep lines of waiting subscribers within reasonable levels.

Pile-ups often occur around the check-out booths of cafeterias or the ticket windows in railroad stations. Customers are eventually taken care of, but capacity is so close to average requirements, in some cases, that long waiting lines can be built up as a result of customers arriving at random in small bunches.

The problem of specifying the number of workmen to tend semiautomatic machinery or the capacity of docks to service freighters is complicated by the fact that the units require service more or less at random, so that again there can easily develop an accumulation of units awaiting service if personnel are not immediately available.

A theory of such processes is growing; it is known as waiting-line theory. This is really a branch of probability theory, and is itself a whole body of mathematical techniques and explicit concepts providing a mathematical framework within which waiting-line and similar problems can be studied.[3]

Some examples of applications in production scheduling are: flow of orders through departments in a job shop; flow of items through the stages in an assembly line; clercial processing of orders for manufacture or shipping; filling orders in a warehouse or stockroom; and setting up shipping or berth facilities to handle trucks or other transport units. In each case, fairly well-fixed crews or facilities have to be set up for handling fluctuating orders or items quickly, avoiding delays in service. A balance between the cost of extra personnel or facilities and delays in taking care of demand is needed.

In applying waiting-line theory to such problems, the flow of orders or demand for goods can be considered as a demand for service, analogous to subscriber cost in a telephone exchange. Orders are handled by one or more processing stations, analogous to telephone trunk lines. When the order or unit is produced, the processing station is free to take on the next order in line, as when a call is completed through the exchange. For example:

---

[3] A technical discussion of waiting-line theory and related applications can be found in W. Feller, *An Introduction to Probability Theory and Its Applications* (New York, John Wiley & Sons, Inc., 1950), Chapter 17.

A wholesale merchandise house planned its order-handling and order-filling activities in advance of peak sales. The company, selling consumer merchandise to a large group of retail dealers, had grown rapidly and in mid-summer had looked forward to serious congestion, delayed orders, and lost customers when the Christmas peak hit. An analysis based on waiting-line theory outlined staff and space requirements to meet the forecast load, showed what jobs were the worst potential bottlenecks, and revealed, incidentally, how the normally inefficient practice of assigning two persons to "pick" one order could in this case help avoid tieups and save space during the critical sales peak.

STAGES OF CONTROL

The choice and use of appropriate techniques for inventory control is not a simple matter. It takes a good deal of research into sales and product characteristics, plus skill in sensing which of many possible approaches are likely to be fruitful.

To describe these techniques, I shall take a case illustration. This case is drawn from a great deal of business experience, but in order to keep the detail and arithmetic within manageable proportions without distorting the essential points, I have simplified and combined everything into one fictional situation.

Any of the stages of the company's progress toward more efficient inventory management—from the original to the final—might be found to exist in the inventory control practices of a number of sizable companies with reputations for progressive and efficient management. These stages of advancement in the refinement of inventory control should not be used to compare the inventory system of one company or division with that of another, for the reasons just mentioned; but they may prove helpful to management in answering the questions, "Where are we now?" and "What could we do better?"

Briefly, the case situation is as follows:

One division of the Hibernian Bay Company makes and sells a small machine part. Sales run slightly over 5,000 units annually, and the price is $100 apiece. Customers are supplied from four branch stock points scattered about the country, which in turn are supplied by the factory warehouse. The machining and assembly operations are conducted in a small plant, employing largely semiskilled female help. The level of production can be changed fairly rapidly but at the cost of training or retraining workers, personnel office expenses, and increased inspection and quality problems. The division management has almost complete autonomy over its operations, although its profit records are closely scrutinized at headquarters in Chicago.

Originally the factory and branch warehouse stocking practices were haphazard and unsatisfactory. In total, nearly four months' stock was carried in branches, in the factory warehouse, or in incompleted production orders. A stock clerk in each branch who watched inventories and placed reorders on the factory warehouse was under pressure to be sure that stocks were adequate to fill customer orders. The factory warehouse reorder clerk in turn watched factory stocks and placed production orders. Production runs or batches were each put through the plant as a unit. Fluctuations in production, even with apparently sizable stocks on hand, caused the management deep concern.

SERVICE IMPROVED

The management decided to try to improve inventory practices and appointed a research team to study the problem. The team suggested using "economical order quantities" for branch orders on the factory warehouse and warehouse orders on production, as a basis for better control. The steps followed were:

The research team suggested that the formula for determining the economical order quantity was $x = \sqrt{2As/i}$, where $A =$ fixed cost connected with an order (setup of machines, writing order, checking receipts, etc.), $i =$ annual cost of carrying a unit in inventory, $s =$ annual movement, and $x =$ "economical order quantity."

The team found that each branch sold an average of 25 units a week, or 1,300 per year; that the cost of a branch's placing and receiving an order was \$19 (\$6 in clerical costs at the branch and factory, \$13 in costs of packing and shipping good, receiving, and stocking); that annual inventory carrying costs in the branches were \$5 per unit, based on a desired 10% return on incremental inventory investment. The reorder quantity for each branch was computed as $\sqrt{2 \cdot \$19 \cdot 1,300/\$5} = 100$ units reorder quantity.

A system was set up where each branch ordered in quantities of 100, on the average, every four weeks. On this basis, without further action, each branch would have had an average inventory of one-half a reorder quantity, or 50 units. (The books would show 75 units, since stock in transit from factory warehouse to branch was also charged to the branch, and with average transit time of one week this would average 25 units.)

The next step was to provide for enough to be on hand when a reorder was placed to last until the order was received. While the average transit time was one week, experience showed that delays at the factory might mean an order would not be received at the branch for two weeks. So sales for two weeks had to be covered.

Statistical analysis showed that sales in any one branch over two weeks could easily fluctuate from 38 units to 62 units and could conceivably go as high as 65–70. The management decided that a 1% chance of a branch running out of stock before getting an order would be adequate.

Calculations then indicated that the maximum reasonable two-week demand to provide for would be 67. (The statistical basis was that sales fluctuate about the average at random; that fluctuations in the various branches are independent of one another; and that the standard deviation is $\sqrt{st}$ where s = sales rate, and t = length of individual time period.)

The branches therefore were instructed to order 100 units whenever the stock on hand and on order was 67 or less. This gave an inventory in each branch made up on the average as follows:

Safety stock	42	(order point, 67, less normal week's usage, 25)
Order cycle stock	50	(one half 100-unit order)
In transit	25	(one week's sales)
Total	117	or 4.7 weeks' sales

The resulting behavior of the reorder system is shown in Exhibit V— both as it would be presumed in theory and as. it actually turned out. Although the actual performance was much less regular than presumed, the two compare fairly well—testimony to the soundness of the procedure.

EXHIBIT V.   ECONOMICAL REORDER SYSTEM OF A
BRANCH WAREHOUSE

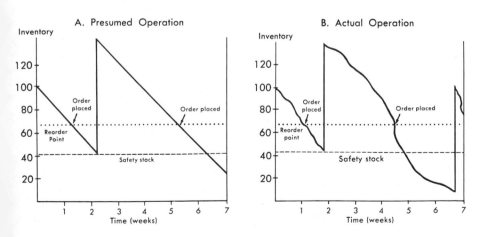

APPLICATION AT THE FACTORY

At the factory warehouse end, the "economical order quantity" scheme worked as follows:

The cost of holding a unit in inventory was $3.50 per year (at 10% return on investment); the cost of placing an order and setting up equipment for each order was $13.50; and, of course, a total of 5,200 units was made each year. These indicated that each production order should be for $\sqrt{2 \cdot \$13.50 \cdot 5{,}200 / \$3.50} = 200$ units.

Factory processing time was two weeks; it would take two weeks for each order to reach the warehouse. The warehouse would need to place its replenishment order on the factory when it had enough on hand or on order to fill maximum reasonable demand during the next two weeks.

On the average, the factory warehouse would receive one order a week from the branches (one every four weeks from each of four branches) under the new branch reorder system. In fact, because of the fluctuations in branch sales described before, it was found that orders on the factory warehouse fluctuated substantially in any two-week period (see Exhibit VI).

EXHIBIT VI.   FLUCTUATIONS OF ORDERS ON FACTORY
WAREHOUSE

Number of branch orders	Number of items ordered	Percentage of weeks
	A. Weekly Periods	
0	0	37%
1	100	37
2	200	18
3	300	6
4+	400+	2
	B. Biweekly Periods	
0	0	13%
1	100	27
2	200	27
3	300	18
4	400	9
5	500	4
6	600	1
7+	700+	1

It was agreed that to give branches service adequate to maintain their own service, stocks at the factory warehouses would have to be high enough to fill demand 99% of the time, i.e., a replenishment order would have to be placed when 600 units were on hand. This meant a safety stock of 600 units minus 200 (normal usage), or 400 units. Cycle stock averaged half a run, or 100 units, and stock in process an additional half run, or 100 units. Total factory stock, then, was:

Cycle stock	100 units
Stock in process	100 units
Safety stock	400 units
Total	600 units

Exhibit VII gives a picture of the apparent costs of the "economical order" system. The stock of 1,068 units equaled less than 11 weeks' sales, a fairly substantial reduction, and the management felt that it had a better control, since clerical procedures were set up to adapt readily to any changes in inventory charges (currently 10% per year) or service level requirements the management might choose to make.

EXHIBIT VII.   COSTS OF REORDER SYSTEM

	Number	Cost each	Annual cost
Inventory			
Factory	600 units	$3.50/year	$2,100
4 branches	468 units	$5.00/year	2,340
Reorder cost			
Branch	52/year	$19.00	990
Factory	26/year	$13.50	350
Total			$5,780

PRODUCTION STABILIZED

But the factory still had problems. On the average, the warehouse would place one production order every two weeks, but experience showed that in 60% of the weeks no orders were placed, in 30% one order, and in 10% two, three, or more orders were placed.

Factory snarls due to these fluctuations occasionally caused the factory to miss deadlines. These in turn led on occasion to warehouse delays in filling branch orders, and forced the branches to hold to the two-week delivery time even though actual transit time was only one week. An analysis revealed the following:

Factory fluctuations were very costly. A statistical regression of costs against operating levels and changes showed that annual production costs were affected more by the average *size* of changes in level than by the frequency of change; a few large changes in operating level were much more costly than many small changes.

Under the "economical reorder quantity" system, production fluctuations were no larger than before, but the average change up or down actually equaled

80% of the average production level. This was estimated to cost $11,500 annually, bringing the total cost of the system, including costs of holding inventories, placing orders, and changing production rates, to $17,280 per year.

This led to the suggestion that the company try a new scheme so that orders on the factory warehouse and the factory would be more regular. A system with a fixed reorder cycle or period was devised, under which branch warehouses would place orders at fixed intervals, the order being for the amount sold in the period just ended. The factory warehouse would ship the replenishment supply, order an equivalent amount from the factory, and receive the order within two weeks or by the beginning of the next review period, whichever was longer.

Under this scheme, each branch warehouse would need to keep its stock on hand or on order sufficient to fill maximum reasonable demand during one review period plus delivery time (tentatively taken as two weeks) on the basis of the reorder rule described previously in this article. The question to be determined was: How long should the review period, that is, the time between reorders, be? Exhibit VIII summarizes inventories and costs for reorder intervals ranging from one to six weeks, based on the following facts and figures:

(1) *Branch safety stock* was determined from a study of branch sales fluctuations, to allow for maximum reasonable demand over the reorder interval plus the two-week delivery period.

"Maximum reasonable demand" was defined to allow a 0.25% risk of being out of stock in any one week (equal to the 1% risk on the average four-week interval under the "economical reorder quantity" system described previously).

(2) *Branch cycle stock* would average one-half of an average shipment. Under this system, the average shipment to a branch each period would equal the average sales by the branch in one period (25 units × number of weeks).

(3) *Transit stock* equaled one week's sales.

(4) *Branch inventory carrying cost* was $5 per unit per year.

(5) *Branch ordering costs* equaled $19 per order, with one order per period. A one-week period would mean 52 orders per year; a two-week period, 26 orders per year; etc.

(6) *Factory safety stock* was set to allow a 1% risk that the warehouse would be unable to replenish all branch shipments immediately.

(7) *Factory cycle stock* in process or in the warehouse would be approximately equal to one-half the sales in any one period.

(8) *Factory inventory carrying cost* was $3.50 per unit per year.

(9) *Factory ordering costs* equaled $13.50 per order (see 5 above).

(10) *Production change costs* were proportional to the period-to-period changes in production level, equal under this system to period-to-period changes in branch sales.

EXHIBIT VIII.   SUMMARY OF REORDER PERIOD
COST COMPARISONS

	Length of period (weeks)					
	1	2	3	4	5	6
Branch warehouse						
Safety stock	24.0	26.0	27.0	28.0	30.0	31.0
Cycle stock	12.5	25.0	37.5	50.0	62.5	75.0
Transit stock	25.0	25.0	25.0	25.0	25.0	25.0
Total units of stock	61.5	76.0	89.5	103.0	117.5	131.0
Annual inventory cost	$ 310	$ 380	$ 450	$ 515	$ 590	$ 650
Ordering cost	990	495	330	250	195	165
Total cost each branch	$1,300	$ 875	$ 780	$ 765	$ 785	$ 815
Total cost four branches	$5,200	$3,500	$3,120	$3,060	$3,140	$3,260
Factory warehouse						
Safety stock	33	33	41	47	52	58
Cycle stock	50	100	150	200	250	300
Total units of stock	83	133	191	247	302	358
Annual inventory cost	$ 290	$ 465	$ 670	$ 865	$1,060	$1,250
Ordering cost	700	350	235	175	140	120
Total cost factory	$ 990	$ 815	$ 905	$1,040	$1,200	$1,370
Production change costs	$1,600	$2,250	$2,760	$3,180	$3,560	$3,900
Total system costs	$7,790	$6,565	$6,785	$7,280	$7,900	$8,530

The figures show that a two-week reorder interval would be most economical for the company as a whole, and this was chosen. Costs were estimated to be $6,600, compared with $17,300 under the "economical reorder quantity" system. While the new system cut total inventories by nearly 70%, most of the gain came from smoother production operations.

Further economies became apparent when the system was in operation:

(1) The reduction in production fluctuations made it possible to meet production deadlines regularly, cutting the effective lead time in deliveries to branches and thereby permitting modest reductions in branch safety stocks.

(2) The inventory system was found well suited to "open" production orders. Instead of issuing a new order with each run, the moderate fluctuations made it possible to replace production orders with simplified "adjusting memos" and at the same time to eliminate much of the machine setups.

"BASE STOCK" SYSTEM

The success with the periodic reordering system encouraged the company to go further and try the "base stock" system referred to earlier. Under this system, the branch warehouses would *report* sales periodically. The factory would consolidate these and put an equivalent amount into production. Stocks at any branch would be replenished whenever reported sales totaled an economical shipping quantity.

Two possible advantages of this system compared to the fixed period scheme were: (1) Branches might be able to justify weekly sales reports, reducing production fluctuations and safety stock needs still further. (2) It might be possible to make less frequent shipments from factory to branches and make further savings. The following questions had to be decided:

How frequently should branches report sales? As noted earlier, cost studies showed that of the $19 total cost of ordering and receiving goods $6 represented clerical costs in placing and recording the order. Here is a summary of the costs affected by the choice of reporting interval:

	Reporting interval			
	One week		Two weeks	
	Number	Cost	Number	Cost
Branch safety stock	100	$ 500	108	$ 540
Production changes		1,600		2,250
Branch clerical costs	4 × 52	1,250	4 × 26	625
Total		$3,350		$3,415

Thus, there appeared to be some advantage to reporting sales weekly from branches to the factory.

How big should replenishment shipments be? Exhibit IX summarizes the system costs related to the size of shipment from factory to branch. Each line shows the total of the cost indicated plus those represented by the line below. The total system cost (top line) is lowest at 82; that point is therefore the optimum shipping quantity from factory to branch warehouse. The same answer can be obtained from the formula given before, $\sqrt{2 \cdot \$13 \cdot 1,300/\$5}$ = 82.

The base stock system therefore was set up with weekly reporting and replenishment shipments of 82 units to branches. The total cost of the base stock system was $5,200 compared with $6,600 under the previous system.

STABILIZED FURTHER

The company, cheered by its successes, decided to see if even further improvements might be obtained by cutting down further on production fluctuations. As it was, the production level under the base stock system was being adjusted each week to account for the full excess of deficiency in inventory due to sales fluctuations. It was proposed that production be adjusted to take up only a fraction of the difference between actual and desired stocks, with added inventories used to make up the difference.

EXHIBIT IX. OPTIMUM SHIPPING QUANTITY FROM FACTORY TO BRANCH WAREHOUSE UNDER BASE STOCK SYSTEM

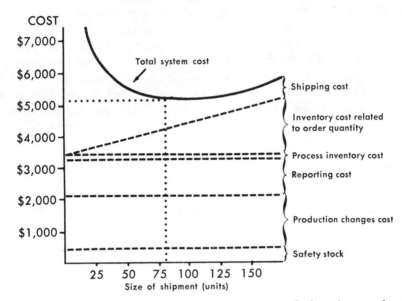

The two costs that would be affected are costs of changing production and costs of holding inventories, in particular safety stocks. These are affected by the fraction of the inventory departure that is made up each week by adjusting production.

The study showed that the cost would be minimized with the rate of response set equal to 0.125. (This compared with a response rate of 1.0 under the base stock system.) The additional savings of $970 brought the annual cost of the system down to $4,200.

SUMMARY

The results of all the changes made by the division management were substantial:

(1) *A major reduction in stocks*—They had been cut 35% from what they were even with the "economical reorder quantity" system.

(2) *A substantial reduction in production fluctuations*—The problems of the case are common even among the best-run businesses and can be solved in much the same way with much the same results. Of course, a large part

of the effort and expense that were necessary in this step-by-step, evolutionary approach could be saved. Technical methods are available for analyzing and measuring the performance of alternate systems so that management can proceed directly to the ultimate system that is most desirable; management does not have to feel its way. Let me emphasize again, however, that no one kind of system should be considered "the goal." The efficiency of any given inventory control plan depends too much on the demand and cost characteristics of the business.

In the discussion thus far, several large questions remain unanswered. What happens when the business is subject to seasonal sales? What more can be done than to insure that desired levels of service are maintained while cutting inventory and production costs? Where do forecasting and scheduling fit into the picture? I shall discuss these questions in the next and final article in this series.

Chapter 11

COMBINED PROBLEMS OF INVENTORY AND PRODUCTION CONTROL

XIII.

Guides to Inventory Policy
III. Anticipating Future Needs*

John F. Magee

Businessmen are prone to view inventories with distaste, as an apparently necessary drain on resources, something that no one has been able to eliminate but hardly a "productive" asset like a new machine or tool. In fact, however, inventories are as productive of earnings as other types of capital investment. They serve as the lubrication and springing for a production-distribution system, keeping it from burning out or breaking down under external shocks. They help to absorb the effects of errors in forecasting demand, to permit more effective use of facilities and staff in the face of fluctuations in sales, and to isolate one part of the system from the next in order to permit each to work more effectively.

* From the *Harvard Business Review,* Vol. 34, No. 3 (1956), 57–70. Reprinted by permission of the *Harvard Business Review.*

In this article let us look at the function of a third type of inventory, one which is of particular importance in long-range planning: anticipation stocks. This type of inventory is most commonly needed where sales are highly seasonal, and where either one or the other of these problems occurs:

1. The "crash" or short-peak season problem which arises, for example, in the toy industry before Christmas or in certain fashion clothing lines at various times during the year.

2. The more conventional seasonal problem arising in industries where sales show a pronounced seasonal swing, with the peak season often extending over several weeks or months, as in the case of automobiles, many kinds of building materials, certain cosmetics, some types of home appliances, agricultural supplies, and furniture.

Stocks built up to buffer production against seasonal fluctuations in sales are not the only form of anticipation stocks. Anticipation stocks may also be carried, for example, to meet a planned intensive sales campaign or to carry sales over a plant vacation or maintenance shutdown. However, the questions and methods of attack which apply to seasonally fluctuating sales also illustrate approaches to control of other types of anticipation stocks; I shall therefore use the former as a basis of discussion in this article.

THE "CRASH" PROBLEM

In the "crash" type of problem, management must balance the risks of not having enough stocks to fill demand and thus losing profit, or of being forced to go to extraordinary measures to buy or produce to fill demand, against the risks of having too much on hand and consequently incurring sizable write-off and obsolescence loss or storage expense until the next selling season.

The question boils down to how much stock to have on hand when the main selling season opens. The objective basically is to have enough on hand so that the company can expect, on the average, to break even on the last unit produced; that is, to carry enough so that on the last unit the expected risk of loss due to inability to fill demand equals the expected cost of carrying the unit through to the next season.

METHOD OF APPROACH

In principle, the solution to the "crash" problem is quite simple. The classic "newsboy" case is as good an illustration as any:

A newsboy has, on the average 10 customers a night who are willing to buy papers costing 5¢ each. The newsboy makes a profit of 3¢ on each paper he sells, and loses 1¢ on each paper he takes out but fails to sell. Let us suppose he has kept records, and that 40% of the time he can sell at least 10 papers and 20% of the time he can sell at least 12 papers.

If the newsboy does not know how many papers he will actually sell in any given day but every day takes out 10 papers, he has a 40% chance of selling all the papers and making 3¢ each, and a 60% chance of not selling all papers and losing 1¢ on each not sold. He can expect the tenth paper to produce, on the average over time, a profit of 0.6¢ (3¢ × 40% − 1¢ ×60%). On the other hand, if he takes 12 papers every night, he can expect the twelfth paper to produce, on the average over time, a loss of 0.2¢ (3 × 20% − 1¢ × 80%).

It would not, therefore, be worth his while to take out 12 papers. As a matter of fact, he would probably make the greatest total profit by taking 11 regularly, since he could expect, on the overage over time, to do slightly better than break even on the eleventh paper (3¢ × 30% − 1¢ × 70%, or 0.2¢).

The newsboy problem is, after all, not so different from many business problems. Certainly from the newsboy's point of view the papers he buys which he may not sell represent a lot of money and a sizable risk of his capital. Indeed, perhaps the most important difference between the news-boy and businessmen in other situations is that the newsboy has to make this decision very frequently and therefore has more of a chance to build up a lot of experience on which to base intuitive judgments—that is, less need for careful calculation or formal statistical methods to wring out of past experience the information which is of value.

REACHING A SOLUTION

Suppose, for example, you are selling cosmetics and you want to make up a special Christmas package in a holiday wrapping containing three normally separate items at a combined price. You have tried a number of deals of this type in the past, and on the whole they have been highly profitable. However, individually they have been unpredictable; some have been very successful, and some that seemed excellent on paper turned out to be failures.

Your market research manager makes a volume prediction each time; on the average, his estimates come fairly close, but rarely on the nose. About half the time they are too high and half the time too low. In fact, 25% of the time your experience shows his estimate to be 20% or more on the high side, and just as frequently he misses as badly in the other direction. About 10% of the time he is as much as 40% off in each direction, and occasionally he really misses and actual sales are 75% or more off from the estimate. You are doing everything you can to improve these estimates, but in the meantime you have to decided how much to make up for your Christmas deal.

EXHIBIT I.   GENERALIZED MATHEMATICAL EXPRESSION OF APPROACH TO "CRASH" PROBLEM

Let:

$V =$ volume of demand

$f(V) =$ the probability density function of demand (i.e., distribution of demand during one period)

$\int_{Y}^{\infty} f(V)\,dV =$ the likelihood of selling an amount Y or more during a season

$n =$ the variable cost of making and holding a unit of stock in inventory during the selling period, including the capital charge for inventory investment, etc.

$m =$ the profit per unit sold

$L =$ the cost per unit of not filling an order (loss of good will), over and above the loss of profit

$P =$ the cost of carrying a unit of inventory if unsold by the end of the period

$K =$ the size of the inventory on hand at the beginning of the season

Then the profit earned during the replenishment cycle is given by:

$$p = mV - P(K - V) - nK; V \leq K$$
$$= mK - L(V - K) - nK; V > K$$

and the expected profit earned during the replenishment cycle, $E(p)$, is given by:

$$E(p) = m \int_{0}^{K} Vf(V)\,dV - nK + mK \int_{K}^{\infty} f(V)\,dV -$$

$$L \int_{K}^{\infty} (V - K)f(V)\,dV - P \int_{0}^{K} (K - V)f(V)\,dV$$

Again, differentiating the expected profit with respect to the inventory on hand at the beginning of the season, K, yields:

$$\frac{dE(p)}{dK} = -n + (m + L) - (M + L + P) \int_{0}^{K} f(V)\,dV$$

The maximum profit will be earned when $dE(p)/dK = 0$; that is, when

$$\int_{0}^{K} f(V)\,dV = \frac{m + L - n}{m + L + P}$$

Cost estimates indicate that if a package is not sold, the items can be repackaged at an extra cost of about $1 per package. If demand exceeds the original run, the extra cost of a special rerun plus emergency shipments to field stocks is estimated to be $1.75 per package. Following reasoning like that in Exhibit I (simply a generalized expression in mathematical terms of the solution to the newsboy case), you or your operations research analyst concludes that you should plan initially to have enough stock so that the chance that demand, as it materializes, will be covered by the initial run equals the ratio of the special makeup cost to the total of (a) special makeup cost plus (b) repackaging loss on unsold items. In other words, you want to make enough so that the chance that total sales will be covered by the initial run equals $1.75 ÷ ($1.00 + $1.75) or 64%. With your past experience on forecasting success, this means about a 10% overstock; that is, your initial run should exceed your estimated needs by about 10%.

This will not eliminate all the difficulties by any means. There is nearly a 40% chance you will have to make some additional high-cost stock, and there is still a good chance you will have unsold goods on hand after the holiday. However, this initial decision is about the best you can do with present forecasting and manufacturing methods to get the right balance between the two risks and thus minimize the over-all cost.

In problems like those noted above, the costs may, superficially at least, look different, and the mathematical details of formulating an approach to the problem and arriving at an answer may differ, but the basic elements are the same—balancing the cost and lost profit opportunities of demand exceeding available stock against the costs and losses of having available unused stock or capacity.

DEVELOPING APPROACH

Sometimes from the scanty experience gained in early-season selling enough information can be developed so that estimates of total season sales and resulting production plans can be adjusted. As more and better information becomes available, mathematical methods can be used to alter the "strategy" for the season slowly, according to predetermined rules.

Such a "developing" approach to inventory problems rests on the basic premises that one does not know the future, that there is therefore no need to plan into it very far in great detail, and that a good strategy for the present is one which puts you in a position to make a good choice the next time you have a chance, whatever actual experience may develop in the meantime. Applications of this general line of approach to problems are beginning to be made in the planning of heating-oil production, seasonal clothing production, and other seasonal, erratic demand problems.

SEASONAL SWINGS

In many industries, the basic yearly pattern of seasonal sales may be quite predictable, and the over-all volume can be reasonably well estimated. There may be only a small error of a few percentage points in estimating either the total volume or the size of the peak. In situations of this sort there are three problems:

1. Adjusting the forecast of expected sales to allow for safety stocks so as to protect against forecast errors. (Examples of an original and an adjusted "maximum" sales forecast are shown in Exhibit II. The latter is the original cumulative forecast increased by the safety stock allowance.)

2. Laying out a production pattern or plan to meet the forecast. (The difference between forecast and production plan will result in a planned inventory as illustrated in Exhibit II. The total costs of inventory and production depend on the form of the production curve, and characteristically the object is to choose this curve or production plan to minimize the expected total of these costs.)

3. Controlling or adjusting the production plan to keep it aligned with the sales forecast, as actual sales experience modifies the forecast and/or results in depleted or excessive inventory as compared with the plan.

MEETING FORECAST ERRORS

The answer to the first problem depends somewhat on that for the third, as the discussion on production control rules in the second article in this series may suggest. In general, however, it is fair to say that in most businesses the risks and costs of back orders so outweigh inventory cost that substantial protection in the form of safety stocks is justified. These

EXHIBIT II.   ILLUSTRATIVE SALES FORECAST AND
PRODUCTION AND INVENTORY PLAN

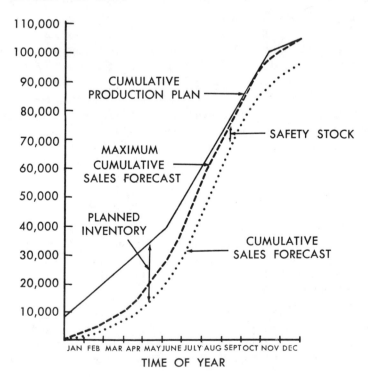

QUANTITY IN UNITS

safety stocks must be large enough so that stocks can be restored after a sudden unexpected sales spurt by a smooth and moderate adjustment in production rate. The production response rules described in the previous article, which take into account the nature of forecast errors, inventory costs, and service requirements, are one way of determining what is "large enough."

Another very similar approach is to begin with a forecast of maximum expected demand, or maximum demand the company is prepared to plan for. The long-range production plan is made out to meet this directly. Then production is adjusted downward from plan as excess inventories accumulate because of actual sales falling below the maximum plan. (More will be said later about this problem of production control.)

PLANNING PRODUCTION

Once the adjusted sales forecast or forecast plus safety stock has been obtained, the task is to plan the production rate or draw in the production curve shown in Exhibit II. The problem is to find a curve or mathematical function that will minimize the total of production and inventory costs. In theory, this sounds like a straightforward mathematical problem often encountered in physics. In practice, the job is not so easy, but a number of techniques have been found useful.

Graphical Techniques. Where the problem of planning production against forecasted seasonal sales is not made too complicated by a variety of items, processes, and stages, simple graphical or arithmetic techniques can often be useful. For example:

Suppose a company has a forecast at the beginning of the year which calls for requirements as outlined in Exhibit III. The first column shows expected sales month by month; the second column shows accumulated expected sales;

EXHIBIT III.   FORECAST OF SALES AND SAFETY STOCKS NEEDED
(In units)

Month	Expected sales	Cumulative sales forecast	Safety reserve	Cumulative total re- quirements*
January	6,000	6,000	3,000	5,500
February	4,000	10,000	2,500	9,000
March	3,000	13,000	2,100	11,600
April	4,000	17,000	2,500	16,000
May	6,000	23,000	3,000	22,500
June	9,000	32,000	3,500	32,000
July	11,000	43,000	4,000	43,500
August	12,000	55,000	4,200	55,700
September	13,000	68,000	4,400	68,900
October	12,000	80,000	4,200	80,700
November	11,000	91,000	4,000	91,500
December	9,000	100,000	3,500	100,000

* Less opening stock of 3,500

the third column shows a safety reserve to cushion the company against forecast errors, allowing time for smooth adjustment (the basis for this reserve will be discussed further below); and the last column shows the total amount that must be produced by the end of each month, allowing for an opening stock of 3,500 units.

The cumulative forecast and cumulative requirements, including opening stock, are shown in Exhibit IV. The company *could* produce at an average annual rate of 100,000 units, or 8,333 units per month—the production plan shown as a straight line in the exhibit. This plan would produce just enough inventory at the end-of-year peak to meet requirements. The month-end inventories (equal to the difference between the production plan and the cumulative sales forecast) are shown in Exhibit V. They average 12,800 units, of which 3,400 are accounted for as safety stock, leaving an average seasonal anticipation stock of 9,400 units. If the annual inventory carrying cost were $45 per unit, the seasonal anticipation stocks would be costing about $425,000 per year.

EXHIBIT IV. ACCUMULATIVE SALES FORECAST AND ALTERNATE PRODUCTION PLAN

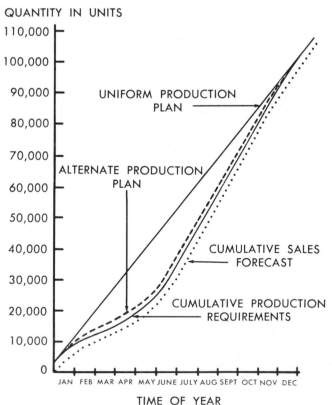

QUANTITY IN UNITS

TIME OF YEAR

Various alternatives might be tried to reduce this cost. For example, operations might be run during the low months of the year at the rate of 4,000 units per month, building up to a peak rate of over 13,000 units per month in September. This plan, shown by the dashed line segments in Exhibit IV, would result in substantially lower anticipation stocks. The average inventory would be 3,700 units, with 3,400 units safety stock, or 300 units seasonal anticipation stock. At $45 a unit, the cost of seasonal stock under this plan would be only $13,000 per year, a saving in inventory cost of over $400,000 per year.

EXHIBIT V.   MONTHLY ENDING INVENTORY
(In units)

January	5,830	July	18,830
February	10,170	August	15,170
March	15,500	September	10,500
April	19,830	October	6,830
May	22,170	November	4,170
June	21,500	December	3,500

Average monthly inventory	12,800
Average safety reserve	3,400
Average seasonal anticipation stock	9,400

The saving, of course, is not all net saving, since it is gained at the cost of adding and laying off the equivalent of some 9,200 units of production capacity. If this were, say, a chemical plant operating well under capacity and the variation from 4,000 to 13,200 units of production a month could be managed by adding and then laying off some 100 semiskilled men, the saving in inventory cost—equivalent to $4,000 per man hired and released—might well justify the change. On the other hand, if the change in operating levels involved adding and laying off some 1,000 to 1,500 employees of various skills, the inventory saving might fall short of offsetting the hiring, training, and layoff costs, not to speak of its effect on community relations. Under these circumstances, the change might not be worthwhile.

This alternative production plan, of course, calls for substantially increased plant capacity—nearly 60% more—for the same average throughput. If the capacity were not available and had to be added, or if it would be gained at the cost of overtime or second-shift premiums, or additional equipment installations, the simple cost calculation just outlined would have to be extended to include these extra costs and investments (not a difficult task if the procedures are well laid out).

By making similar trial calculations under other operating patterns, one can quickly get a picture of the influence of operating pattern on cost, and can arrive at a pattern which comes close to giving the minimum over-all cost. This plan then represents the basis for procurement, employment, and inventory control during the coming months until new forecasts call for an adjustment.

The operating plan summarized in Exhibit VI is essentially a minimum-cost plan, under the conditions that: (a) inventory costs are $45 per unit; (b) the cost of hiring and training an employee is $300 (typical of many industries); (c) a change of 750 units in the monthly rate of output requires employment or release of 100 men. The cost of seasonal inventory equals 2,150 units (average seasonal anticipation stocks) × $45 per unit, or about $97,000. The plan calls for varying the production rate from a low of 5,000 units per month to a maximum of 11,000 units—a change of 6,000 units; this requires hiring and training 800 new employees at a cost of $240,000. (If the hiring and subsequent layoff of 800 employees is considered an undesirable employment variation, the solution must be sought within whatever are set as the feasible or tolerable levels.)

Thus, under the plan in Exhibit VI the total of seasonal anticipation inventory stocks and hiring and training costs is $337,000. This represents a net saving of nearly $90,000 per year compared either with the uniform production plan or the alternative plan in Exhibit IV. (With the hiring and training costs taken into account according to the conditions assumed for Exhibit VI, the alternative plan with its extreme employment variation comes out about the same as the uniform plan.)

Advanced Techniques. Sometimes the problem of planning production to meet seasonal demand is too complicated for simple graphical techniques, and more specialized techniques are needed. One of these is linear

EXHIBIT VI. MINIMUM OVER-ALL COST PLAN
(In units)

Month	Sales forecast	Monthly production plan	End-of-month inventory (including safety reserve)
January	6,000	5,500	3,000
February	4,000	5,000	4,000
March	3,000	5,000	6,000
April	4,000	5,000	7,000
May	6,000	5,200	6,200
June	9,000	11,000	8,200
July	11,000	11,000	8,200
August	12,000	11,000	7,200
September	13,000	11,000	5,200
October	12,000	11,000	4,200
November	11,000	10,800	4,000
December	9,000	8,500	3,500
Average monthly inventory			5,550
Average safety reserve			3,400
Average seasonal anticipation stock			2,150

programming. The problem just described *might* have been attacked by linear programming methods in order to cut through the repeated trials to a good solution, but this approach was not necessary because trial and error did not involve a prohibitive amount of time and effort. Linear programming has been found useful in circumstances where the problem is complicated, for instance, by one or more of these conditions:

Several product lines using the same facilities or staff.
Possibilities of planned use of overtime to meet peak needs.
Need for considering extra-shift premiums.
Several stages in manufacturing, with seasonal storage possibilities between.
A number of alternate plants, with different cost and employment situations, to meet demand.
Joint planning of plant operations and of the assignment of branch warehouses to the plant.

When the seasonal planning problem is attacked as a linear programming problem, the objective is to minimize the total of costs incurred in carrying inventories forward in slack periods to meet future sales peaks, changing the production level to meet sales requirements, or resorting to overtime. The objective has to be reached within the limitations imposed by: (a) capacity restrictions on the amount which can be produced at normal or overtime rates in any month; (b) the requirement that inventories in each line or product be planned large enough to meet sales requirements; and, possibly, (c) the amount of variation that can be tolerated in the planned production rate.

Illustrations of production planning problems formulated in linear programing terms can be found in technical literature on the subject.

CONTROLLING PRODUCTION

Once the production plan has been made, it and the sales forecast dictate a sequence of planned inventory balances. However, as sales experience accumulates, actual stocks will fall below or exceed the planned balances. The minimum inventory balance or safety stock which has been (or should have been) set up will absorb the immediate effects of departures of actual sales from forecast, but it will be necessary to keep adjusting production plans *periodically* to bring inventories into line. The size of the needed safety stock, it should be emphasized, depends on the way production adjustments are made.

The task is comparable to that of adjusting production in the face of demand fluctuations, described in the preceding article in this series. There it was pointed out that methods used generally take this form: adjusted production = original production plan (or forecast sales level) ± *some fraction* or part of the deficiency or excess of inventory compared with "normal" or "par." The idea is to keep adjusting production to bring inventory back into balance in the face of fluctuations in demand. If the fraction is large (close to one), production is made very responsive to sales fluctuations, and the inventory needed is smaller. If the fraction is small, the inventory acts to absorb sales fluctuations, and must be larger; production changes from original plan are smaller.

Production plans to meet seasonal sales have to be kept in adjustment in much the same way, and basically similar control systems can be used. In this case, the original plan is the production plan (e.g., Exhibit VI) worked out to meet seasonal sales. The "normal" inventory is not a fixed level, as in the other case, but varies from month to month; it is the planned inventory of Exhibit VI, including the safety stock. The steps to take in planning production are these four:

1. From a study of forecast errors or possible differences between sales and forecast, and of costs of holding inventory and changing production, choose the desired fraction or rate of adjustment in production and the corresponding safety stock, using methods of the type described in the preceding article.

The choice of safety stock does not involve production levels, just the costs of changing production and holding stocks, along with anticipated forecast errors.

2. Add the safety stock so chosen to the cumulative sales forecast month by month to get the accumulative production required.

3. Plan production period by period to meet requirements, as described earlier.

4. Periodically adjust the planned production by the specified fraction (chosen in Step 1) of the departure of actual inventories from the plan for the period.

For those interested in the actual working through of a problem, Exhibit VII shows the mathematical expression of the production control rule.

RELATIVE IMPORTANCE

The relative importance of anticipation stocks and of lot size stocks and fluctuation stocks (described in the previous articles) will differ from case to case. A study of sales and production characteristics is basic in finding out what inventory functions are important, and what the significant costs and policies related to these functions happen to be.

EXHIBIT VII. PRODUCTION CONTROL RULE EXPRESSED
MATHEMATICALLY

The rule can be written formally as:

$$\hat{P}_i = P_i^* \pm k(I_{i-1}^* - I_{i-1}); 0 < k \leq 1$$

where:

$\hat{P}_i$ = adjusted production plan for period i
P_i^* = original production plan for period i
I_{i-1}^* = planned closing inventory for period $i - 1$
I_{i-1} = actual closing inventory for period $i - 1$
k = fraction of inventory departure adjusted for in production

P_i^* and I_i^* are chosen by the methods described earlier to minimize total inventory and operating costs and meet the production requirements:

$$R_i = F_i + S_i$$

where:

R_i = production required up through period i
F_i = accumulated forecast of sales through the period i
S_i = safety stock needed for period i

The safety stock, S_i for each period is in general proportional to expected forecast errors and related to the value of k that is chosen. Thus, if forecast errors from period to period are independent,

$$S_i = A \sqrt{\frac{1}{2k - k^2}} \, \sigma_i$$

σ_i being the standard deviation of forecast errors for the period; and A a parameter which depends on the percentage of customer orders which management desires to fill directly from stock (typical values range from 1.3 to 2.5, corresponding to 90% and 99% protection).

SALES CHARACTERISTICS

Sales characteristics which strongly influence the production and inventory control system (and the relative importance of the different inventory functions) include:

1. *The unit of sales*—Are sales made in dozens, tons, or carloads? Planning must be done in terms of this characteristic unit. It is obviously not enough, for example, to have several tons on hand if the usual unit required is a carload.

2. *The size and frequency of orders*—Are there a few large orders each day or week, or a steady stream of small orders? This is related to the question of unit of sales, but the same total volume sold in a large number of small orders can characteristically be supported by substantially less inventory than if sold in a few large orders, unless special measures are taken to reduce the uncertainty about the time when individual large orders will be placed.

3. *Uniformity or predictability of sales*—Do sales show predictable seasonal fluctuations? Or do they show large short-term fluctuations, uncontrollable or

self-imposed (as by special sales campaigns)? Handling large, unpredictable fluctuations requires flexibility and additional capacity in inventory production as well as carefully designed rules for adjusting or controlling inventory balances. But where fluctuations are predictable, advance planning techniques can be used.

4. *Service requirements or allowable delay in filling orders*—Where allowable delays are small, inventories and production capacity must be correspondingly greater; care is required to be sure the control system is really responsive to needs.

5. *The distribution pattern*—Do shipments go direct from factory to customer, through field warehouses, through jobbers, retailers, or consignment? The more stages there are, characteristically, the more inventory is required. Field inventories in fact serve basically to improve service to jobbers or retailers and thereby to remove from them some of the burden of keeping stocks.

Where the product moves through several stages of handling from factory to ultimate consumer, prompt reports or estimates of movement, as close to the consumer level as possible, are important in minimizing the amount of uncontrollable fluctuation in demand which the factory has to contend with. Often the reordering habits of retailers and jobbers can seriously exaggerate the basic uncertainty in consumer demand for a product, and thereby compound the inventory and production control problems of the plant.

6. *The accuracy, frequency, and detail of sales forecasts*— Fluctuation stocks exist basically because forecasts are not exact. Thus the inventory problems of a business are directly related to its inability to forecast sales with precision. This does not mean that lack of precise sales forecasts is an excuse for sloppy control. Sometimes it is more economical to accept the forecasting uncertainties and stick to the plan, whether it means overproduction or underproduction, than to pay the price in inventories or production fluctuations. But the responsibility of forecast errors for inventory needs should be clearly recognized, and the control system should be adapted to the type of forecasts that are possible.

PRODUCTION CHARACTERISTICS

The production characteristics which influence the scheme of production and inventory control are:

1. *The form of production organization*—Job-shop type organization is an expensive way of getting flexibility; a company using it should be sure it really needs that degree of flexibility. The inventory and production control scheme can be considerably simpler under a product-line organization than in a job shop.

2. *The number of manufacturing stages*—Where a number of stages in manufacturing exist, the inventory control scheme must be set up to take advantage of differences in cost and obsolescence risk which are likely to exist.

3. *The degree of specialization of the product at specific stages*—Is each end product distinct from the raw material stage on, or are the different products more or less the same up to the final processing, assembly, and packaging? Where the latter is true, economies are often possible in keeping the right

balance of stocks in the semifinished state and by simplifying the control and scheduling of preliminary stages where the types of product are not diverse.

4. *Physically required processing times at each stage*—Processing times affect the length of delay, after issuing a replenishment order or adjusting a production rate, before the action becomes effective. The length of this delay, in turn, directly influences the size of the inventory needed.

5. *Capacity of production and warehousing stages*—Capacity obviously affects the size and frequency of reorder.

6. *Production flexibility*—How rapidly can management vary production rates, shift personnel among product lines or departments, and change equipment from one product to another? Management of inventories and production control are basically a question of striking a balance among production flexibility and capacity, inventory levels, and customer service needs. No company is free to pick all three at will. A realistic inventory control system must be set up to recognize the limitations in flexibility which exist.

7. *Kind of processing*—Are batches of materials of a certain size needed in production? If so, the quantities and combinations must obviously be taken into account in scheduling for production.

8. *Quality requirements, shelf-life limits, or obsolescence risks*—These set important upper limits on the extent inventories can be used to buy flexibility and free production operations from fluctuations in demand.

These sales and production characteristics cannot be readily distinguished as having one type of effect or another on the production planning and inventory control scheme. Nor is it true that one type of characteristic dictates one approach while another kind of product always requires something else. However, the job of setting up a sound production and inventory control system is not just a job of setting up the right clerical routines and staff organization; it is a research job to find out how the product sales and production characteristics can be exploited to get an economical balance between production flexibility, inventory investment, and customer service.

ROLE OF FORECASTING

The need for estimates of future sales to control inventories is clearest in the case of anticipation stocks, but it exists in the case of the other functions as well. Whether forecasts are needed or possible is not the question; they are made formally or informally every time a decision is made whether to build or replenish an inventory. The question is whether the necessary forecasts are being made as well as they might be if formally recognized and if available statistical and market research techniques were used. Without going into the methods of forecasting, which is a considerable subject of its own, the following points are significant here:

Economical inventory plans depend on realistic estimates of need—not just sales goals or quotas. Even so, there are bound to be forecasting errors—and the bigger the possible errors, the bigger the inventories must be to guard against them.

A single forecast figure, without specifying the estimated error or limits of error, is not enough. Sometimes the need may be met by a maximum sale forecast indicating the upper limit of demand which the production or distribution organization will be required to service.

To estimate the limits of error requires a comparison of past forecasts and sales—and often this is hard to do, either because the earlier forecasts were made informally, or the records were discarded and hopefully forgotten.

In any event, forecasting errors bear so importantly on inventory economy that to keep the control system up to date requires systematic review of past errors and effort to improve the forecasting method.

PRODUCTION SCHEDULING

The task of translating inventory policy into practice, of reacting to demand as it materializes and utilizing the inventory balances and planned production capacity, is a function of production scheduling. Considerable effort has gone into the development of techniques—board displays, filing systems, card systems, and so on—to facilitate scheduling and control of progress on orders scheduled. These techniques can be extremely useful *if* they are adapted to the nature of the product and manufacturing facilities and *if* they are used in a framework of self-consistent inventory balances and production operating levels. The essence of the control problem is setting this framework in the light of management policy, not making the actual schedules.

Conventional scheduling methods are often worked out to cope with the complexities of job-shop production, where each order is unique and no set sequence of operations exists.

Scheduling operations in this way through a large number of stages or departments is difficult. Fortunately, however, the need for so doing is not nearly so common as one might gather. Many businessmen, in discussing inventory and production control, give the impression that their organization with its large product line—whether several hundred or several tens of thousands—is saddled with job-shop operations from top to bottom. They look with longing toward the lower operating costs and simpler management problems of assembly-line operations. They frequently fail to recognize that almost all products and product lines are capable of being manufactured under a wide range of organizational forms intermediate to the extremes of either pure job-shop or assembly-line operation.

Taking advantage of this latitude has been a source of considerable operating economy in some businesses—and could be in many more.

CONTROL SYSTEMS

A comprehensive inventory control system should be closely co-ordinated with other planning and control activities, such as sales forecasting, cash planning, and capital budgeting, since it affects all of these activies in many ways. The specific steps and timing will vary from one company to another, depending on product and process requirements, but the essentials of an inventory control system can be grouped into three broad classes: long-range inventory planning, short-range planning, and scheduling.

EXHIBIT VIII. SCHEMATIC DIAGRAM OF INVENTORY PLANNING

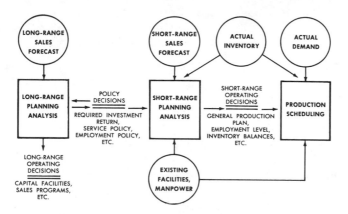

Exhibit VIII shows the three basic planning functions in boxes, with the arrows indicating the flow of information to and from the analysis. More specifically:

1. The *long-range* plan makes use of: (a) sales forecasts, with error or range estimates, and (b) preliminary policy decisions on capital allocation and value and on the amount of risk to be assumed. The purpose is to show the implications of policy choices so they can be refined and sharpened, and then to provide a basis for long-range operating decisions concerning construction, purchase, and sale of facilities, adjustment of sales and promotion programs, and so on. The analysis results may also lead to further forecasting effort by showing the production and capital costs resulting from poor forecasts.

2. At the intermediate stage, the short-range plan uses as its "raw materials" or inputs: (a) the results of policy decisions, (b) short-term demand forecasts, (c) existing facilities and manpower, and (d) inventories. The outputs are bases for short-range operating decisions—the general production plan to follow, adjustments in the employment rate, corrections in inventory balances.

3. Finally, within this framework *scheduling* can react to demand as it actually materializes.

Chapter 12

RELATED LOT-SIZE AND DYNAMIC PROBLEMS

XIV.

An Investigation of Some Quantitative Relationships Between Break-Even Point Analysis and Economic Lot-Size Theory*

Wayland P. Smith

Two common tools utilized to evaluate the economic potential of alternative ways of performing a specified task are (A) Break-Even Point Analysis, and (B) Economic Lot-Size Theory.

These two techniques have become the basic devices around which many courses in Engineering Economics have been built over the past 40 years. Most engineering undergraduate students at some time are exposed to these two fundamental methods. Industrial Engineers, in particular, find a persistent recurrence of problems that utilize one or the other of these models in their solution.

In retrospect one wonders why these two schemes have never been combined into one common model. On the other hand, they have primarily

* From *The Journal of Industrial Engineering*, Vol. 9, No. 1 (1958), 52–57. Reprinted by permission of *The Journal of Industrial Engineering*.

been developed to solve two problems that at least on the surface appear to be quite divergent. The purpose of this paper is to show that these problems are not divergent, that they have much in common, and that they are actually very much interrelated. In short, a single mathematical formulation will be developed that relates the two theories.

Before presenting such a combined formulation, a brief review is presented of the two basic techniques in very simple form. The purpose of this review is twofold—1. to re-establish the assumptions on which these two techniques are based, and 2. to establish a common set of symbols that will be helpful for the combined formulation.

A SIMPLIFIED BREAK-EVEN POINT MODEL

The historical development of break-even analysis and the break-even chart would be exceedingly difficult to trace. Like many other techniques, it was simultaneously created and developed by many people with the rapid growth of the scientific management movement during the early years of the twentieth century. It was one of the techniques that was quickly exploited.

Certainly Dr. Walter Rautenstrauch was one of the principal developers and proponents of this technique (7). It is to be found in practically all books which deal with engineering economy problems (1) (2) (3) (4) (10) (13).

Generally, it is treated in its most simple form for solving short-range problems and the time-value-of-money aspect of the problem is omitted. This is not always the case, and more sophisticated methods involving different basic assumptions have been developed. One of these is the MAPI formulation (6) (9).

Although many types of problems lend themselves to break-even analysis, a specific type of problem is of concern here—the economic comparison of two alternative methods of performing a task (actually any number of alternatives can be compared simultaneously by this procedure).

Costs for each alternative are divided into two categories and called either fixed costs or variable costs. The fixed costs are those costs that occur only once during the life of the alternative. Once these costs have been expended, they are not recoverable. Examples of such costs are:

1. Set up and tear down cost.
2. Cost of special tooling.
3. Paper work and clerical cost required to schedule a job.

In other words, the fixed costs are those costs that are not incurred by every unit of production. If we were to plot cost versus the number of units produced, these costs would appear as step functions. In the most simple problem, only those fixed costs that occur prior to the first unit of production are included. This is frequently done when the other fixed costs are assumed to be negligible.

Conversely, variable costs are those costs that are incurred by every unit of production. Examples of such costs are:

1. Direct labor cost per piece.
2. Direct material cost per piece.
3. Depreciation.

Once both types of costs have been identified for each alternative, it is possible to write a total cost equation for each one of the alternatives in terms of production quantity.

Total cost = (summation of all fixed costs) + (the production quantity) $\times$ (the summation of all variable costs)

Where: C_i = total cost of the ith alternative
           f_{xi} = an initial cost of the ith alternative
           F_i = summation of all initial fixed cost for the ith alternative
           v_{xi} = a variable cost of the ith alternative
           V_i = summation of all variable cost for the ith alternative
           N = the quantity to be produced   Eq. 1.

Then $C_i = (f_{1i} + f_{2i} + \cdots) + N(v_{1i} + v_{2i} + \cdots)$
Or $C_i = F_i + NV_i$

If C_i is plotted against N for each alternative, a simple graphical relationship results (Fig. 1). F_i becomes the y intercept and V_i becomes the slope of the straight line that this equation represents. If the two alternatives have been selected such that the one having the lower F_i has the higher V_i, then the two lines will intersect at some positive value of N. This point is called the break-even point. It represents the quantity at which the total costs are the same for both alternatives. When the demand for the product is greater than this break-even quantity, then the alternative with the lower V_i is more economical. When the required quantity is less than the break-even point, then the alternative with the lower F_i is the more economical.

In a quantitative manner this analysis tells us what we recognize intuitively—that a production method with relatively low fixed costs and high variable costs will be more economical at lower quantities while a production with relatively high fixed costs and low variable costs will be more economical at higher quantities.

It also reminds us that no single production method is best for all quantities of production. Since minor and major methods variation are easy to conceive through changes in machines, tools, men, motion patterns, etc.,

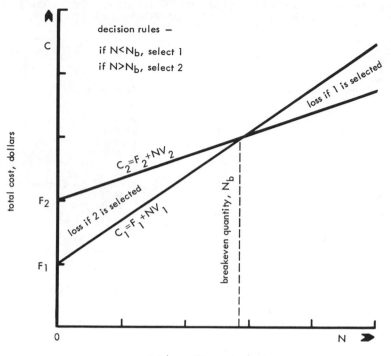

FIGURE 1. A BREAK-EVEN CHART FOR TWO ALTERNATIVES

it should not be too difficult to imagine an almost infinite number of possible production methods from which to choose—each with its own small range of production quantities over which it is more economical than any other alternative (Fig. 2).

A SIMPLIFIED PRODUCTION ECONOMIC LOT-SIZE MODEL

Like break-even analysis, economic lot-size theory was developed during the period from 1910 through 1930. Its historical development has been clearly traced by Fairfield E. Raymond in his monumental treatise on the subject (8). Since this book tells the story so well and contains a complete bibliography, it would be superfluous to repeat it here. However, a table from this text showing the development of economic lot-size formulas has been reproduced here because it is so revealing.

TABLE 1. EQUATIONS EMPLOYED TO SHOW THE STAGES IN THE DEVELOPMENT OF FORMULAE FOR ECONOMIC LOT SIZES

First appearance	Form	Authorities	Approx. date of record
1912	Cubic equation not published	G. D. Babcock	1912
1915	$Q = \sqrt{\dfrac{P \cdot S}{c}} \cdot k$	F. W. Harris D. B. Carter General Electric Co. J. A. Bennie P. E. Holden K. W. Stillman Benning and Littlefield J. M. Christman G. H. Mellen	1915 1922 1922 1923 1924 1925 1925
1917	Special adaptation	Eli Lilly & Co.	1917
1917	$Q = \sqrt{\dfrac{P \cdot S}{c \cdot i}} \cdot k$	S. A. Morse W. E. Camp Heltzer Cabot Co. N. R. Richardson	1917 1922 1924 1927
	$Q = \sqrt{\dfrac{P \cdot S \cdot k}{c \cdot (i + f_i)}}$ where $f_i =$ allowances for insurance, storage costs, etc.	H. T. Stock B. Cooper	1923 1926
1918	$Q = \sqrt{\dfrac{P \cdot S \cdot D'}{c \cdot i(D' - S)}} \cdot k$	G. Pennington E. T. Phillips W. L. Jones J. W. Hallock	1927 1927 1929 1929
1918	$Q = -\dfrac{P}{c} + \sqrt{\dfrac{P^2}{c^2} + \dfrac{P \cdot S \cdot D'}{c \cdot i(D' - S)}} \cdot k$	E. W. Taft	1918
1923	$Q = \sqrt{\dfrac{P \cdot S \cdot k}{c \cdot i \cdot f_d + \dfrac{a \cdot b}{h}}} \cdot k'b$	G. Pennington F. H. Thompson R. C. Davis C. N. Neklutin	1927 1923 1926 1929
1924	$Q = \sqrt{\dfrac{P \cdot S \cdot k}{c \cdot i + (m + c) \cdot t_p \cdot S \cdot i}}$	A. C. Brungardt P. N. Lehoczky	1923 1927

The operations research movement stemming from the success of operations evaluations groups in the various services during World War II has given a rebirth to economic lot-size theory. It is interesting to note, however, that the recent writings of many operations researchers seem oblivious of the work done during the 1920's. At least there appears to be some hesitancy towards acknowledging this earlier work (5) (11). Economic lot size as it relates to inventory control has also been treated recently by T. M. Whitten in the theory of inventory management (12).

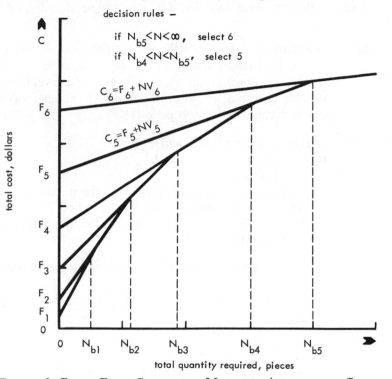

FIGURE 2. BREAK-EVEN CHART FOR MULTIPLY-ALTERNATIVE CASE

In the production of goods when the rate of production exceeds the rate of demand, the production must proceed in batches if the maximum production rate of the process is to be fully utilized. Otherwise, a ponderous growing stock pile will soon exist. The question arises as to the size of these batches or length of the run or the number of batches or lots to be started each year (in other words, four ways of stating the same problem).

In order to achieve the lot size that is most economical, two opposing cost elements must be considered. On the one hand, there are the costs that are incurred for each new lot, namely, set-up cost of the process including necessary scheduling, handling, paper work, etc. These costs are relatively proportional to the number of lots and would tend to make the lot size large. On the other hand, there are the costs incurred due to the storage of items necessitated by the production rate being higher than the demand rate. When long production runs are made, the amount of storage space required and the amount of money involved in inventory would increase. These costs would tend to make the lot size small.

Economic lot-size theory as does break-even analysis involves the development of the total cost equation for any specific situation of this kind.

Total cost = (the number of lots) × (the preparation and set-up costs) + (the production quantity) × (the sum of all variable costs) + (average inventory quantity) × (the inventory cost per unit during a given time period) × (number of time periods during the demand period)   Eq.2.*

Where C_i = total cost of the ith alternative
       N = total quantity to be produced
       n = lot size quantity
       F_i = sum of preparation and set-up costs for the ith alternative
       V_i = sum of the variable costs for the ith alternative
       P_i = production rate (after set-up) costs for the ith alternative
       D = the demand rate

$\frac{n}{2}(1-N/P_i)$ = the average inventory quantity (assuming a constant demand rate)

       I = sum of storage and inventory costs per unit during a given time period

Then $C_i = \left(\frac{N}{n}\right)F_i + NV_i$

$$+ \left(\frac{n}{2}\right)\left(1 - \frac{D}{P_i}\right)\left(\frac{N}{D}\right)I$$

Or $C_i = N\left[\left(\frac{I}{2}\right)\left(\frac{1}{D} - \frac{1}{P_i}\right)n^1 + V_i n^0 + F_i n^{-1}\right]$

If C_i is plotted against n for a specific alternative, a simple graphical relationship results for any specified value of D. This represents the graphical sum of the three costs in Eq. 2. (Refer to Fig. 3.)

By setting the first derivative of cost with respect to the lot size equal to zero, it is possible to find the lot size which yields minimum cost.

$$\frac{dC_i}{dn} = 0 = N\left[\frac{I}{2}\left(\frac{1}{D} - \frac{1}{P_i}\right) - \frac{F_i}{n^2}\right] \qquad \text{Eq. 3.}$$

---

* This only is true where $P > D$.

$$n = \sqrt{\frac{2F_i}{I\left(\dfrac{1}{D} - \dfrac{1}{P_i}\right)}}$$ Eq. 4.

If this value of n is substituted back into Eq. 2., a total cost equation results which is the minimum cost for any value of N.

$$\min_{c_i} = N\left\{\left(\frac{I}{2}\right)\left(\frac{1}{D} - \frac{1}{P_i}\right)\sqrt{\frac{2F_i}{I\left(\dfrac{1}{D} - \dfrac{1}{P_i}\right)}}\right.$$

$$\left. + V_i + F_i\sqrt{\frac{I\left(\dfrac{1}{D} - \dfrac{1}{P_i}\right)}{2F_i}}\right\}$$ Eq. 5.

$$\min_{c_i} = N\left\{\sqrt{\frac{I\left(\dfrac{1}{D} - \dfrac{1}{P_i}\right)F_i}{2}}\right.$$

$$\left. + V_i + \sqrt{\frac{I\left(\dfrac{1}{D} - \dfrac{1}{P_i}\right)F_i}{2}}\right\}$$

$$\min_{c_i} = N\sqrt{I\left(\frac{1}{D} - \frac{1}{P_i}\right)F_i} + NV_i$$

When this result is compared with Eq. 1., there is considerable similarity. The variable cost term is identical. The coefficient of the fixed cost term in the economic lot-size formulation is considerably more complex than that of the break-even formulation. In the break-even formulation, this coefficient is unity.

It should be apparent from the foregoing simple formulation of economic lot size that the concept of alternative manufacturing methods is totally ignored. Economic lot-size theory as developed here assumes one and only one manufacturing method. While this may be realistic enough after production methods have been established, it is not realistic at the time the manufacturing method is being established.

Thus two methods have been explored. Both of these methods purport to select the best method of doing a job. But these two techniques are based upon assumptions that are radically different. *Break-even analysis ignores inventory cost and assumes a single set up while economic lot-size theory ignores the possibility of different manufacturing methods with their accompanying differences and fixed variable cost patterns.*

THE COMBINED MODEL

There are two possible ways of approaching combined formulation of break-even analysis and economic lot-size techniques. The simpler case is the discrete case which assumes a limited finite number of possible production alternatives. The more complex case is the continuous one which assumes an infinite number of alternative production methods. The first case selects the optimum method from several stated possibilities. The second case selects the cost pattern of the optimum alternative and then searches for the method which actually matches this cost pattern. Only the first case is discussed in this report.

To fully explore the discrete case, we will examine a problem involving three alternatives: namely, the age-old problem of whether it is better to use an engine lathe, a turret lathe, or an automatic lathe to perform a specified manufacturing operation.

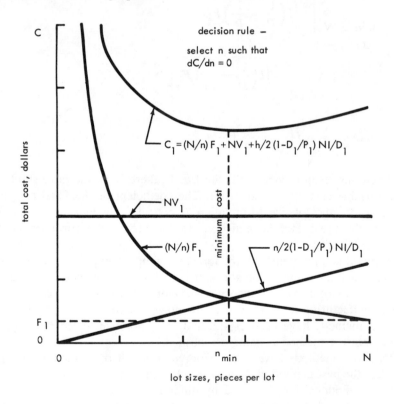

FIGURE 3. GRAPHIC FORMULATION OF ECONOMIC LOT FOR
A SINGLE ALTERNATIVE

To make this combined formulation as realistic as possible, the following values have been assumed:

1. Sum of costs that are incurred each time the job is set up (F_i).
   a. Engine lathe, $F_1 = \$1$
   b. Turret lathe, $F_2 = \$30$
   c. Automatic lathe, $F_3 = \$70$
2. Sum of all variable costs including direct labor, direct material, and manfacturing expense (V_i).
   a. Engine lathe, $V_1 = \$.20$ per unit
   b. Turret lathe, $V_2 = \$.10$ per unit
   c. Automatic lathe, $V_3 = \$.05$ per unit
3. Sum of all storage and inventory costs per unit of production when stored for *one month*. This amount is the same for all three alternatives (I).
   $I = \$.25$ per month per unit.
4. Production rate (P_i).
   a. Engine lathe, $P_1 = 5,000$ pieces per month
   b. Turret lathe, $P_2 = 15,000$ pieces per month
   c. Automatic lathe, $P_3 = 45,000$ pieces per month

All of these values are inherent in the particular production method and storage system. In a sense, these are fixed values. In addition, we must know or assume values relative to customer demand. We wish to examine what happens at different levels of customer demand.

To make this formulation more realistic the following levels have been assumed:

5. Demand rate (D).
   Case No. 1, $D_1 = 100$ pieces per month
   Case No. 2, $D_2 = 1,000$ pieces per month
   Case No. 3, $D_3 = 5,000$ pieces per month

Now it is possible to calculate the total cost equation for each alternative according to Eq. 5. This is done in the three steps shown as follows:

Step No. 1 (the basic equation)

Engine lathe

$$\min_{c_1} = N \sqrt{\frac{1}{4}\left(\frac{1}{D_j} - \frac{1}{5,000}\right)} 1 + .2N \qquad \text{Eq. 6.}$$

Turret lathe

$$\min_{c_2} = N \sqrt{\frac{1}{4}\left(\frac{1}{D_j} - \frac{1}{15,000}\right)} 30 + .1N \qquad \text{Eq. 7.}$$

Automatic lathe

$$\min_{c_3} = N\sqrt{\frac{1}{4}\left(\frac{1}{D_j} - \frac{1}{45,000}\right)70} + .05N \qquad \text{Eq. 8.}$$

Step No. 2 (let $K_{ji} = \sqrt{\frac{1}{4}\left(\frac{1}{D_j} - \frac{1}{P_i}\right)F_i}$

and find the K value for each alternative at each demand rate
—9 cases in all.)

	D_1	D_2	D_3
K_1	.049	.014	0
K_2	.274	.084	.031
K_3	.42	.132	.056

Step No 3 (substitute K values into Eq. 6., 7. and 8. and combine terms)

	D_1	D_2	D_3
$\min_{c_1}$	.249N	.214N	.2N
$\min_{c_2}$	.374N	.184N	.131N
$\min_{c_3}$	.425N	.182N	.106N

It is now possible to plot the total minimum cost of each alternative against the demand rate. Figure 4 shows this relationship.

When a smooth curve is drawn through the points for each alternative, three break-even points become apparent. The engine lathe is the most economical method when the demand rate is greater than 0 and less than 450 pieces per month. The turret lathe is the most economical when the demand rate is greater than 450 pieces per month and less than 900 pieces per month. The automatic lathe is the most economical when the demand rate is greater than 900 pieces per month.

How do these answers compare with those obtained from the typical break-even analysis? In the first place, it should be pointed out that these answers are entirely independent of the total quantity required (N). Thus the answer obtained is much more general. To compare these answers with the standard break-even analysis, it is necessary to assume various values of N.

Substituting known values into equation 1 yields the following total cost equation for each alternative according to the break-even analysis model which has been developed previously:

Engine lathe,	$C_1 = 1 + .2N$	Eq. 9.
Turret lathe,	$C_2 = 30 + .1N$	Eq. 10.
Automatic lathe,	$C_3 = 70 + .05N$	Eq. 11.

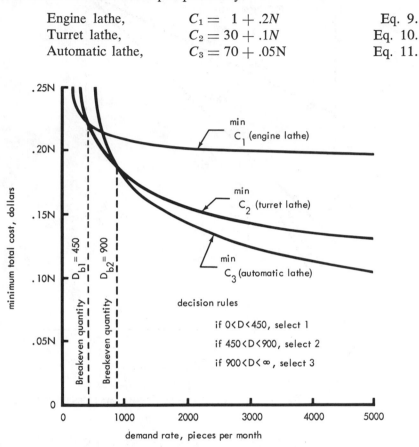

FIGURE 4. COMBINED FORMULATION FOR THREE ALTERNATIVES

When the C_i versus N curves are plotted, three break-even points are once again apparent. The engine lathe is the most economical method when the quantity required is greater than 0 and less than 290 pieces. The turret lathe is the most economical method when the quantity required is greater than 290 pieces and less than 800 pieces. The automatic lathe is the most economical when the quantity required is in excess of 800 pieces. This relationship is shown in Figure 5.

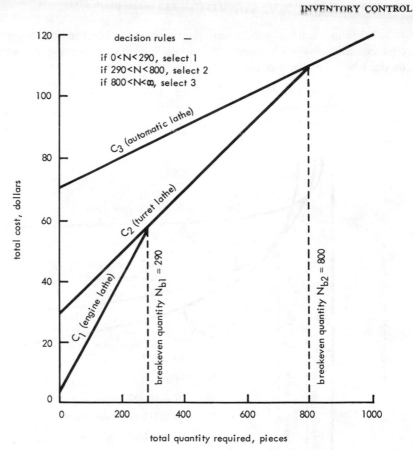

FIGURE 5. BREAK-EVEN CHART FOR THREE ALTERNATIVES

COMPARISON OF RESULTS

The next problem is to find a convenient and graphic way of portraying the errors that would have been generated in this specific problem if the simple break-even method had been used to solve the problem. Or to state it another way, what savings would have been derived by using the more complicated, combined model in determining the best production method?

A glance at the decision rules which are established in this example by the break-even model and the combined model is revealing because in most situations the two methods result in different courses of action rather than the same course of action. Figure 6 clearly reveals the disparity between the two methods. Listed below are the types of errors that can be made. These are shown graphically in Figure 6. In each case the area over which the error can be made is a rough approximation of the probability of this type of error. The actual loss at a specified point in the Figure 6 matrix may be determined from Figure 4.

TYPES OF ERROR

Type of Error	Breakeven Model Chooses	Combined Model Chooses
1	Engine Lathe	Turret Lathe
2	Engine Lathe	Automatic Lathe
3	Turret Lathe	Engine Lathe
4	Turret Lathe	Automatic Lathe
5	Automatic Lathe	Engine Lathe
6	Automatic Lathe	Turret Lathe

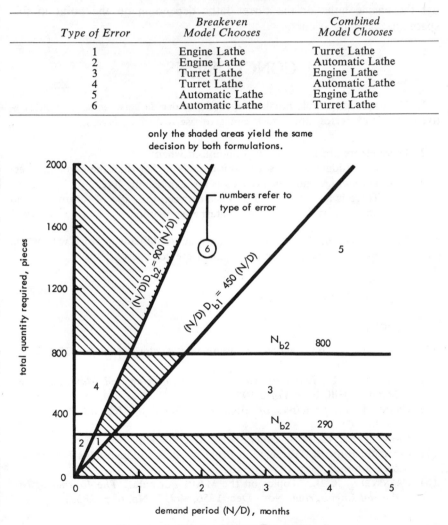

FIGURE 6. ERROR SPACE DIAGRAM

Generally a sales forecast would be able to limit to some degree the space in this figure that is actually pertinent. Let us say in this example that we are reasonably certain that the total volume required will be between 1,200 and 2,100 pieces and that the demand rate will be between 200 and 700 pieces per month. If this were the case checking Figure 6, it is apparent that the break-even model would give us the wrong decision over this entire space. According to the break-even model, we should always use the automatic lathe. According to the combined model, we should either use the engine lathe or the turret lathe depending on the point in this space that actually occurs.

CONCLUSIONS

1. The use of the simple break-even model to decide between several alternative methods of performing a task can give rise to serious errors.

2. These errors are particularly pronounced when—
   a. The production rates are considerably higher than the demand rates.
   b. The storage and inventory costs are significantly large.
   c. There is a substantial difference between the ratio of set-up cost and storage cost for the several alternative methods.

3. The combined model is not significantly more difficult to work with when modern computing techniques and equipment are considered.

References

(1) BULLINGER, C. E., *Engineering Economic Analysis*, McGraw-Hill, New York, 1950.
(2) EIDMANN, F. L., *Economic Control of Engineering and Manufacturing*, McGraw-Hill, New York, 1931.
(3) GRANT, E. L., *Principles of Engineering Economy*, Ronald Press, New York, 1950.
(4) KNOEPPEL, C. E., *Profit Engineering*, McGraw-Hill, New York, 1933.
(5) LATHROP, JOHN B., "Production Problems Bow to Operations Research," *SAE Journal*, May 1954, p. 46.
(6) ORENSTEEN, R. B., "Topics on the MAPI Formula," *The Journal of Industrial Engineering*, Nov.–Dec. 1956, Vol. 7, No. 6, p. 283.

(7) RAUTENSTRAUCH, WALTER, AND VILLERS, RAYMOND, *The Economics of Industrial Management*, Funk & Wagnalls Co., New York, 1949.

(8) RAYMOND, FAIRFIELD E., *Quantity and Economy in Manufacture*, McGraw-Hill, New York, 1931.

(9) TERBORGH, GEORGE, *Dynamic Equipment Policy*, McGraw-Hill, New York, 1949.

(10) THUESEN, H. G., *Engineering Economy*, Prentice-Hall, Inc., New York, 1950.

(11) VARNUM, EDWARD C., "The Economic Lot Size," *The Tool Engineer*, Nov. 1956, p. 85.

(12) WHITIN, THOMSON M., *The Theory of Inventory Management*, Princeton University Press, Princeton, N.J., 1953.

(13) WOODS, B. M., AND DE GARMO, E. P., *Introduction to Engineering Economy*, Macmillian, New York, 1953 (2nd Edition).

Chapter 13

SIMULATION IN INVENTORY CONTROL

XV.

Determining the "Best Possible" Inventory Levels*

Kalman Joseph Cohen

INTRODUCTION

We shall be concerned here with the problem of how inventory levels should be established. This is an important problem, for inventories play a role in all phases of business and industry, whether retail, wholesale, or manufacturing. Rather than considering all aspects of inventory problems, however, we shall concentrate on the function of inventories in the distribution of commodities, in particular, in the wholesaling operations, and we shall not be concerned with the part that inventories play in manufacturing.

In a distributional business, the reason for having any inventory is to sell goods. Usually, you cannot sell anything to a customer unless you have it in stock. These considerations would tend to make wholesalers or retailers carry large inventories, for the more items there are in stock, the greater are the chances of having what customers want when they want it.

* From *Industrial Quality Control* (1958), 4–10. Reprinted by permission of *Industrial Quality Control*.

However, there are limits to the size of the inventories which any business would want to have, these limits arising because it costs money to hold inventory. Inventories can be considered to be too large when the costs of carrying the commodities exceed the benefits obtained from having them in stock. On the other hand, inventories are insufficient when the additional gains from having more inventory are greater than the additional costs which would be generated. Somewhere in between there exists the *best possible* level of inventory, i.e., that level of inventory which results in the largest possible profit for the business. How to find the level of inventory which *is* best is the subject of this article.

THE WAREHOUSE NETWORK

The particular work which we shall discuss was done for the Replacement Division of Thompson Products. This Division does no manufacturing, so we need not consider the functions of inventories in manufacturing operations. Replacement Division is a large distributor of automotive engine and chassis parts for replacement use. This Division buys these parts in bulk from various manufacturers and sells them to wholesalers or jobbers, who in turn sell them to independent garagemen, car dealers, and fleet operators.

Replacement Division has one central warehouse in Cleveland and 36 branch warehouses scattered throughout the United States. Most of the sales are made at the branches. The central warehouse serves mainly as a supply depot, from which all branch stocks are sent.

The inventory problem at the branch warehouses consists in determining the best possible amounts of inventory which should be carried in stock. The magnitude of this problem can be appreciated from the fact that approximately 15,000 items are sold at each of the 36 branches, so there are more than half a million branch warehouse inventory levels to be established.

SALES DEMAND AT THE BRANCHES

If it were possible to say exactly how many parts would be sold each week at every branch and how long it would take to get these parts to the branches from the central warehouse, then it would be relatively easy to specify the best possible inventory levels at each branch warehouse. The problem that we have to deal with is considerably more difficult, however, because of two unavoidable elements of uncertainty: uncertainty about the sales demand at the branches and uncertainty about the time required to send parts from the central to the branch warehouses.

The uncertainty in the sales demand for an item which occurs at the branches is illustrated in Fig. 1, where we see a typical pattern in the fluctuations of weekly demand. It looks as though we could say with some degree of assurance that the sales demand for that part at the branch will average ten units per week, but what it will be in any particular week, we cannot say. Some orderliness can be derived from this chaos, however, if we ask, not what the demand will be in any particular week, but how frequently we can expect weekly demands of different amounts.

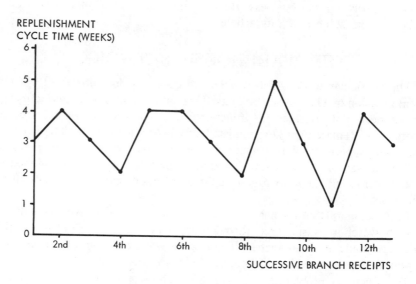

FIGURE 1. VARIATIONS OF DEMAND FOR AN ITEM AT A BRANCH

If we look at the weekly demands for a part at a branch over a large enough number of weeks, there will become evident a stable pattern of the relative frequencies with which different levels of demand occur. Over a long enough period of time, the pattern of weekly demand that we saw in Fig. 1 will build up into the frequency distribution of weekly demand shown in Fig. 2. Here we see that the most frequently occurring weekly demand is the average demand of ten units per week, the next most frequently occurring demand is nine units per week, and so forth. Furthermore, a weekly demand of ten units occurs three times as frequently as a weekly demand of five units, etc.

Statisticians apply the name "Poisson distribution" to describe the type of frequency distribution shown in Fig. 2. For our purposes, we need know only that the shape of the Poisson distribution is completely determined by its average value, and that we can use this distribution to describe the uncertainties in the weekly demand for a part at a branch warehouse.

Because of the fluctuations in sales demand, it sometimes happens that a branch is out of stock on an item when a customer wants it. This results in a *lost sale,* for when a customer cannot immediately obtain a particular part from the local branch warehouse, he will usually purchase it from a competitor. Thus, lost sales are lost business, and if a branch is out of stock when an item is requested, Replacement Division foregoes the profit that could have been made by selling that item.

THE REPLACEMENT SYSTEM

The branch warehouses are not autonomous in their operations. The central warehouse maintains rigid inventory control over the branches, determining what their inventory levels should be and actually shipping all stocks for the branches from Cleveland. Whenever a part is sold at a branch, a copy of the sales slip is immediately sent to Cleveland, so that the central warehouse can prepare an invoice for the customer. Cleveland accumulates the sales slips from a branch for a whole week, and it then prepares a replenishment shipment to restore the branch warehouse's inventory, replacing each part which has been sold during the week on a one-for-one basis. Thus, sales of all parts for a week are automatically replaced on a weekly basis, and a replenishment shipment is sent each week to every branch warehouse.

REPLENISHMENT CYCLE TIME

The period between the first sales slip for a week being sent from a branch to Cleveland and the receipt of the corresponding replenishment shipment at the branch can be called the *replenishment* cycle. Another

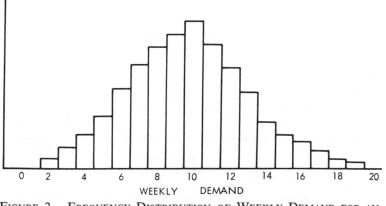

FIGURE 2. FREQUENCY DISTRIBUTION OF WEEKLY DEMAND FOR AN ITEM AT A BRANCH

major element of uncertainty in the system is the length of the replenishment cycle, for this varies from week to week. Fig. 3 shows a typical pattern in the fluctuations of replenishment cycle times. While the average replenishment cycle time shown here seems to be three weeks, there are substantial variations from one week to another. We can deal with the uncertainty of

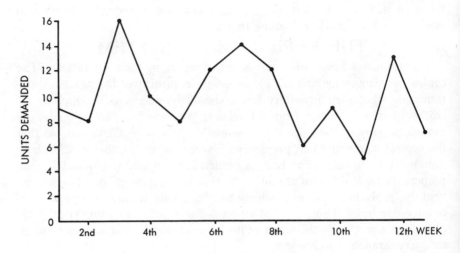

FIGURE 3.   VARIATION OF REPLENISHMENT CYCLE TIME FOR A BRANCH

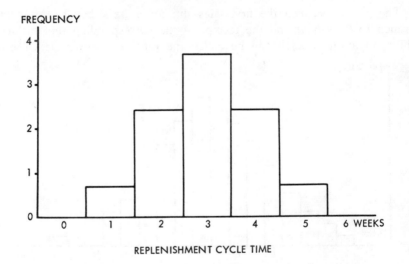

FIGURE 4.   DISCRETE FREQUENCY DISTRIBUTION OF REPLENISHMENT CYCLE TIME

the replenishment cycle time as we dealt with the uncertainty in weekly sales demand. That is, we shall ask not what the replenishment cycle time will be in any particular week, but how frequently we can expect replenishment cycles of different lengths.

If we look at the replenishment cycle time over a large enough number of weeks, there will become evident a stable pattern of the relative frequencies with which different lengths of replenishment cycles occur. Over a sufficiently long period of time, the pattern of replenishment cycle times that we saw in Fig. 3 will build up into the frequency distribution of replenishment cycle times shown in Fig. 4. Here, we see that the most frequent replenishment cycle time is three weeks, which occurs about 38 percent of the time. Replenishment cycles of two or four weeks each occur about 24 percent of the time, and replenishment cycles of one or five weeks each occur about 7 percent of the time.

Statisticians apply the name "normal distribution" to the type of frequency distribution shown in Fig. 4. For our purposes, we need know only that the shape of the normal distribution is completely determined by its average value and its standard deviation, and that we can use this distribution to describe the uncertainties in the replenishment cycle time at a branch warehouse.

The uncertainties in replenishment cycles are actually somewhat more complicated than those indicated by the distribution shown in Fig. 4. How long the replenishment cycle will be in one week seems to depend on how long it was in the previous week, since there is a positive correlation in the lengths of successive replenishment cycles. Although over a long period of time, the relative frequencies with which different replenishment cycles occur is adequately described by the normal distribution, the positive correlation between successive replenishment cycles times means that the magnitude of the weekly fluctuations will be lessened. The "correlated" time series is much more sluggish than the "independent" time series. Without going into complicated mathematical details, we can say only that the positive correlation between successive replenishment cycles can be superimposed on the distribution of replenishment cycle times, the result being that statisticians would describe the uncertainties in replenishment cycle time as a serially correlated, normally distributed random variable. (Since we have momentarily lapsed into statistical jargon, we can mention in passing that statisticians would similarly describe the uncertainties in weekly sales demand as a Poisson distributed random variable.)

THE RELATION BETWEEN LOST SALES AND INVENTORY LEVELS

Let us once again look at the schematic relation between the central and branch warehouses. This is illustrated in Fig. 5, where we have introduced roulette wheels to indicate the uncertainties in weekly sales demand and replenishment of cycle time. These two elements of uncertainty make it impossible for a branch always to have parts in stock when customers want them. The frequency with which a branch is out of stock on items that customers want depends upon the size of that branch's inventories, for the branch warehouse inventories function as buffers which mediate the uncertainties of sales demand and replenishment cycle time. Therefore, a necessary step in determining the best possible levels for branch inventories is first to determine the relation between lost sales of an item and the level of inventory for that part at a branch.[1]

If sufficient historical data were available, it would be possible to determine directly how lost sales depend upon inventory levels. The required data were not available, however, so it was necessary to adopt an alternative approach. Essentially, what we did was to reconstruct or simulate the history of branch warehouse operations on a high-speed electric computer.[2] From this reconstructed history, we were able to obtain the required data, and thus, the dependence of lost sales on inventory levels.

Technically, this simulation of history on a computer is called a "Monte Carlo" approach, after the gambling casino of the same name. Anybody who has watched the roulette wheels at Monte Carlo or Las Vegas can understand the reasoning behind this approach.

---

[1] An analytical method for determining the relation between average lost sales and inventory level for the special case in which successive replenishment cycle times are uncorrelated has been developed in William Karush, "A Queuing Model for an Inventory Problem," *Operations Research,* Vol. 5, No. 5 (Oct. 1957), p. 693–703, and in Philip M. Morse, *Queues, Inventories and Maintenance,* New York: John Wiley & Sons, Inc., 1958, p. 139–146.

[2] This Monte Carlo approach has been discussed in: (a) Kenneth C. Lucas and Leland A Moody, "Electronic Computer Simulation of Inventory Control," p. 107–121 in *Electronics in Action: The Current Practicality of EDP,* Special Report No. 22, American Management Association, New York, 1957. Figures 2, 4, 5, 8, and 9 were taken from the Lucas and Moody paper; (b) Jack K. Weinstock, "An Inventory Control Solution by Simulation," p. 65–71 in *Report of System Simulation Symposium* (Sponsored by the American Institute of Industrial Engineers, The Institute of Management Sciences, and the Operations Research Society of America, held in conjunction with the 8th National Convention of the American Institute of Industrial Engineers, New York, May 16, 17, 1957), 1958; (c) Andrew Vazsonyi, "Electronic Simulation of Business Operations (The Monte Carlo Method)," Second Annual West Coast Engineering Management Conference, May 27–28, 1957, Los Angeles, California, sponsored by the Management Division, Southern California Section, The American Society of Mechanical Engineers.

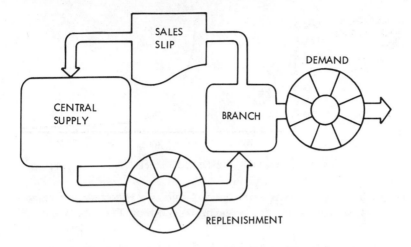

FIGURE 5. BRANCH WAREHOUSE SUPPLY SYSTEM

Let us look again at Fig. 5, which shows the relation between the central and branch warehouses. With the one-for-one replenishment system which is being used, the number of sales during any week of a part at a branch (and the number of lost sales) depends only upon the sales demand during that week and the inventory on hand at the start of the week. This starting inventory depends, in turn, upon sales during previous weeks, the lengths of time required for replenishment cycles during preceding weeks, and the level of inventory which was initially established.

Thus, in order to determine the actual sales and lost sales which can be expected to result from a given initial inventory level, it is necessary to know only the patterns of sales demand and replenishment cycle times which occur. Both demand and replenishment times are uncertain, but typical patterns for them can be constructed from the frequency distributions which describe them. Conceptually, we can think of generating these patterns by each week spinning the two roulette wheels shown in Fig. 5. Since actually doing this would require too much of our own time, we let the electronic computer calculate the values which result from spinning the roulette wheels. A high-speed computer can run through calculations of this type very, very quickly, and in a brief time it is possible to determine the average number of lost sales which will occur each week for any particular initial inventory level.

Using the computer to simulate history resulted in a set of curves similar to the one shown in Fig. 6. For a given average weekly sales demand, the percentage of sales which will be lost decreases as the inventory level in-

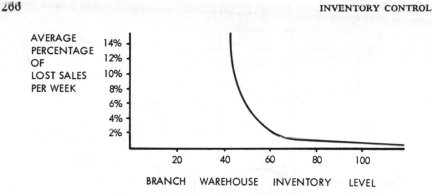

creases. However, as we see in Fig. 7, the exact relation between the average percentage of lost sales per week and branch inventory level depends upon the average weekly demand.

THE *SOBIL* (SIMULATED OPTIMAL BRANCH INVENTORY LEVELS) *SYSTEM*

Once we know the relation between average lost sales and inventory levels, we are ready to use this knowledge to establish the best possible branch warehouse inventory levels. By "best possible" inventory levels, we mean those levels of inventory which will result in the largest total expected profits from the operations of the branches. By balancing the expected gain resulting from the sales that branch warehouse inventories will support against the expected cost of carrying this inventory, normal inventory levels can be established for every part at each branch in a way which leads to the largest possible total profits. For convenience, we have invented the name "SOBIL System" to refer to the use of the simulation curves of Fig. 10 for establishing branch warehouse inventory levels which are optimal in accordance with the expected profit maximization criterion.

The gross gain each week from holding inventory is the product of the average weekly sales that will result from this inventory and the gross margin per unit sold, where the gross margin on a part is the difference between its selling price and material cost. The reasonableness of this can be seen from the following three considerations.

First, lost sales, as measured by the simulation curves of Fig. 7, are lost business. This is substantially true, for customers are usually unwilling to wait for a part when a branch is out-of-stock. Of course, for very minor delays of a day or two pending receipt of a shipment already in transit,

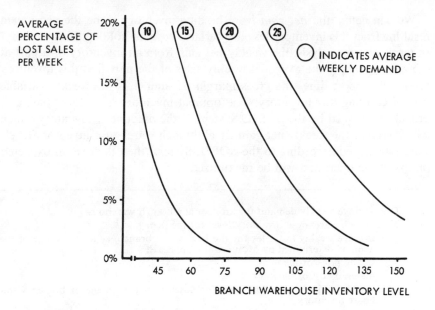

AVERAGE PERCENTAGE OF LOST SALES PER WEEK

○ INDICATES AVERAGE WEEKLY DEMAND

BRANCH WAREHOUSE INVENTORY LEVEL

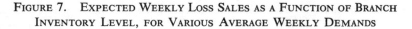

FIGURE 7.   EXPECTED WEEKLY LOSS SALES AS A FUNCTION OF BRANCH INVENTORY LEVEL, FOR VARIOUS AVERAGE WEEKLY DEMANDS

some customers may be willing to wait, but this possibility has in fact already been taken into account by the manner in which the simulation curves were derived.

Second, in those rare instances when a customer who requests a part from a branch which is out of stock is willing to experience a substantial delay in obtaining it, i.e., to allow his order to be back-logged, there are considerable extra costs incurred in processing, expediting, handling, and shipping this order. These extra costs probably eliminate profit which would have accompanied a normal sale of the item.

Third, the administrative and processing costs of handling customer orders are the same regardless of whether those customer orders result in direct sales or lost sales.

On the opposite side of the ledger, the penalty attached to holding inventory is the cost of carrying this inventory. Specifically, we must consider those variable elements of inventory carrying costs which depend upon the size of inventories actually held, as e.g., the cost of invested capital, obsolescence, insurance and taxes, handling and labor costs, and space costs. In Replacement Division, the variable costs of holding inventory at a branch warehouse are proportional to the value of that inventory, where inventory is valued at material cost per unit times the number of units.

We can define the *net gain* from holding inventory to be the gross gain resulting from this inventory less the variable costs of holding this inventory. In terms of our analysis, the weekly net gain from an inventory of a part at a branch is simply the expected weekly sales of the part that this inventory level will support times the gross margin per unit, less the weekly variable cost of carrying this inventory. The optimal inventory level for a part at a branch, as defined by the SOBIL System, is the amount of inventory which will maximize the weekly net gain. If all branch warehouse inventory levels were established according to the SOBIL System, then the overall expected profits of the operation will be maximized.

D = average weekly demand for an item at a branch warehouse

X = branch warehouse inventory level for the item

$l(X)$ = average weekly lost sales for the item at the branch, as a percentage of the demand determined by Monte Carlo approach

P = selling price of the item

C = material cost of the item

v = weekly variable inventory carrying costs, as a percentage of branch warehouse inventory value

$G(X)$ = weekly net gain from a branch warehouse inventory level of X for the item

Criterion: the optimal branch warehouse inventory level for the item is that X that maximizes $G(X)$. This value of X must satisfy the inequality

$$G(X - 1) < G(X) > G(X + 1),$$

where

$$G(X) = (P - C)[1 - l(X)]D - vCX.$$

The inequality is equivalent to

$$(P - C)Dl(X - 1) - vC > (P - C)Dl(X) < (P - C)Dl(X + 1) + vC.$$

The value of X that satisfies this inequality can be closely approximated by solving the equation obtained by setting the derivative of $G(X)$ with respect to X equal to zero. This leads to

$$-\frac{dl(X)}{dX} = \frac{vC}{(P - C)D}.$$

This means that the solution is equal (or very nearly equal) to the value of X where the negative slope of the $l(X)$ curve is equal to $vC \div (P - C)D$.

FIGURE 8.   THE SOBIL SYSTEM

The procedure for establishing the best possible inventory level is shown symbolically in Fig. 8. The weekly net gain from holding an inventory of a part at a branch is a function of the size of that inventory. In order to find the optimal size of that inventory, we can set the derivative of the weekly net gain from holding inventory equal to zero, and then solve this equation for the optimal inventory level. When we do this, it turns out that the best possible inventory levels do not depend upon the height of the simulation curves of Fig. 7, but, rather, they depend upon the *slopes* of these curves.

In particular, in order to establish the optimal inventory levels, we have to know the relation between the rate of increase in average weekly sales and branch warehouse inventory levels. The form of this relation is shown in Fig. 9, where we see that for any given level of average weekly demand, the rate of increase in average weekly sales decreases as the inventory level increases. The electronic computer can be used to produce these new curves shown in Fig. 9, as well as the simulation curves shown in Fig. 7.

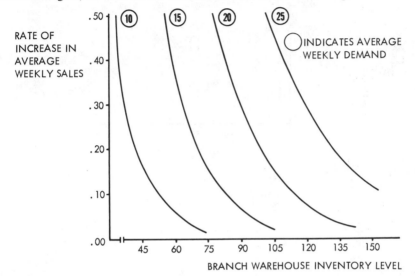

FIGURE 9. RATE OF INCREASE IN EXPECTED WEEKLY SALES AS A FUNCTION OF BRANCH INVENTORY LEVEL, FOR VARIOUS AVERAGE WEEKLY DEMANDS

To determine the optimal inventory level for a part of a branch, we first select the curve from Fig. 9 which corresponds to the average weekly sales demand for the item. Suppose that this particular curve is the one shown in Fig. 10. Next, we divide the variable cost of carrying one unit of inventory for a week by the gross margin on the part. The resulting value, as we see in Fig. 10, is found on the vertical axis. From there, we move horizontally from the curve, and then we move vertically from the curve to the horizontal axis. The level of inventory which is then indicated on the horizontal axis is the best possible inventory level for the part at the branch.

If desired, rather than using this graphical procedure, the determination of optimal branch inventory levels can readily be programmed for an electronic computer.

It must be emphasized that while the SOBIL System provides an automatic way of determining branch warehouse inventory levels, this neither restricts management's prerogative nor eliminates the need for sound business judgment. Management always has the discretion to establish branch

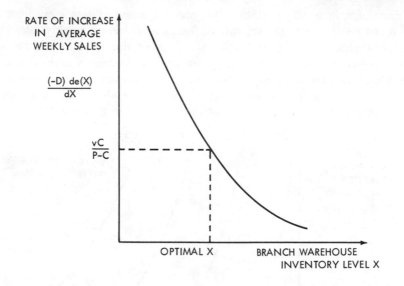

FIGURE 10.   SOBIL SYSTEM, GRAPHICAL DETERMINATION OF OPTIMAL
BRANCH INVENTORY LEVELS

warehouse inventory levels other than those indicated by the SOBIL System, if policy considerations should so dictate. Indeed, management might want to do so because of a desire to give exceptional service to favored customers, to maintain a particular share-of-the-market, or aggressively to develop a new market. In such cases it is easy to determine the net gain from holding inventory *which is foregone* by establishing a branch warehouse inventory at some level other than that indicated by the SOBIL System. This provides additional information which management would not otherwise have, information which can help management decide whether the special policy considerations are worthwhile. Figure 11 shows the form in which this information could easily be provided if the calculations of optimal branch warehouse inventory levels are done on an electronic computer.

FORECASTING REQUIREMENTS FOR THE SOBIL SYSTEM

In order to make effective use of the SOBIL System, it is necessary to forecast the average weekly demand for every item at each branch. This may not be easy to do, for these average weekly demands slowly change over time.

Over a long period, the local demand for an automotive replacement part will vary because of the changing size and age distribution of the existing stock of automobiles and trucks, the changing number of models in which the part has been used, competition, seasonal factors, and random fluctuations.

Many alternative methods for forecasting demand by item by branch should be investigated. Perhaps the simplest procedure is to use a moving average or linear trend extrapolation based on recently experienced demand. More sophisticated would be the use of a life cycle growth and decay curve based on the number of models in which a part has been used and the elapsed times since the part was first and last incorporated in a new model.

Even more elaborate would be a mortality, age-distribution, share-of-the-market model. The size of the market for a replacement part would be estimated by considering the size and age distribution of the existing stock of automobiles and trucks, the probability of the part becoming defective as a function of the age of the machine in which it is housed, and the models in which the part has been incorporated. The size of the market for the part is then multiplied by each branch warehouse's assumed share-of-the-market to yield the forecasts of the average demand for that part at the various branch warehouses.

Any or all of these forecasting procedures might be improved by making adjustments for seasonal variation.

How often the forecasts of average weekly demand should be revised depends upon how frequently the branch warehouse inventory levels should be changed. This, in turn, depends upon the clerical and data-processing costs required to reset the branch inventories, the net gain from holding inventories which is foregone because of using incorrect estimates of average weekly demand, and any changes which might occur in the values of critical parameters, such as the means or variances of the replenishment cycle times, the cost of capital, or other inventory holding costs.

TESTING THE SOBIL SYSTEM

Before completely accepting the worthwhileness of the SOBIL System, it is desirable to estimate the magnitude of the increased profits which should result from the use of this procedure. There are two general ways of making such an estimate, either through a careful analysis of historical data or through a program of controlled experimentation.

The cheapest and fastest way of estimating the amount of increased profits which should result from adopting the SOBIL System is to assume that the equation defining the net gain from holding inventories and the simulation curves expressing the dependence of average lost sales on branch warehouse inventory levels are all accurate. On this basis, it is possible to compare the net gain from holding inventories which was actually experienced with the net gain from holding inventories which would have occurred had the branch warehouse inventories been established at the levels indicated by the SOBIL System.

Using historical data on actual sales, lost sales, and branch warehouse inventory levels, it is possible to compute what the net gain from holding inventories actually was during some past period. This can be done for a randomly selected sample of items and branches, or, if time and budget permit, for all items and branches.

From the same historical data on actual demand, it is possible to determine the potential performance of the system, i.e., the net gain from holding inventories which would have resulted from optimal inventory levels. The results of these two calculations should then be compared. The difference between the net gain from holding inventories had optimal branch warehouse inventory levels been established and the actually experienced net gain indicates the increased profits which should results from using the SOBIL System.

The conclusive test of the SOBIL System can come only from a controlled experiment, however. Using proper experimental design principles, a randomized sample of branch warehouses should have their inventory levels established as indicated by the SOBIL System. In the remaining branches, the inventory levels should continue to be determined by the present system. The worthwhileness of the SOBIL System can then be determined by comparing the profitability of those branches where it was employed with the remaining branches. In order to get a meaningful basis of comparison which is independent of size, what should be considered is the percentage change in profits of the branch warehouses, not the absolute profits themselves. Then, the measure of effectiveness of the SOBIL System would be the ratio of the percentage change in profits of those branches using this new system to the percentage change in profits of those branches using the present method.

CONCLUSION

In this article we have described a procedure, which we have called the SOBIL System, for establishing the best possible branch inventory levels in a network composed of one central and several branch warehouses using a one-for-one replenishment system. Since the branch warehouse inventories function as buffers mediating the uncertainties of weekly sales demand and replenishment cycle time, there is a probabilistic dependence of weekly lost sales on branch inventory levels. A Monte Carlo approach, that is, a simulation of the history of the system on an electronic computer, was used to determine the relation between average weekly lost sales and inventory levels. By balancing the expected gain resulting from the average weekly sales that branch warehouse inventories will support against the expected cost of carrying inventories, our knowledge of the relation between average weekly lost sales and inventory levels can be used to determine optimal branch warehouse inventories, i.e., the levels of inventory which yield the longest possible net gains from holding inventory.

In addition to outlining the conceptual framework of the SOBIL System, we have indicated graphical and computational techniques which could be used in implementing the procedure, discussed the nature of the forecasts which must be made, and presented ways of determining the amount of increased profits which should result from adopting this system.

In a warehouse network such as we have described, adoption of the SOBIL System should result in several advantages. First and foremost, the total profits of the business should be increased, because of the optimal

Part P	Branch Warehouse B	Average Weekly Demand 10	
Branch Warehouse Inventory Level	Average Percentage of Lost Sales	Net Gain from Holding Inventory	Foregone Net Gain from Holding Inventory
40	20.0	6.40	1.10
45	11.5	7.05	.45
50	6.5	7.35	.15
55	3.0	7.50	Optimal Branch Inventory Level
60	1.7	7.43	.07
65	.8	7.32	.18

FIGURE 11. SOBIL SYSTEM, COMPUTER PRINT-OUT

balancing of revenues and costs generated by inventory. Furthermore, for any given amount of capital invested in inventory, the best possible distribution of this inventory can be obtained between the branches and for the different items, and the total investment in inventory can be controlled merely by changing the cost of capital. Finally, when policy considerations dictate establishing branch warehouse inventories at levels other than those indicated as optimal by the SOBIL System, the amount of short-run profit which is foregone by this policy is readily calculable.

ACKNOWLEDGMENTS

This article discusses some continuing research which is being done for the Replacement Division of Thompson Products by the Management Sciences Department of The Ramo-Wooldridge Corporation. This work represents a team effort, and it is difficult adequately to delineate the parts for which various people are responsible. The members of the Ramo-Wooldridge team who, at various times, were involved in this project include Mr. W. R. Hydeman, Dr. William Karush, Mr. L. A. Moody, Mr. A. F. Moravec, Dr. A. Vazsonyi, Mr. Jack K. Weinstock, and Dr. David M. Young. The author's own contributions, conceived in close collaboration with Mr. Moravec, were mainly connected with developing the decision rules for determining optimal branch warehouse inventory levels (based on the relation between expected lost sales and inventory) and the general economic analysis of the Monte Carlo model's relevance to the Replacement Division's operations.

The members of the Management Sciences Department's study team are especially grateful to Mr. Kenneth C. Lucas of Thompson Products' Replacement Division for his patience, advice, and cooperation during this project. The author wishes to thank Messrs. Hydeman and Moravec for their personal help and encouragement while the three of us were in Cleveland working on the implementation of the Monte Carlo model.

EDITORS' NOTE

In the preceding article, two important pieces of information, weekly sales and replenishment cycle time, were obtained by a simulation technique called Monte Carlo.

To illustrate how these data were actually obtained, we can start with Figure 2 from the article. In the diagram below, assumed values for the frequency have been inserted on the vertical axis.

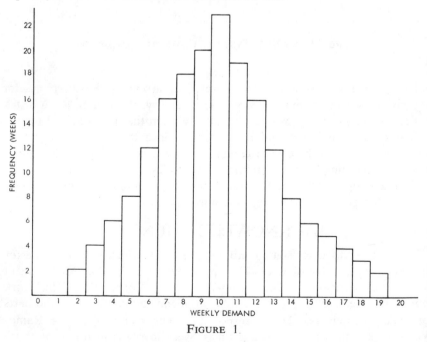

FIGURE 1

From the frequency distribution of weekly demand, a probability function is easily derived. The frequency distribution represents 184 weeks of experience (the summation of all the vertical bars). Since a weekly demand of 2 units occurred twice during the 184 weeks, we can say that the probability of a demand of 2 units in any given week is $\frac{2}{184}$ or slightly over 0.01. Similarly, the probability of a demand of 10 units is $\frac{23}{184}$ or 0.125. When these probabilities are plotted against the possible values of weekly demand, we get the discrete (since we are dealing with whole demand units only, excluding demands like 4.7 units) probability function shown below in Figure 2.

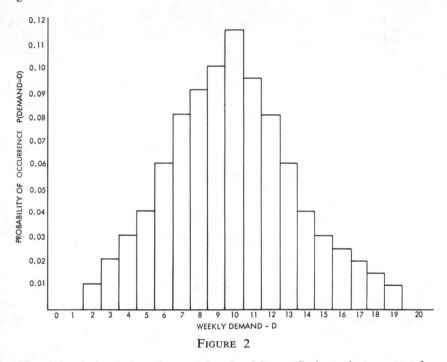

FIGURE 2

The job of simulating demand by the Monte Carlo technique can be made somewhat easier if this probability function is transformed into a "cumulative" probability function. Whereas the probability function in Figure 2 shows the probability that weekly demand will equal a certain number of units, a cumulative probability function shows the probability that weekly demand will be equal to *or less than* a given amount. As an example, in Figure 2 the probability of a demand of 4 units per week is 0.0326. The probability of a demand of 4 units or less would be the sum of the probability of a demand of 0 units, plus the probability of a demand of 1 unit (which can be written $P(D = 1)$ where D denotes demand) plus

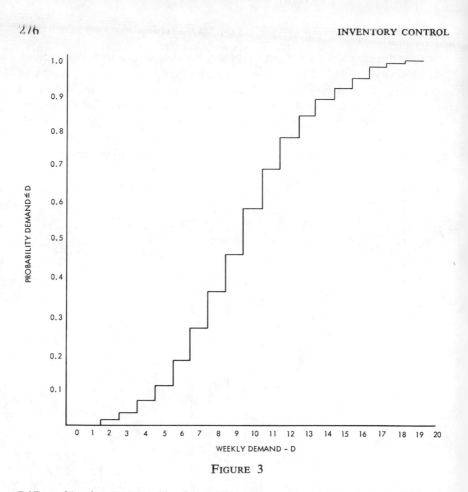

FIGURE 3

$P(D = 2)$ plus $P(D = 3)$ plus $P(D = 4)$ or $0 + 0 + 0.011 + 0.022 + 0.033 = 0.066$. It should be clear that the cumulative probability for the highest demand shown on Figure 2 (i.e., 19 units) is 1.0, since demand in every week of the 184 weeks shown in Figure 1 was 19 units *or less,* $P(D \leq 19) = {}^{184}\!/_{184} = 1.0$. Figure 3 is the cumulative probability function plotted from Figure 2. Table I presents the same information in tabular form.

This cumulative probability function is the basis for simulating demand by the Monte Carlo method.

Suppose now we determine a three digit random number. Possible sources of random numbers would include a computer routine which generates random numbers such as the one used in this article, a random number table, drawing one number from each of three jars containing balls numbered 0 through 9, or throwing a ten sided die three times. There are 1000 possible numbers that may show up on the draw of a three digit random

TABLE I

Demand D	Probability That Weekly Demand Is Less than or Equal to D
0	0
1	0
2	0.011
3	0.033
4	0.066
5	0.109
6	0.174
7	0.261
8	0.359
9	0.467
10	0.592
11	0.696
12	0.783
13	0.848
14	0.891
15	0.924
16	0.951
17	0.973
18	0.989
19	1.000

number—000 through 999. The probability of drawing any given number is $1/1000$ and is the same for all possible numbers. That is, $P(\text{Number} = 000) = P(\text{Number} = 001) = \ldots = P(\text{Number} = 999)$. Looking back at Table I, we see that the desired probability for a weekly demand of 2 units or less is 0.011. This demand can be simulated by saying that every time a random number which is between 001 and 011 is drawn we will automatically set weekly demand equal to 2 units. Carrying on in this vein, if the random number is 012 to 033, we will set demand equal to 3 units. Similarly, if the random number is 784 to 848, demand equals 13 units; and demand equals 19 units for random numbers from 990 to 000. (We interpret 000 as the number 1000 rather than 0.)

Looking back at this procedure, let us check the results with Figure 2. The probability of a random number falling between 001 and 011 is $11/1000$ or 0.011, which, according to Figure 2, is exactly the probability that demand equals 2 units. The probability of a random number falling between 990 and 000 is also $11/1000$, which is exactly the probability of demand equal to 19 units per week. Thus, we have a technique which enables us to simulate exactly the distribution or probability function of weekly demand.

One question still remains. The Monte Carlo method insures that demands occur with the same relative frequencies as shown in Figure 2. Using a simple average demand, however, would also yield the same total demand over the 184 week period. Why, then, bother with Monte Carlo simulation? The important difference between such a straightforward reproduction of total or average demand and the Monte Carlo technique is that Monte Carlo allows a randomized arrangement of individual weekly demands. Thus, unlikely, but nonetheless possible, combinations of demand like 2 units in one week and 19 units the next will pop up occasionally in the Monte Carlo method. When such fluctuations arise, the response of the inventory system can be observed. Simulating demand at a single, average rate would never allow the testing of the inventory rules under fluctuations in demand that are certain to exist in the real world. In this article, variations in demand are very important since the magnitude of the inventory level is specified to protect against such variations.

The replenishment cycle time, which was also simulated by the Monte Carlo method, could be developed by using a procedure very much like the one developed for simulating weekly demand.

Chapter 14

STATISTICAL METHODS IN INVENTORY CONTROL

XVI.

*Physical Inventory Using Sampling Methods**

Marion R. Bryson †

INTRODUCTION

Business, industry, and government are all faced with the task of periodically taking a physical inventory of all goods on hand. The most commonly used method of performing this physical inventory is to make a complete count of all stocks once each period, usually annually. All counts of stocks are made within a short period of time, say within a week. At the close of such an inventory, it is assumed that accurate knowledge of the quantity and value of all stocks on hand has been obtained. Unfortunately, in most cases this may be a false assumption.

In most of the larger and many of the smaller establishments a continuous record is kept of stocks. These records are altered as activity

* From *Applied Statistics,* Vol. 9, No. 3 (1960), 178–188. Reprinted by permission of *Applied Statistics.*

† The author wishes to express his thanks to Professor R. F. Rinehart, who critically read the manuscript and made many helpful suggestions.

changes the quantity on hand. If the records were completely accurate it would, obviously, be unnecessary ever to make a physical count of stocks. Many of the records are inaccurate for the following reasons: the previous inventory was in error causing the record to reflect the wrong balance from the beginning of the fiscal period; some receipts and/or issues were made without correct alteration of the records; items were lost; items were pilfered; records were lost; and other record adjustments, such as price changes or reserve stock levels, were incorrectly processed. Hence it is the purpose of the inventory to correct the records which reflect wrong information.

The question which immediately arises is 'How accurate are the records at the close of the inventory?' The personnel employed in the inventory are relatively untrained in inventory methods since this activity occurs during only one week out of the year. During this week personnel are drawn from all parts of the establishment to perform the counting and clerical duties incidental to the inventory. Many of these people are not interested in inventory work, and if they are doing satisfactory work at their normal job they know they will not be dismissed or demoted if their poor inventory work is detected.

Because of the suspected inaccuracies in inventory and because operational record errors occur and remain undetected for as long as one year, an agency of the U.S. Government sponsored a research project to determine what could be done about improving inventory methods.

DESCRIPTION OF SUPPLY CENTERS

The government agency mentioned above maintains supply centers in various parts of the country. Each of these supply centers has in its storage areas from 5,000 to 150,000 different types of item stored. Hereafter the term 'item' will be used to denote a type of item and the term 'piece' to denote an individual part. From zero to more than one million pieces of each item may be on hand at any given time. The storage areas are in the nature of huge stockrooms whose function it is to receive and store incoming goods and issue and ship goods ordered by their customers. The supply center maintains records of stocks on hand and the records department receives orders for shipments, processes them, and instructs the stockroom to issue the stock. It also processes all receipt vouchers and instructs the stockroom to store the stock in an assigned location.

Each item has an assigned location or locations in the stockrooms. When an order comes in to the records department, the records are checked to determine whether the stock in this quantity is available for issue. If it is not, the order is sent to a master records centre which will re-order the stock from another storage center. If the stock is available, a shipping order is drawn up and sent to the stockroom. This shipping order designates the item number, location, and quantity to be shipped, among other facts. If the item is stored in more than one location, one of the locations is designated as the master location. The recorded balances are kept by item number and not by location; hence the single balance kept by the records department reflects the sum of the quantities in each storage location. The records department adjusts its balance to reflect the issue. Receipts are processed in essentially the same way.

BASIC PLAN OF OPERATION

One such supply center was selected by the government agency as the site of the study. After nine months of preliminary work at this center, an additional center was assigned for further study and testing. Each of these two centers has approximately 100,000 items in its stockrooms.

Various methods of quality control have been used from time to time in the actual taking of a shut-down inventory. These have been principally confined to quality control of the individual counter and quality control of the areas of the stockroom after the counting was complete. These methods have not proved to be very successful in the inventories taken by the agency which sponsored this research.

The basic concept of the present project is the continuous quality control of the storage areas. Those areas which are deemed to be out of control are completely inventoried. This serves the same purpose as 100% inspection of a rejected lot of pieces produced on a production line.

The stockrooms of a supply center are stratified by physical location. All lots are of approximately equal size. An attempt is made to store the more active items together in one or more lots and to store the less active items in different lots. In addition to the advantage this 'popularity' storage has of placing the active items nearer the shipping facilities, it also serves to increase the between-lot variance of the error rates.

QUALITY CONTROL PROCEDURE

To initiate the quality control once the stratification is complete, a sample of items in each lot is selected. A physical count of the number of pieces of each of these items in the stockroom is made and this count is compared with the recorded balance. If the count disagrees with the balance by more than the 'leeway,' the item is said to be 'discrepant' or 'in error.' This leeway is established for the discrepancies so that a minor discrepancy may be ignored. In this study an item is classed as discrepant if and only if the difference between the count and the balance is greater than 1% of the balance, or the monetary value of the discrepancy is greater than $1 (approximately 7s.).

Following the count, an estimate of the percentage of items in each lot which are discrepant is made. The simple binomial estimator

$$\dot{P} = \frac{100 d_i}{n_i}$$

is used. Here

$\dot{P}_i =$ the estimated percent discrepant in the i-th lot; (hereafter called 'estimated error rate').

$d_i =$ number of discrepant items in the sample from the i-th lot.

$n_i =$ sample size in the i-th lot, i.e., the number of items.

The variance of this estimator is the usual one:

$$\operatorname{var} \dot{P}_i = \frac{\dot{P}_i(100 - \dot{P}_i)}{n_i}$$

Next, an acceptable limit for the estimated error rate is established. In this project the limit is 10%.

Hereafter the words 'sampling' or 'sample' refer to the process of taking a physical count on only a sample of items in a lot. The word 'inventory' will refer to a complete count of every item in the lot and the reconciliation of this count with its recorded balance.

The results of the sample are then observed. If more lots have an estimated error rate of above 10% than can be inventoried by the counting crew in a three-month period (quarter), only enough of the highest error-rate lots are rejected to consume one quarter of inventory time. The remainder of those above 10% are temporarily accepted.

In the first quarter of the year, those lots rejected on the initial sample are inventoried. Those lots which were accepted, whether or not their estimated error rates were above 10%, are resampled as before during this quarter. From this group of resampled lots the inventory load for the second quarter is chosen. It will be seen that those lots inventoried in the first quarter cannot be inventoried again during the second quarter since they were not included in the resampled lots during the first quarter. They will be resampled during the quarter following their inventory, i.e., during the second quarter in this case, so cannot be rescheduled for inventory before the third quarter.

If the lots whose estimated error rates are above 10% do not constitute a full quarter of inventory work, either the acceptable limit can be lowered or the size of the inventory crew can be reduced.

OPERATION OF INITIAL STUDY

In October of 1958 the project was initiated at supply center number one (SC-1). For the first nine months the work was confined to methods of stratification and methods of counting an item without freezing activity on the item. A team of 15 men was assigned to work on the project. The center was stratified into 25 lots and two samples were taken in each lot, the time between samples being about four months.

A completely random sample of items in each lot was drawn. First, for sampling purposes, every piece of a given item was considered as being stored in the lot with the master location of the item. A cumulative list of all possible storage locations was drawn up. This list is not the same as that kept in the 'location file' from which issues are drawn up. For example, a given rack may have as many as three items stored on it, all of which have the same numbered location in the location file. This rack was considered as three 'item locations' even though the records showed it as only one location. It was because of this that it was not possible to sample from the location file. This would result in clusters of items in the sample, the cluster size varying from one to twenty-four items.

The sample size was not rigidly fixed in advance. A sample of item locations was drawn from the cumulative list, using random number tables, and each of these locations was visited. If the location was the master location of some item, this item was included in the sample. If it was a reserve location or an empty location to which no stock number was assigned, the location was dropped from the sample. If the final sample size was too small, a second sample was taken to augment the first one. A sample size of between 200 and 300 was selected in all but a few small lots. The average lot size was about 4000.

The count on the sample items was taken without affecting the normal center operation. In simplified form the steps followed were:

(1) Count all pieces of an item in the stockroom.
(2) Obtain the recorded balance for the item.
(3) Compare the two figures.
(4) If the figures agree, *classify it as a non-discrepant item.*
(5) If the figures disagree, they may disagree because
   (*a*) A miscount has occurred.
   (*b*) An activity has occurred in the record section but has not yet occurred in the stockroom.
   (*c*) The item is discrepant.
   This item is set aside for two weeks.

(6) Two weeks after the first count, retrace steps 1–4 if the item is in disagreement.

(7) If the two figures now agree, *it is a non-discrepant item.*

(8) If they disagree by the same quantity as they did on the first count, *the item is classed as a discrepant item.* Points (*a*) and (*b*) in step 5 are improbable in this case since the same miscount is unlikely and no activity should be in process for two weeks.

(9) If the item disagrees by an amount different from the first discrepancy, *set it aside for another two weeks.*

(10) A third count is taken on all items falling into step 9 and steps 1–4 and 8 are followed.

(11) For items which are still not reconciled, an investigation is conducted to determine their true nature.

Several minor refinements can be and have been made in the above procedure but basically it has been operated successfully using this system.

The purpose of the second sampling was to estimate the error rates which existed in each of the 25 lots. The error rates obtained in this sample were then compared with the results of the annual shut-down inventory which was taken immediately following the second sampling phase.

RESULTS OF THE INITIAL STUDY

Table I gives the lot sizes, sample sizes, and the error rates of both the sample and the shut-down inventory.

From the table it will be noted that the difference between the sample results and the findings of the inventory is significant at the 95% level for more than half of the lots. Since it was the purpose of both the sample and the inventory to estimate the true error rate of the lot it appears that something is wrong. It could be one or both of two things:

(1) the sample was drawn incorrectly, biasing the results;

(2) the sample does not estimate the percentage found by the inventory but some other quantity; either or both may differ from the true error rate.

Let us look at the first of these two possibilities. In order to check the accuracy of the sampling, the *inventory* findings on the *sample items only* were compared with the inventory findings on the entire lot. The difference between these two figures represents sampling error only. Table II gives the results of this comparison.

In this comparison only three of the twenty-five lots had differences which were significant at the 95% level. This leads one to believe that the sampling was without bias with the possible exception of lots 1 and 10. Since one of these is negative and the other is positive, and since there are

TABLE I. ERROR RATES (%)

Lot No.	Lot Size	Sample Size	Estimated Error Rate from Sample	Shut-down Inventory Error Rate	Difference (Inv.-Samp.)
1	7,818	310	61.9	52.3	− 9.6†
2	7,191	291	57.7	53.0	− 4.7
3	1,809	217	51.6	54.8	3.2
4	2,344	66	46.9	50.9	4.0
5	6,717	285	43.5	50.5	7.0*
6	3,228	220	41.8	32.9	− 3.9*
7	7,945	300	39.0	41.5	2.5
8	3,493	212	37.3	47.0	9.7*
9	3,676	207	37.2	31.2	− 6.0
10	3,136	217	36.9	53.7	16.8†
11	1,908	207	35.3	33.3	− 2.0
12	5,053	259	34.8	50.5	15.7†
13	7,271	287	33.1	47.5	14.4†
14	2,930	213	31.9	34.3	2.4
15	6,920	239	31.4	37.5	6.1*
16	2,885	234	29.5	41.0	11.5†
17	614	72	29.2	39.9	10.7*
18	3,004	222	27.5	37.4	9.9†
19	7,004	233	27.0	25.7	− 1.3
20	1,918	226	26.5	31.2	4.7
21	2,266	197	24.4	28.6	4.2
22	3,175	216	22.2	33.4	11.2†
23	6,248	260	21.9	25.4	3.5
24	1,491	192	20.3	25.5	5.2
25	2,872	242	16.5	25.6	9.1†
TOTAL	192,376	5,624	—	—	—
MEAN	—	—	34.7	40.7	6.0

* Difference significant at 95% confidence level.
† Difference significant at 99% confidence level.

equal numbers of plus and minus differences, no consistent bias is evident.

Let us look now at the second possible cause of the large differences shown in Table I.

Since the differences in error rates given by Inventory (Inventory denotes this particular inventory) and the estimates given by the sampling plan (hereafter referred to as SQC) are not due primarily to the sampling technique of SQC, these differences must be due in large part to mechanical mistakes by SQC, or mistakes by Inventory, or change in discrepancy status of items from one count to the other. The latter group is regarded as not significant. It becomes then a question of determining the relative order of magnitude of the mistakes made by SQC and those made by Inventory.

Information on the mistakes of SQC and those of Inventory is provided through a study of the items counted by both SQC and Inventory. The results of this study follow:

1. Inventory and SQC agree on a total of 81 percent of the items, the non-discrepant items in agreement being 58 percent, and the discrepant items 23 percent.

2. Inventory found a discrepancy, SQC found no discrepancy, on 7.75 percent of the items. In a further study it was found that Inventory mistakes account for 7 percent of these, and the other 0.75 percent are actual discrepancies which occurred after the sampling count was completed.

3. SQC found a discrepancy, Inventory found no discrepancy, on approximately 15 percent of the items. Essentially all of these differences result from SQC mistakes.

4. SQC and Inventory both found a discrepancy, but disagreed about its magnitude, on 9.75 percent of the items. By special investigation on these items, it was found that SQC and Inventory shared about equally in the mistakes, but that about 2% of the mistakes were due to an actual change in the size of the discrepancy between the time of the sample count and the time of the inventory count.

TABLE II. ERROR RATES (%)

Lot No.	Inventory Error Rate on Sample Items	Inventory Error Rate on All Items in Lot	Difference (Lot-Sample)
1	61.3	52.3	− 9.0†
2	55.5	53.0	− 2.5
3	57.8	54.8	− 3.0
4	47.8	50.9	3.1
5	50.7	50.5	− 0.2
6	39.3	32.9	− 6.4
7	46.2	41.5	− 4.7
8	45.5	47.0	1.5
9	41.4	31.2	−10.2*
10	43.3	53.7	10.4†
11	39.2	33.3	− 6.2
12	46.5	50.5	3.9
13	43.8	47.5	3.7
14	32.7	34.3	1.6
15	35.5	37.5	2.0
16	40.6	41.0	0.4
17	40.6	41.0	0.4
18	34.7	37.4	2.7
19	29.3	25.7	− 3.6
20	31.3	31.2	− 0.1
21	28.6	28.6	0.0
22	29.2	33.4	4.2
23	30.4	25.4	− 5.0
24	26.8	25.5	− 1.3
25	22.4	25.6	3.2
MEAN	39.9	40.7	0.8

* Difference significant at 95% confidence level.
† Difference significant at 99% confidence level.

From this analysis we arrive at the figures in Table III. In accordance with this table, for example, the SQC technique results in 22 mistakes for every 1000 good items counted, and in 122 mistakes for every 1000 discrepant items counted. The rate of mistakes in general is 5.5 percent of the time for SQC and 11 percent of the time for Inventory. The general conclusion is that overall the SQC technique makes only half as many mistakes as the Inventory technique.

TABLE III. FREQUENCY OF MISTAKES, INVENTORY
COMPARED WITH SQC

	Non-discrepant Items	Discrepant Items	All Items
SQC	2.2%	12.2%	5.5%
Inventory	10.4%	12.2%	11.0%

This explains the differences shown in Table I. Of the thirteen significant differences shown there, only two of them are negative and in these two cases the difference is largely explained by sampling bias or sampling error, as indicated in Table II.

There are two major reasons for the superior performance of the SQC team. They are:

(1) The procedure of accepting no count unless it agrees with a previous count or with the recorded balance virtually eliminates the possibility of a miscount.

(2) The team is experienced in inventory and interested in the work.

Results of Second Study

After the first study at SC-1, the project was initiated at a second supply center (SC-2). It was also expanded to include the physical inventory of the rejected lots. In these two centers, no shut-down inventory is being taken.

After some study it was decided that a center should be divided into sixteen lots of equal size. If more than three lots had an estimated error rate of more than 10%, the three lots showing the highest percentage error in any quarter would be completely inventoried the following quarter. The principal advantage of this is that the work load in each quarter is the same so that it is not then necessary to have a variable-sized inventory team.

In any given quarter thirteen lots are sampled and three lots are inventoried that each year an equivalent of three-quarters of the lots in the entire center is inventoried completely. Actually some lots may be inventoried twice in a year so that more than one-quarter of the centre may miss inventory entirely. Adjustments in the recorded balances for discrepant items are made.

It might at first sight be thought paradoxical that the recommended plan should include a proportion of complete inventory work, since the earlier results indicated that more mistakes were made in a complete inventory than in a sample count. However, it must be stressed that the earlier comparison was between an experienced SQC team and relatively untrained personnel carrying out the inventory. A team specialising in inventory work would be expected to have a low mistake rate. Furthermore, the periodic complete inventory allows proper adjustment of erroneous balances to be made.

Since the purpose of the sampling is to rank the lots from most erroneous to least erroneous, the question whether recounts were necessary in the sampling arose. If only one count is taken on the sample items and the item is classed as discrepant if its count does not agree with its balance, ignoring the possibility of miscounts and documents in flow, what effect would this have on the ranking? This question was studied using the data on the 5624 items in the sample at SC-1. Each item was classed as a discrepant or a non-discrepant item on the basis of the first count only and the lots were ranked. The ranking thus obtained was compared with the ranking using the recount procedure. The results of this are presented in Table IV.

TABLE IV.   COMPARISON OF RANKINGS OF FIRST COUNT OF
LOTS BY DIFFERENT METHODS

Rank by Single Count	Rank by Multiple Count	Rank by Inventory
1	1	4
2	2	3
3	3	1
4	4	5
5	5	6
6	6	18
7	7	10
8	8	9
9	11	17
10	9	19
11	10	2
12	12	7
13	17	12
14	16	11
15	13	8
16	14	15
17	15	13
18	18	14
19	20	20
20	19	12
21	21	21
22	23	25
23	22	16
24	24	24
25	25	23

Spearman's rank correlation coefficient has the following values:

(1) single count v. multiple count $r_s = 0.984$
(2) single count v. inventory $r_s = 0.754$
(3) multiple count v. inventory $r_s = 0.775$

The single count agrees extremely well with the multiple count and both are in reasonable agreement with the inventory findings.

On the basis of the foregoing results, it was decided that for the sample items, only a single count would be taken. This saves considerable time in the counting. No adjustments are made on the basis of the sample findings.

During the first quarter, SC-2 was sampled, without stratification. On the basis of this sample, the error rate in each section of each stockroom was estimated. The sections were then grouped together into lots, sections with similar estimated error rates being put into the same lots. The three lots with the highest error rates were inventoried, and the remaining lots were resampled in the following quarter. In the quarter following the inventory, the three inventoried lots were resampled.

The results of the samples and the inventories at SC-2 are given in Table V.

TABLE V.   RESULTS OF STUDY AT SC-2

Lot No.	Error Rate on First Sample (%)	Error Rate on Inventory (%)	Error Rate on Second Sample (%)
1	40.0	29.5	5.9
2	39.8	32.6	5.5
3	34.9	30.1	4.9
4	26.7		24.4
5	25.6		30.1
6	24.0		18.8
7	20.6		24.2
8	19.5		30.1
9	19.4		12.0
10	14.3		11.5
11	12.7		18.8
12	12.0		13.2
13	11.8		10.0
14	11.7		10.4
15	11.1		14.3
16	*		*
MEAN	21.6	30.7	15.6
MEAN OF LOTS 4.15	17.5		18.2

* No results available.

It will be noted that the inventory in the first three lots reduced the error rate radically. It had an overall effect of reducing the center-wide error rate by six percentage points. It will be noted also that the error rate in the lots which were not inventoried did not grow significantly during the quarter.

There are no significant differences between the sample estimates in the first and second quarters except for lot 8. In this instance, much stock was moved into the lot during the quarter. The stock which was moved in was believed to have a high error rate by the center personnel.

COMPARISON OF INVENTORIES

The direct cost per item of the SQC inventory is about 70–80% of the direct cost of the shut-down inventory. The saving in cost is the result of more efficient operation of the SQC inventory and the lack of necessity for training a large group of people for inventory. Other advantages of the SQC inventory are:

(1) No shut-down period is necessary, so that normal operation is carried on throughout the year.

(2) At any given time the records have a higher degree of accuracy.

(3) A trained team is available for any special inventories which may be necessary.

(4) Inefficient or error-making procedures are quickly identified and eliminated.

(5) An incentive for more efficient centre operation is produced.

(6) State of preservation of stocks is constantly reviewed.

XVII.

Inventory Policy by Control Chart*

J. W. Dudley

THE INVENTORY–PRODUCTION–SALES RELATION

The economic advantages of adequate inventory control in relation to sales and production at a manufacturing plant are not only important in the continual struggle against competition, but also reasonably self-evident to most plant managers.

The average plant manager fully appreciates the value of effective inventory control and usually believes that he has an active, accurate and

* From *Industrial Quality Control*, Vol. 16, No. 7 (1960), 4–7. Reprinted by permission of *Industrial Quality Control*.

effective policy for defining and controlling production and inventory in relation to sales. However, when he is asked to objectively define his policy, or to critically examine the dollar results of his policy to see whether it has accomplished the desired and defined ends, the existing policy may prove to be a rule of thumb, or worse, a rule of many thumbs. In fact, he may be fortunate if any reproducible policy can be discovered in a group of related products.

FACTORS AFFECTING CHOICE OF CONTROL METHODS

When we try to determine what is adequate inventory control in a particular plant for a particular type of product, we find that many factors affect our selection of an inventory control policy and procedure. Some of these are:

a) The number of different grades, types or catalogued items produced. A mail order house with thousands of items probably has several inventory policies, each applying to similar or homogeneous groups of items.
b) The approximate demand rate or sales of each item.
c) The relation between clerical costs and the sales price of items in inventory. Consider the diversity in handling paper clips, jewelry, and perishable foods.
d) The cost of holding items in stock.
e) The reliability in predicting future sales, changes in design or production methods, etc. Many items depend on the vagaries of weather, styles, fads, and the like.
f) Customer relationships.

THE IN–PRO–SALES CONTROL CHART

Variations in the foregoing factors may result in several policies of inventory control, ranging from simple rules to highly elaborate formulas requiring computers to handle hundreds or thousands of separate items. In the writer's opinion, there is a broad middle ground where a simple control chart technique with low clerical work load can handle the inventory problem on generally similar and homogeneous items with economical effectiveness. This technique is easily adaptable to computers on a large scale, if required.

It is not within the scope of this discussion to describe the fundamental basis and mathematical background for statistical control charts. Most companies have been using these charts in many applications for many years. One of the most important provisions in setting up such a chart is that the subgroups which are used for computing expected variation and control limits shall consist of items which are considered to be similar, or as the statistician says, homogeneous. We believe that most plant managers, even those to whom control charts are relatively new, will not attempt to impose similar inventory policies on items of material which are fundamentally different in handling costs, volume required for storage, etc. Obviously, judgment must be exercised in deciding how broad the coverage should be in this application of control charts. We believe that a similar type of judgment would have to be exercised for any method of inventory control.

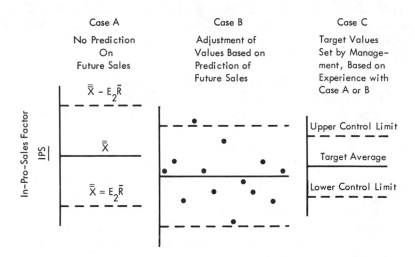

Items of Product, in Order of Increasing $ Sales/30 Days

FIGURE 1. STAGES IN DEVELOPMENT OF INVENTORY CONTROL

STEPS IN CONTROL

In this article, this control chart method is described for the following situations, as illustrated in Figure 1.

Case A

The case where future sales of product cannot be firmly and accurately predicted and where it may be desired to balance the production of several items considered to be similar, statistically homogeneous, and made from common raw materials or using common machines.

Case B

The case of similar items where total sales can be predicted with fair accuracy.

Case C

A case similar to Case B, in which top management has a well-defined policy based on economic lot sizes and past experience for proportioning inventory, production, and sales.

The study of economic lot sizes for the producer or the consumer has been discussed in many previous papers and textbooks.[1] The control chart method described here is useful, regardless of whether it is or is not desirable to attempt calculations of economic lot size.

In applying this control chart method and deciding whether to use Case A, B, or C, it is quite possible that the user might make an error in judgment as to which case is most suitable for the problem at hand, or he may attempt to include non-similar items on a single chart. For example, he may think that his inventory policy is so well established that he can proceed immediately to Case C. If he is too optimistic in this assumption, the completed chart will probably correct him in short order. Also, in a case of improper selection of non-similar items, the chart will tend to be self-correcting.

CONTROL CHART DEVELOPMENT

In developing a control chart technique for co-ordinating inventory, production and sales, it is desirable to use dollar values which are combined into a single factor for chart study. This combined factor may be called the In-Pro-Sales factor, abbreviated as *IPS*.

For the purpose of our discussion, it will be assumed that the proposed chart will be based on some convenient fixed operating interval, such as a calendar month, and that production and sales rates will then be corrected to a 30-day basis. The following data are required to compute a value for *IPS:*

$I = $ \$ value of inventory physically on hand at end of previous monthly interval

$S = $ \$ value of sales during previous monthly interval, prorated to 30 day basis

$P = $ \$ value per 30 days, gross sales value of production, based on rate of production at *end* of previous monthly interval

---

[1] See, for example, Hoehing, W. F., "Statistical Inventory Control," *Industrial Quality Control,* Vol. XIII, No. 7, Jan. 1957, pp. 7–13.

$O =$ \$ value of outstanding orders *not* shipped at end of previous monthly interval

Using the above information, the *IPS* factor is defined as:

$$IPS = \frac{I - O + P}{S + 1}$$

It should be noted that the value of unity is added in the denominator to cover the situation when monthly sales are zero. When sales are zero, it is still desirable to have a definite value of *IPS* for the particular item, because *if production is not stopped, IPS* may be still larger the following month, indicating neglect of the control chart warning.

PROCEDURE FOR CASE A

In Case A, where future sales cannot be firmly predicted, the procedure for preparing the control chart is as follows:

Step 1: Tabulate $(I - O)$, P and S for the items to be controlled.

Step 2: Calculate *IPS* for each item.

Step 3: Retabulate the items in the order of increasing values of sales, S.

Step 4: Using a suitable subgroup size, calculate upper and lower control limits for *individual IPS* values using the grand average $(\overline{X})$ of *IPS* and the average Range $(\overline{R})$ of subgroups with standard control chart formulas for "No Standard Given":

$$UCL = \overline{\overline{X}} + E_2\overline{R} = \overline{\overline{X}} + 2.66\overline{R}$$
$$LCL = \overline{\overline{X}} - E_2\overline{R} = \overline{\overline{X}} - 2.66\overline{R}$$

with subgroups of two.

Step 5: Plot the control chart using the results of steps 2 and 4.

The control limits are always calculated for *individual values* of *IPS,* using the following values of E_2, taken from *Manual on Quality Control of Materials,* American Society for Testing Materials, 1951.

Subgroup Size n	Factor for Individuals E_2
2	2.660
3	1.772
4	1.457
5	1.290
6	1.184
7	1.109
8	1.054
9	1.010
10	0.975

Whenever a value of *IPS* falls above the upper limit, inventory and/or production is too high in relation to sales, and adjustments should be made accordingly. Similarly, the converse is true for items where *IPS* falls below the lower control limit.

It will be noted that *when there are no sales during a given period,* the value of *IPS* usually becomes relatively very high. Such values of *IPS* should not be included in computing averages, ranges and limits for the control chart. Usually, those values will be found to be far above the upper control limit when the chart is completed. Nevertheless, these extra-high values act as a valuable red flag to the user of the chart, and should therefore be identified each time they occur, if there is any hope of future sales on the item. The value of *IPS* in such cases becomes the dollar value of non-moving inventory on a very unprofitable item! Naturally, the chart says they don't conform to good inventory policy.

Since Case A is not dependent on a prediction of future sales, management will normally strive to establish a target or desirable average value for the *IPS* factor. A new chart and new limits are computed each month. Gradual production changes based on a study of *IPS* values falling outside of limits will tend to reduce the width of the control chart limits so that the entire group of similar items approaches a balanced and controlled inventory condition, thereby approaching the management policy goal. When this has been attained, management can then decide whether the average *IPS* value should be raised or lowered, depending on several of the factors listed at the beginning of this article. The monthly control chart will therefore be a continual guide to management in adjusting production rates to conform with desired inventory policy.

PROCEDURE FOR CASE B

If management has been operating for some time under Case A, and finds that it may be possible to predict future sales of the group of similar items, then the value $\overline{\overline{X}}$ on the control chart may be multiplied by the factor:

$$\frac{\text{Total \$ Sales during last period}}{\text{Total \$ Sales predicted for next period}}$$

since *IPS* is almost inversely proportional to sales. The control limits are then shifted accordingly, based on the predicted value for $\overline{\overline{X}}$. This is considered operation under Case B, and obviously should not be continued unless reasonably accurate sales predictions can again be made for the next future time period.

PROCEDURE FOR CASE C

After operating successfully for a time under Case B for a group of similar items, management may wish to establish a firm policy covering a standard central value for *IPS* and also standard control limits based on past experience. This would be considered Case C, which represents a very desirable goal for management. Such *standardized control values for one group of products might be considerably different from controls for another group.*

It is again emphasized that this In-Pro-Sales control chart is a flexible

Item	Rank in order of sales	(I—O) $	P $	S $	IPS* Value
1	4	9070	8880	13640	1.32
2	27	44640	28770	39680	1.85
3	29	47320	34170	42300	1.93
4	8	43710	40230	23240	3.61
5	15	48340	32300	32010	2.52
6	25	45310	32590	36960	2.11
7	19	51320	35510	34050	2.55
8	3	16180	5030	11540	1.84
9	16	27760	40560	32090	2.13
10	30	48810	31620	47340	1.70
11	28	44230	9910	41620	1.30
12	2	9390	2080	6180	1.86
13	24	24130	30800	36530	1.50
14	10	40110	23810	25310	2.53
15	22	37740	35790	34680	2.12
16	11	48140	44270	28340	3.26
17	6	11890	8930	17080	1.22
18	12	23840	50310	29660	2.47
19	7	42710	34280	22020	3.50
20	21	42440	40330	34670	2.39
21	1	5490	1680	5610	1.28
22	23	26170	34780	36210	1.68
23	26	37800	33700	38740	1.85
24	5	40040	13400	17070	3.13
25	14	23350	25070	30770	1.57
26	9	28720	28490	23770	2.41
27	17	42830	19330	32380	1.92
28	20	20240	31760	34200	1.52
29	13	46310	41260	30140	2.91
30	18	35240	29570	33370	1.94

TABLE I. EXAMPLE OF DATA FOR CASE A

$$*IPS = \frac{I - O + P}{S + 1}$$

tool which in no way interferes with calculation of economic lot size or other well known production control methods which may already be in use at the plant. The *IPS* technique, particularly in the stage described as Case A, serves as a simple and rational check on other parts of the production control system. If management is operating either under Case B or Case C, and a radical change occurs in the overall market for the group of products, the situation should be resurveyed by again using the methods described under Case A.

TABLE II.   EXAMPLE OF CALCULATIONS FOR CASE A

Item	Rank in order of sales	IPS	Range R_2
21	1	1.28	
12	2	1.86	0.58
8	3	1.84	
1	4	1.32	0.52
24	5	3.13	
17	6	1.22	1.91
19	7	3.50	
4	8	3.61	0.11
26	9	2.41	
14	10	2.53	0.12
16	11	3.26	
18	12	2.47	0.79
29	13	2.91	
25	14	1.57	1.34
5	15	2.52	
9	16	2.13	0.39
27	17	1.92	
30	18	1.94	0.02
7	19	2.55	
28	20	1.52	1.03
20	21	2.39	
15	22	2.12	0.27
22	23	1.68	
13	24	1.50	0.18
6	25	2.11	
23	26	1.85	0.26
2	27	1.85	
11	28	1.30	0.55
3	29	1.93	
10	30	1.70	0.23

Averages	2.131	0.553
$E_2\bar{R}$	1.471	
Upper Control limit, UCL	3.602	
Lower Control limit, LCL	0.660	

EXAMPLE OF CASE A

Let us assume that a textile producer is manufacturing 30 types of cloth (different weights, weaves, color, etc.). Following the procedure for Case A:

Step 1: The 30 items are entered in Table I, with the values of $(I - O)$, P, and S. (Also a rank number based on S.)

Step 2: IPS is calculated for each item and entered in Table I.

Step 3: Rearrange the items by sales rank number as shown in Table II.

Step 4: Using a subgroup of 2 for this case, compute $\overline{\overline{X}}$, $\overline{R}$, and the control limits, as shown in Table II.

Step 5: Plot the chart (Fig. 2).

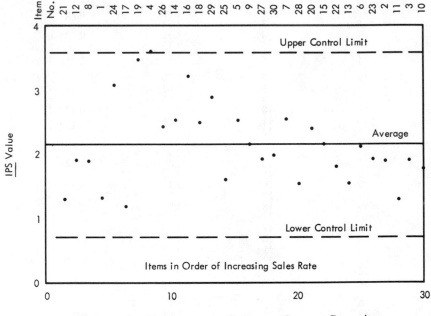

FIGURE 2.   EXAMPLE OF CONTROL CHART, CASE A

When more than 60 items are involved, it may be desirable to increase the subgroup size to 3, 4, . . . 10. In accordance with control chart theory, subgroup size should not exceed about ten when ranges are used, and a subgroup size of two to five is preferable in this application.

Several conclusions may be drawn from the *IPS* control chart by the plant manager:

a) Since the average value of *IPS* in this example is 2.131, the sum of monthly production and inventory is approximately twice the average sales rate over the 30 items.

b) Since the lower control limit on the chart is less than unity, there is a possible risk of certain items running out of stock, with inventory plus production running behind sales, although no specific item had an *IPS* less than 1.00 on the chart.

c) Item 4 has an *IPS* value above the upper control limit, with items 19, 16, and 24 high enough to warrant an extra check on sales forecasts and production planning, so as to bring *IPS* values closer to the target average value desired by the manager on his next control chart.

It should again be emphasized that this control chart procedure is intended for use on individual values of *IPS* only. The use of small subgroups is in accordance with usual control chart practice to estimate the expected *variation* occurring among items having a relatively close current dollar sales rate. If certain items are not turning over rapidly, the subgroups for these items will then have internal variations of *IPS* value which will then be compared on the chart with other subgroups of items which are turning over rapidly. The plant manager may then find that one of two situations occurs on his chart:

a) Various values of *IPS* may fall outside of control limits in a random manner across the chart. Such a situation simply indicates that the production rates for these items need to be corrected if they are to be maintained in a condition of inventory control on the same policy as the other items.

b) In another situation, the manager may find that all of the items at one end of the chart are out of control with respect to those at the other end. The manager must then decide whether he wishes to maintain a consistent policy over the entire group of items, or whether he actually has a single policy or whether he should select the right-hand end of his chart) which should actually have been charted under a separate policy. This is the situation where the chart tends to be self-correcting, so that it will tell the plant manager whether he actually has a single policy or whether he should select a breakpoint and change his inventory policy for a certain portion of the products having an exceptionally high (or low) turnover rate.

It may be noted that the chart also calls the manager's attention to the ranking of items in order of sales value, and obviously this relative ranking will change from month to month. It appears to the writer that this type of ranking for setting up the chart is the one fundamentally of greatest interest and utility to the plant manager. The subgroup size selected for setting up the chart is only for the purpose of computing upper and lower control limits for individual values, since the *averages of subgroups are not plotted*. In case a plant manager who is statistically minded, should question whether this method of grouping is in accordance with normal control chart theory, we suggest that the purpose of the chart itself is to tell him whether the values of *IPS,* so arranged, form an approximately normal universe of values. If they do not, then considerable numbers of *IPS* values will fall outside of the control limits, which indicates that the manager *does not really have a consistently successful inventory policy,* but only thinks he has, for the group of items being considered.

When the sales rate (*S*) of an item *approaches* zero, obviously the value of *IPS* can have relatively large positive or negative values. This property of *IPS,* together with the random fluctuations of sales, production difficulties and delivery changes, makes the *IPS* factor a suitable and effective parameter for impartial studies of inventory policy by the control chart method.

Those who are familiar with the many other applications of control charts will recognize that the values of E_2 given in this paper are based on estimated limits extending three standard deviations above and below the average. These limits are conservative and will only rarely give a false indication that a value of *IPS* is too far from the target or central value. If tighter limits are desired, the values of E_2 may be multiplied by ⅔ to cut the limit to two standard deviations. When such narrower limits are used, about 5 percent of the *IPS* values will tend to fall outside of limits by pure chance, causing the plant manager a little additional worry. When one is learning to use the charts, however, the narrower limits may promote interest and result in a more rapid improvement in overall inventory control.

PART III
Facilities Planning

Chapter 15
INTRODUCTION TO PART III

Although often not the most frequent of operating decisions, facilities plans can be the most significant. The facilities plan affects many other decisions, not the least consequential of which are the production and work force employment plans. The facilities plan establishes cost structures and capacity constraints and, in so doing, goes a long way toward determining optimum production plans.

The relationship between cost structure and capacity constraints on one hand and production plans on the other was examined in Part I. It is sufficient to suggest at this time that production plans are usually developed with facilities planning in retrospect; that is, the facilities and their resultant cost structures and capacity constraints are considered known values. This sequence represents the normal procedure, since in most cases the facilities are already in existence when production plans are laid. However, in Part Three we will consider the entire facility a variable and will examine the process of evaluating alternative facilities to create the most favorable cost structures for future production plans. Moreover, the relationship of work force employment plans and given cost structures was examined through linear decision rules in Chapter 5. In this Part, the facilities will be considered as they influence an ideal cost structure which in turn determines work force employment plans through the derivation of linear decision rules. In short, Part I used facilities as known values and determined work force and production plans accordingly; whereas in this part neither the facilities nor the production plans are considered fixed.

Facilities planning is not restricted in this analysis to plant location and plant expansion decisions; rather, facilities planning includes any decisions which affect the makeup of the productive plant. Each equipment addition or replacement decision constitutes facilities planning because these decisions in their aggregate recast the over-all production facility and modify the cost structures and capacity constraints used in formulating production and employment plans. The individual facilities decisions and deliberations can, over an extended period of time, modify the facility substantially and, therefore, are just as much facilities planning as are new plant and relocation decisions.

Too often individualized equipment decisions are not considered facilities planning and are regarded as separate engineering or modernization projects. It is our purpose to place these decisions in a general management planning framework.

Conventionally these decisions are determined in a capital budgeting framework. That is, the facilities alternatives are considered as financial investments and evaluated accordingly. This approach emphasizes the profitability of alternative facilities plans under the assumption that the alternatives which exhibit the greatest profitability will be undertaken. In this way, it is thought, only the facilities plans which are superior in an investment sense are adopted. Moreover, only the facilities plans which are more profitable than financial investments would be considered. Implementation of this approach tends to budget the available capital to high-return investments and should therefore result in the creation of the optimum type of facility for production and employment planning, because only the facilities plans which show a profitable return will be undertaken. In other words, facilities plans are screened on the basis of profitability and only the most profitable alternatives are accepted.

This approach places great importance on the measure of profitability, because profitability determines whether alternatives are accepted or rejected. Any projects which are accepted and built into the on-going production facility modify the existing cost structure and capacity constraints and, therefore, constitute facilities planning according to our definition. The measure of profitability used in the screening process is, therefore, of crucial significance because it can determine which facilities plans are undertaken.

The simplest and most common measure of profitability used in the capital budgeting approach to facilities planning is the simple "payback" period. The payback period is the number of years (or, more generally, the period of time) required for the proposal to recover through cost savings the amount of capital invested. The proposed alternative or plan usually is a lower cost alternative than the present facility used in performing the same function and generally requires an added investment. The relative magnitude of the added investment compared to the generated cost savings is a measure of the profitability of the alternative.

Specifically, if

>$I =$ the added capital required by the proposed alternative;
>$N =$ the net cost savings generated by the alternative; and
>$P =$ the payback period measure of profitability; then

$$P = \frac{I}{N} \tag{15.1}$$

Obviously the alternatives with a large I and a small N are relatively undesirable; while those with a small I and a large N are more favorable. Therefore, the smaller the payback period, P, the more favorable the plan. If N is in dollars per year, P is also in years.

P has the advantage of being simple to calculate and compare with alternative facilities. Its meaning is apparent. For example, if $P = 1$, the alternative will "pay for itself," that is, recover the I, in one year. If, however, $P = 5$, five years will be required to recover the I. P has the disadvantage of being entirely relative. To verify this statement, ask yourself what P is good and what is bad. $P = 3$ is good in some industries and bad in others. The auto industry which completely retools every two years might not be interested in a facilities plan wherein $P = 3$; however, in the petroleum industry, a project with $P = 3$ might be considered very favorable. In addition, $P = 3$ has no significance in comparison with financial investments wherein the profitability is measured in terms of rate of return. P does not, therefore, provide an adequate criterion to budget capital between facilities plans on one hand and financial plans on the other. In summary, the payback measure is simple and straightforward, but is not sufficiently powerful to handle the general facilities planning—capital budgeting problem.

The second measure used in conventional approaches, the simple rate of return, makes up for some of the disadvantages of the P measure. First of all, the simple rate of return compares the net cost savings to the average amount of added capital in terms of the percentage rate of return. This percentage rate of return can be compared to alternative financial investments and thereby provides a criterion which is more generally applicable than P. If:

>$R =$ the simple rate of return as a percentage per year,

$$R = \frac{N - A}{\dfrac{I}{2}} \tag{15.2}$$

In this measure, the net earnings N are reduced by a factor A which specifically allows for the recovery of the added investment I. If N and

A are constants per year, the average investment is $\dfrac{I}{2}$. Therefore, R is a percentage rate of return which measures the profitability over and above recovery of the added investment I. R can, therefore, be compared directly to the rate of return of interest bearing securities or other financial investments. A is usually determined by dividing I by the shortest life of the plant so that R is the rate of return under the worst conditions. If the actual life exceeds that used in computing A, the rate of return R would be higher in actuality than originally computed. Specifically,

$$A = \frac{I}{T} \qquad (15.3)$$

when T equals the shortest possible use life.

Unfortunately neither of these criteria explicitly considers the time value of money. Under the assumption that any cost savings from the first year will be reinvested at the current rate of interest, $1 now is worth more than $1 a year from now. In fact, $1 now is worth $1 + $1i a year from now when i is the prevailing rate of interest. Clearly the original dollar has grown to include interest earned. Two years from now, the original $1 will be worth $1 + $1i + i($1 +$1i) = $1 + 2i($1) + i^2 = (1 + i)^2$.[1]

Turning this concept around, a flow of earnings (or cost savings) of $1 per year for each of five years is worth *less* than $5 now, the product of 5 times $1, because some amount I (less than $5) invested now at i percent rate of return will yield a flow of $1 per year for five years. For example, $3.791 invested now at 10% will yield $1 per year for each of five years. The formula used in determining this value is:

$$V = \sum_{t=1}^{5} \frac{1}{(1 + .10)^t} = \$3.791$$

In general terms, the present value, V, of N dollars per year for t years is:

$$V = \sum_{t=1}^{t} \frac{N}{(1 + i)^t} \qquad (15.4)$$

Formula (15.4) is used to determine elaborate tables found in most basic financial management or managerial accounting texts to give V for various values of t and i. For example, to select a few applicable values, one such table contains V equivalents for flows of earnings reinvested at 1 percent to 50 percent for one to fifty years. Such tables are of immeasurable value in avoiding the computation of V in accordance with formula (15.4).

---

[1] This method of computation assumes that the $1 is received and reinvested in the first day of the current year.

TABLE I

_____ Invested now at ____% is equal to ___ per year for ___ years

$3.791	10	$1	5
$6.145	10	$1	10
$7.606	10	$1	15
$8.514	10	$1	20
$9.915	10	$1	50
$2.991	20	$1	5
$4.192	20	$1	10
$4.675	20	$1	15
$4.870	20	$1	20
$4.999	20	$1	50
$2.035	40	$1	5
$2.414	40	$1	10
$2.484	40	$1	15
$2.497	40	$1	20
$2.500	40	$1	50

Source: Robert N. Anthony, _Management Accounting_, Richard D. Irwin, Inc., 1956, p. 496.

Certain relationships are apparent from Table I. Given i, the present value of $1 per year increases as N increases, but not in proportion to N. For reasons previously examined, V increases less rapidly than N because of the added value of reinvested earnings. Correspondingly, given N, V decreases as i increases, again because of the reinvestment effect. A detailed examination of this present-value concept is outside the scope of this book, although it is certainly a topic which is usually examined in basic accounting, managerial economics, or financial management texts.

The concept of present value analysis is applied to facilities planning problems by employing an economic model (or mathematical expression) of the planned facilities investment. In this approach, a more explicit formulation of the plan is used to specify the criteria of the decision more carefully.

The value of any facility is equal to the earnings stream it generates plus its market or disposal value, less the amount of added investment required to produce the earnings stream. If:

V = economic value
D = disposal value
I = investment cost
N = earnings stream
T = the economic or use life, whichever is less,

then

$$V = NT + D - I \qquad (15.5)$$

But (15.5) is not in present value terms; that is, the flow and disposal value are in terms of their value when they accrue rather than as of the present time. To convert (15.5) to present value, we need only recall (15.4) which expresses the present value of a flow of cost savings N as $V =$ $\sum_{t=1}^{T} \frac{N}{(1+i)^t}$. Similarly, the present value of the disposable market value is $V = \frac{D_t}{(1+i)^t}$ when D_t is the disposable market value as of the point in time t, for example, as of the end of the fifth year. Finally, since I is already in present value terms,

$$V = \sum_{t=1}^{T} \frac{N}{(1+i)^t} + \frac{D_t}{(1+i)^t} - I \tag{15.6}$$

Expression (15.6) gives the present value of a facilities investment assuming that the funds are reinvested at the beginning of each year t to earn the rate of return i. To employ (15.6), we need only determine the sum of the present value less the investment cost. If this value, V, is positive, using an i equal to the cost of capital, then the facilities investment should be favorably considered. When several alternatives are considered, the one with the largest V should be accepted.

In order to make the V of model (15.6) more precise, we can consider the effect of reinvestment (or rediscounting) instantaneously rather than at the beginning of each year under analysis. To accomplish this precision, we can introduce the relationship that

$$\sum_{t=1}^{T} \frac{N}{(1+i)^t} \longrightarrow \int_{0}^{T} Ne^{-it}dt$$

which indicates that the calculus integral expression is approximated by the formula we have been using. The integral expression rediscounts instantaneously the flow of earnings N at the rate of interest i over the time period T. Expression (15.6) becomes

$$V = \int_{0}^{T} Ne^{-it}dt + De^{-iT} - I \tag{15.7}[2]$$

which is an exact economic model for a facilities investment.

---

[2] Based upon an analysis in Chapter 12 of Bowman and Fetter's, *Analysis for Production Management*, Richard D. Irwin, Inc., revised 1961.

To maximize V, we set the derivative of (15.7) equal to zero and solve for T.[3]

$$\frac{dV}{dT} = Ne^{-iT} + D'e^{-iT} + De^{-iT}(-i) - 0 = 0$$

Therefore, V is maximized when

$$Ne^{-iT} + D'e^{-iT} = iD_Te^{-iT}$$

Dividing through by e^{-iT},

$$N + D' = iD_T \qquad\qquad (15.8)$$

Expression (15.8) says that V is a maximum when the net earnings less the change in disposable value (D' is decreasing) equals the interest on the disposable value. In this expression, iD is the opportunity cost of retaining the investment or the income which could have been obtained by not making the investment. Therefore, as long as the net earnings less the decline in disposable value exceed the opportunity cost (iD), more can be obtained by undertaking the facility plan than by rejecting it. Expression (15.8) would be used to determine T given N, D_t and i, and that value would be used to determine the V in (15.7). If the V thus determined is positive, the investment is acceptable.

It would be useful to reconcile (15.7) and (15.2), since the simple rate of return (15.2) is a special case of the present value analysis (15.7). By definition, the simple rate of return does not consider the present value of money and considers N constant over time.

Therefore,

$$V = \sum_{t=1}^{T} N + D - I = TN + D_T - I$$

Furthermore, in the simple rate of return analysis, the rate of change of salvage value is $\dfrac{I}{T}$ (assuming straight line amortization of I). Therefore,

$$D_T = I - TD = I - T\frac{I}{T} = 0$$

---

[3] $\dfrac{de^u}{dx} = e^u \dfrac{du}{dx}$ Therefore, $\dfrac{d}{dT} e^{-iT} = e^{-iT} \dfrac{d}{dT}(-iT) = e^{-iT}(-i)$

Finally, the rate of return over time period T equals $\dfrac{V}{\dfrac{I}{2}}$ where $\dfrac{I}{2}$ is the average investment. But

$$V = TN + D_T - I$$
$$= TN + 0 - I$$
$$= TN - I$$

Therefore,

$$R = \frac{V}{\dfrac{I}{2}} = \frac{TN - I}{\dfrac{I}{2}} \tag{15.9}$$

Dividing (15.9) by T,

$$R = \frac{N - \dfrac{I}{T}}{\dfrac{I}{2}} \tag{15.10}$$

Thus the R of (15.10) is expressed as a percentage per year; furthermore the $\dfrac{I}{T}$ of (15.10) equals the A of (15.2) and the conditions of (15.10) and (15.2) are identical. In other words, the conditions which apply to the simple rate of return analysis (15.2) apply if (1) the time value of money is ignored, (2) the rate of amortization, A, is constant and equal to $\dfrac{I}{T}$, and (3) the disposable value, D_t, is zero at time T. In order for the disposable value to be zero at the end of period T (the economic life), the use life must be at least equal to T. The use life is equal to the period of time from installation to obsolescence or complete failure, whichever is less; and the economic life is defined as the period of time when V is maximal. Therefore, in order for the simple rate of return to apply, the facility investment must reach a maximum value and be declining when failure or obsolescence sets in. Under these conditions, plus conditions (1) and (2) listed above, the simple rate of return can be used as an approximation of the present value model.

So much for the conventional treatment. It is apparent that none of these traditional models considers certain conditions which are present in many operating decisions in the facilities planning area. The first of these is the problem of uncertainty. The net earnings, N, are a significant variable in determining the present value, V, of the facilities investment and, hence, the simple rate of return. However, N can only be estimated in any planning-type analysis. And yet there is always some uncertainty in forecasting a value for N. In other words, perfect forecasting is impossible; hence, uncertainty obtains in the facilities plan. Any general formulation of the facilities planning problem must incorporate a means of adjusting to various forecasts. Chapter 16 treats this problem by putting facilities planning in a game theory (uncertainty) format, an approach which is further generalized by an editorial note.

The second gap in the conventional approach concerns analyzing the over-all effect of individual decisions. Each factory is part of a general system which processes materials and distributes the resulting products. Individual facilities plans must be built into the system of plants which comprise the entire firm's production facility. Chapter 17 treats this problem by developing a linear programming model for the interrelated-units aspect of facilities planning.

Finally, none of the conventional measures considers the general problem of determining the total size of a facility. The application of capital budgeting methods will result in planning the most efficient facility given a level of demand, because the net earnings, N, are dependent upon a particular demand forecast. The conventional procedure will not necessarily accept plans to expand facilities in anticipation of forecasted increases in output. This problem area is called scale (or size) of operations and is analyzed in a fairly general form in Chapter 17.

These three chapters, therefore, constitute a reasonably complete analysis of the general facilities planning problem.

Chapter 16

UNCERTAINTY PROBLEMS IN FACILITIES PLANNING

XVIII.

Capital Budgeting and Game Theory*

Edward G. Bennion

The purpose of this article is to do two things: (1) to suggest a more rational approach to capital budgeting, which is a perennial and imperfectly solved problem for business, and (2) to test the applicability of game theory to the kind of decisions which are involved in capital budgeting.

In a sense, this is singling out a particular problem and a particular technique. However, the problem happens to be one of the most important and least clarified of the top-level issues faced by businessmen, just as the technique happens to be one of the most intriguing and least understood of the statistical devices which have recently been presented to businessmen as aids to top-level decision making. In combination, they offer an unusual opportunity to push progress ahead in an area where it is needed and at the same time put some realism into a methodology whose value may be overestimated at its present stage of development.

ROLE OF FORECASTS

The whole subject of capital budgeting is, of course, too big and complicated to be critically examined within the scope of one brief article. But

* From the *Harvard Business Review,* Vol. 34, No. 6 (1956), 115–123. Reprinted by permission of the *Harvard Business Review.*

perhaps some new light can be thrown on one important problem aspect: the relationship that should obtain between the budget and the economic forecast.

It hardly seems necessary to prove that economic forecasts play a significant—sometimes an almost determining—role in shaping the business-man's investment decisions. The traditional explanation is simple:

In order to decide how much a company should invest or what kinds of assets it should acquire, we need a sales forecast for the firm—to establish its anticipated level of activity.

But the firm's sales forecast cannot be made without some estimate of what the industry is going to do. And the industry's sales forcast in turn depends in large measure on the predicted level of activity in the economy as a whole.

Q.E.D.—the capital budget of any individual firm has a unique and important relation to the general economic forecast.

UNRELIABLE GUIDE

If it is obvious that forecasts are necessary, it is still more obvious that they are likely to be unreliable:

It is impossible to make an economic forecast in which full confidence can be placed. No matter what refinements of techniques are employed, there still remain at least some *exogenous variables*—i.e.,variables, such as defense expenditures, the error limits of whose predicted values cannot be scientifically measured.

It is thus not even possible to say with certainty how likely our forecast is to be right. We may be brash enough to label a forecast as "most probable," but this implies an ability on our part to pin an approximate probability coefficient on a forecast: 1.0 if it is a virtual certainty, 0.0 if it is next to an impossibility, or some other coefficient between these extremes. But, again, since we have no precise way of measuring the probability of our exogenous variables behaving as we assume them to do, there is no assurance that the *estimated* probability coefficient for our forecast is anything like 100% correct.

In spite of such drawbacks, businessmen are willing to pay for having general economic forecasts made, and to use them in deciding among alternative investment opportunities for capital funds. For example, the more certain is prosperity, the wiser it will usually be to invest in new plant and equipment; whereas the more certain is depression or recession, the safer it looks to invest in government bonds or other securities. In other words, the businessman uses economic forecasts, to assess the relative advantages of investing in fixed or liquid assets, in the light of the expected business-cycle phase.

COMMON ERROR

At this point, the businessman stands before us, his economic forecast in one hand, his proposed investment alternatives in the other. His next step is the one where he is most apt to go wrong. When some one phase of the business cycle is forecast as "most probable," it is likely to look logical to him to go ahead and put his funds into whichever investment alternative maximizes profit in the phase expected.

Looking at the situation superficially, this step appears to be quite sensible. But actually a businessman armed with only a single most probable forecast is in no position to make a wise investment decision—*unless* his forecast is 100% correct, and this, as we have seen, is an impossibility.

A NEW APPROACH

In the following pages, a more rational way to use an economic forecast is suggested. Furthermore, adoption of the method proposed here permits the businessman to learn the answer to another question over which he probably has spent some sleepless nights if he has ever known responsibility for making a decision on the capital budget. *Just how far off can the forecast be before it leads to a "wrong" investment decision?*

Because the fundamentals of this new approach are most easily grasped if a specific problem is attacked, let us see how it can be applied in concrete cases. We shall look first at a simplified hypothetical case, and then at a case based on actual experience (slightly disguised). For the sake of the clearest possible focus on the problems involved, no explicit reference will be made to the role of game theory while we are working out their solution. Following their presentation, however, we will meet the theory head-on and discover in the process that we have already drawn from it just about as much as is possible.

SIMPLIFIED CASE

This first case, although hypothetical, is not unrealistic. Further, it has the advantage of reducing the problem and method of solution to the simplest possible proportions.

ALTERNATIVE INVESTMENTS

The specific issue of whether to invest in plant or securities is a good one for illustrative purposes because it can be defined so sharply. Suppose we have even more exact information than most businessmen generally assemble before exercising their judgment to reach an investment decision.

Under these circumstances we might know that:

The most probable forecast is for a recession.

In recession, investment in plant will yield 1% as compared with a 4% yield for securities.

In prosperity, plant will yield 17%, while securities will yield 5%.

Placing these data in diagram form, we get the following 2 × 2 "matrix":

| | | Cycle-Phase Alternatives | |
		Recession	Prosperity
Management Investment Alternatives	Securities	4%	5%
	Plant	1%	17%

Under this condition no businessman worth his salt is going to want to settle for securities—but how can he justify any other course, given his forecast of a probable recession?

MORE DATA NEEDED

To begin with, our businessman needs to recognize that the data so far placed at his disposal, rather than limiting his choice, do not provide the basis for a decision at all. Two further questions first require an answer:

(1) How probable is the "most probable" forecast? To answer this, the forecast needs to be complete by assigning a *probability coefficient* to each cycle phase considered.

(2) How probable does a recession have to be before the earnings prospects of the more conservative choice look just as attractive as the returns available from adopting a bolder course of action? In other words, what are the *indifference probabilities* of recession and prosperity, given the rate of return each will yield?

PROBABILITY COEFFICIENTS

Establishing probability coefficients on the economic forecast is a job we can relinquish, more than willingly, to the company economist. We are not concerned here with what kind of crystal ball he gazes into, but rather with how top management uses his findings, whatever they may be. So, in order to get on with our problem, let us simply suppose that our forecaster thinks the chances of recession are 6 out of 10 and so has assigned a probability coefficient of 0.6 to his predictions for a recession (which automatically means 0.4 for prosperity).

INDIFFERENCE PROBABILITIES

The handling of indifference probabilities is not going to be quite so simple, but it can be done readily enough by anyone who can recall his high school course in algebra (he does not have to be blessed with "total recall," either):

Suppose we say, in elementary algebraic terms, that the recession probability coefficient $= R$, and the prosperity probability coefficient $= P$. In that event, we know from our matrix figures that over any period:

  I: $4R + 5P =$ the return on securities
  II: $1R + 17P =$ the return on plant

From this, it is clear that the return on securities will be the same as the return on plant when:

  III: $4R + 5P = 1R + 17P$

Solving this last equation for R in terms of P, we get:

  IV: $R = 4P$

Since the sum of the probability coefficients $(R + P)$ has to equal 1.0, we can say that $R = (1 - P)$ and substitute $(1 - P)$ for R in IV:

  V: $1 - P = 4P$, or
  VI: $P = 0.2$, and $R = 0.8$

This merely means that if the probabilities of a recession and prosperity are 0.8 and 0.2 respectively, then the chances are that the company will be just as well off investing in securities as in plant, and vice versa. In other words, it appears to be a matter of *indifference* which alternative is chosen.

ASSEMBLING THE DATA

For the sake of convenience, let us reassemble all our information in the compact easy-to-read form of a matrix:

| | | Cycle-Phase Alternatives | |
		Recession	Prosperity
Management Investment Alternatives	Securities	4%	5%
	Plant	1%	17%

Indifference probabilities: $R = 0.8$ $P = 0.2$
Forecasted probabilities: $\hat{R} = 0.6$ $\hat{P} = 0.4$

Here, at last, our businessman has all the information he needs to decide what course of action maximizes his chances for success. So long as the forecasted probability coefficient for a recession is not equal to or greater than the indifference probability coefficient for this phase of the business cycle, the businessman can know that he is not making an *avoidable* mistake by playing for high stakes and building a plant. *The alternative to choose is the one that has a higher forecasted probability than indifference probability.*

ADVANTAGE GAINED

The little technique outlined above thus does two things:

1. It makes clear that the best paying investment alternative in the most probable situation is not necessarily the alternative that management should choose.

2. With indifference probabilities, it is possible for us to see what margin of error is permissible in any estimated probabilities before these estimates result in an erroneous decision.

ACTUAL CASE

With this much understanding of the 2×2 matrix, we are now in a position to apply indifference probabilities to our actual but more complicated case:

An integrated petroleum company anticipates the need for a refinery in Country A, has determined that Alpha City is the best location, but is uncertain as to the appropriate size.

Operating at approximate capacity, internal economies of scale exist up to a refinery size of R barrels per day (B/D).

However, once sales exceed Z barrels per day (with $Z < R$), further economies could best be effected by building a second refinery elsewhere. This puts a ceiling of Z barrels per day on the Alpha City unit.[1]

Whatever size refinery is built, it can be completed in 1965. It is also agreed that depreciation and obsolescence will make the refinery valueless by 1978.

As an aid in determining the size required in 1965, it is known that consumption growth is highly correlated with industrial output.

Unfortunately, there is less than perfect unanimity as to the expected growth rate of industrial output between the present and 1965. The economics department has forecasted a rate of 2.5%, the foreign government officially estimates a rate of 5%, and the company top management wonders what would happen if the growth rate turned out to be 7.5%.

---

[1] This ceiling decision, it might be noted, involves the solution to a problem to which linear programing conceivably might aptly be applied. Taking this solution as given obviously does not mean it is necessarily easy to come by. See Alexander Henderson and Robert Schlaifer, "Mathematical Programming: Better Information for Better Decision Making," reprinted in this book on page 53.

Careful analysis leads to the conclusion that a growth rate of 2.5% requires a refinery of X barrels per day capacity; that a growth rate of 5% necessitates a refinery of Y barrels per day capacity; and that a growth rate of 7.5% requires a refinery of Z barrels per day capacity, this last being our previously established ceiling size.

Pending further study, all agree to work on the assumption of a zero growth rate after 1965.

To evaluate the three alternative refineries, anticipated integrated income (covering refining, marketing, producing, and transportation) will be computed for each facility under each growth rate, and the percent return on integrated investment will then be calculated and compared.[2]

MATRIX AND PROBABILITIES

With three sizes of refineries to consider, and three growth rates, we will get a 3 $\times$ 3 matrix on this problem. The figures on the diagram, representing return on integrated investment, are more or less what common sense tells us to expect. For example:

The small X B/D refinery shows the highest rate of return if the growth rate is a low 2.5%, bringing in an 8.8% return against only 2% for the large Z B/D unit with its much higher cost of investment.

On the other hand, if the growth rate should reach a high of 7.5%, the large Z B/D refinery can return an average of 12.6%, while the small X B/D facility with its limited output is tied to its 8.8% ceiling yield.

But filling in the matrix does more than verify our common-sense conclusions. It also equips us to see *how much* better one refinery is than another under each possible condition.

	Pre-1965 Growth Rate Alternatives		
	Low 2.5%	Moderate 5.0%	High 7.5%
Z B/D	2.0%	7.3%	12.6%
Y B/D	3.7%	11.0%	11.0%
X B/D	8.8%	8.8%	8.8%

Refinery Investment Alternatives (labels for the rows Z B/D, Y B/D, X B/D)

Indifference probabilities: $L = 0.301$ $M = 0.114$ $H = 0.585$

Forecasted probabilities: $\hat{L} = 0.333$ $\hat{M} = 0.333$ $\hat{H} = 0.333$

---

[2] While the matrix figures of this case are based on careful engineering estimates, this venture is still in an experimental stage and hence does not constitute a part of the budget procedure of Standard Oil Company (New Jersey), with which I am associated.

The indifference probabilities here were calculated by just the same algebraic procedures as were followed in our previous example. The forecasted probabilities simply reflect the fact that no one in the company could decide which of the three forecasts was most likely, and therefore each was treated as equally "valid" (i.e., chances of 1 out of 3, or $0.33\frac{1}{3}$).

THE SOLUTION

A quick look at our diagram now reveals that the extra-large Z B/D refinery should be ruled out, since its return will be greater only under a 7.5% growth rate, and the real probability for a 7.5% growth rate is too small to justify considering that alternative. (Remember that an alternative cannot be chosen unless its forecasted or estimated true probability is equal to or above the indifference probability.)

On the other hand, both the X B/D and Y B/D refineries are still in the running. So, with two possibilities still remaining, new indifference probability calculations are needed in order that we may choose between them:

Suppose (as before) we use the letter L to represent the indifference probability for the low 2.5% growth rate; M for the moderate 5% rate; and H for the high 7.5% figure. In this event we read off the matrix that:

I: $3.7L + 11.0M + 11.0H =$ the return on the Y B/D refinery
II: $8.8L + 8.8M + 8.8H =$ the return on the X B/D refinery

From this it is clear that the return on Y B/D will be the same as the return on X B/D when:

III: $3.7L + 11.0M + 11.0H = 8.8L + 8.8M + 8.8H$

Solving this equation in terms of L we get:

IV: $L = 0.43 (M + H)$

This means that if the estimated true probability of a 2.5% growth rate is greater than 0.43 of the combined estimated true probabilities of the 5% and the 7.5% growth rates, the X B/D refinery is a better bet than the Y B/D refinery. This has to be true because the X B/D refinery is the best-paying alternative, given the 2.5% growth rate.

Since the estimated true probability for the 2.5% growth rate is actually 0.33, which is slightly greater than $0.43 \times (0.33 + 0.33)$, we would conclude that the X B/D refinery is a little better bet than the Y B/D refinery, with the Z B/D refinery showing a very poor third.

A CHANGED ASSUMPTION

Now that we have reached an answer to the problem as originally stated, let us (realistically if provokingly) proceed to alter some of our assumptions, and see just what this will do to our choice:

Suppose that top management, having injected the 7.5% growth rate into the original problem for comparative purposes, concludes that the probability of a 7.5% growth rate is really nil, and that the probabilities of the 2.5% and 5% growth rates are each 0.5. The indifference equation then becomes:

$$3.7L + 11.0M = 8.8L + 8.8M, \text{ or } L = 0.43M$$

Since the estimated true probability of 0.50 for 2.5% growth rate is, in this instance, a great deal bigger than 0.43×0.50, we would conclude that the $X\ B/D$ refinery is a lot better bet than the $Y\ B/D$ refinery, and that no one in his right mind would even consider building a $Z\ B/D$ unit.

Thus we come to the same general conclusion as before, only a bit more cocky, as a result of writing off the 7.5% growth rate and distributing its former probability in such a way as to make the 2.5% and 5% growth rates equally probable.

A RADICAL REVISION

It is clear, however, that the above conclusion is suspect unless we expect no economic growth in Country A after 1965. If we do expect further growth, the $X\ B/D$ refinery loses much of its \$-sign allure. It will not be large enough to take advantage of Country A's expanding economy and so can never return any more than 8.8% on investment.

In contrast, the $Z\ B/D$ refinery will show an increasing rate of return as A's expanding market permits it to produce more and more per year, perhaps ultimately reaching its capacity. Thus, instead of spurning the $Z\ B/D$ refinery (as in our last example), we must acknowledge its potential attractiveness—provided A's economy does not get stalled after 1965, as was previously assumed.

With this possibility in mind, let us make some alterations in our problem and see what we should do. There are two new conditions:

1. After 1965, it is now agreed, the growth rate of Country A will be a steady 2.5% each year.

2. It would be possible to build an $X\ B/D$ or $Y\ B/D$ refinery that would be expansible to $Z\ B/D$; such units would cost more than nonexpansible facilities, but less than two separate refineries with a combined $Z\ B/D$ capacity.

At this point our real problem becomes one of deciding whether to build a $Z\ B/D$ refinery or an $X\ B/D$ or a $Y\ B/D$ refinery expansible to $Z\ B/D$. It may be helpful, first, to consider how the figures in this new matrix should differ from those presented earlier:

Most of the figures are higher than before, reflecting the fact that average earnings are increased by higher sales toward the end of the productive life of each unit.

To a limited extent, the higher investment costs of the two expansible units operate as a drag on their earnings. Thus two of the figures happen to be lower than before, and the expansible refineries have a lower maximum return than is possible with a $Z B/D$ unit.

On the whole, the figures in the matrix tend to be squeezed closer together; i.e., they no longer range between such wide extremes.

Now our revised matrix reads like this:

		Pre-1965 Growth Rate Alternatives		
		Low 2.5%	Moderate 5.0%	High 7.5%
	Z B/D	4.6%	9.9%	12.6%
Refinery Investment Alternatives	Expansible Y B/D	7.2%	10.5%	11.1%
	Expansible X B/D	8.0%	9.7%	10.4%

Indifference probabilities: $L = 0.338$ $M = 0.129$ $H = 0.533$

Forecasted probabilities: $\hat{L} = 0.333$ $\hat{M} = 0.333$ $\hat{H} = 0.333$

Again, we work our algebraic equations to find the indifference probabilities, while the forecasted probabilities result, as before, from assigning equal weight to each forecast.

In this instance, the expansible $Y B/D$ refinery is a shoo-in. This can be intuitively seen by recognizing that the $Y B/D$ refinery is the best paying one given the 5% growth rate, and this growth rate is the only one with an *indifference* probability lower than its *estimated true* probability. By somewhat similar reasoning, the $Z B/D$ refinery is distinctly the worst choice.

The new matrix also reveals another significant conclusion. One does not have to be a mathematician to perceive, just from inspection, that the cost of a poor decision here is a good deal lower than it was for our earlier versions of this problem. The result, of course, flows from the fact that the differences in the row and column vectors have been greatly narrowed. The *absolute* cost of a mistake is by no means insignificant, but *relatively* it is much less than in the previous matrix. This piece of information is in itself of considerable value. At a minimum, it will help the budget-maker to do less agonized tossing in his bed.

MORE TINKERING

Just for fun, let us tinker with our problem once more before dropping it, and again assume that management rejects as of nil probability the growth rate of 7.5% between the present and 1965, giving the 2.5% and 5% growth rates equal probabilities (i.e., chances of 1 out of 2, or 0.5):

This eliminates the top row and right column of the 3×3 matrix, leaving it 2×2.

The indifference probabilities equation for the X B/D and Y B/D refineries then becomes:

$$8.0L + 9.7M = 7.2L + 10.5M, \text{ or } L = M$$

This means that the *indifference* probabilities for both L and M are 0.5.

These, however, are also the values for the *estimated real* probabilities for the 2.5% and 5% growth rates.

Consequently, we have here the unusual case in which the X B/D and Y B/D refineries are equally good bets, with the Z B/D refinery being no bet at all,

No matter which way we look at the problem, therefore, the Z B/D refinery is the poorest choice. But, under one probability assessment, the expansible Y B/D refinery is a better choice than the expansible X B/D refinery; under the other, the expansible X and Y B/D refineries are toss-ups. This conclusion is, of course, decidedly different from that reached for the previous matrix, in which the influence of post-1965 growth was ignored.

OTHER BUDGET QUESTIONS

So far we have managed to explore only one small corner of the capital budget domain. Let us look at some further problem areas.

PROBLEM OF TIMING

Our new technique can also be put to work on a timing problem. Since all but one of the figures in the following matrix have been chosen somewhat arbitrarily (although the choices can easily be defended), they call for no explanation. The only exception is the 9.6% prosperity return for the Y B/D refinery which appears in the lower right-hand corner; this is the *weighted average* return from this investment under the three possible rates of growth, assuming equal probability for each.

		Pre-1965 Cycle-Phase Alternatives		
		Depression	Recession	Prosperity
	Government Bonds	3.5%	3.0%	2.5%
Management Investment Alternatives	Other Securities	2.0%	5.0%	3.0%
	Y B/D Refinery	−2.0%	3.0%	9.6%

Indifference probabilities: $D = 0.43$ $R = 0.24$ $P = 0.33$

It would be a tedious repetition of now familiar principles to attempt to bleed this matrix dry. Let us content ourselves, therefore, with just one reasonable (and relatively simple) interpretation:

Since depression is comparable to the 1937–1938 decline in this country, we might well reject this as being of nil probability in the period between now and 1965.

Should we do so, the left column of the 3 × 3 matrix would be eliminated, as would the top row, since government bonds would not be a logical investment except under depressed conditions.

In the remaining 2 × 2 matrix, the indifference equation for other securities and our *Y B/D* refinery then becomes:

$$5.0R + 3.0P = 3.0R + 9.6P, \text{ or } P = 0.3R$$

In other words, unless we think the true probability of a recession is something more than twice as great as that of prosperity, the construction of the *Y B/D* refinery ought not to be deferred.

INVESTMENT PRIORITIES

Whenever more than one investment alternative is available, there arises the problem of assigning an order of priority among them. To assess and compare each possible project, the method followed in the previous problem can be used to advantage again:

(1) Using a 2 × 2 matrix, calculate indifference probabilities for investing in securities and in plant (or other assets to be used in the company's own business).

(2) Repeat this process for each contemplated internal use of company funds. The top row will be the same in all of these matrices, but the bottom rows will not in general be the same. Consequently, the indifference probabilities for the numerous matrices may vary widely. Any company

project with an indifference probability coefficient for prosperity that is lower than the estimated true prosperity probability coefficient is a good bet.

(3) Instead of arraying the projects in order of descending return *for the most probable cycle phase* (which would incur all the defects already shown to exist in tying investment decisions to a single most probable forecast), array them in order of descending *weighted average* return— weighted according to the estimated probabilities of recession and prosperity or of different rates of growth.

In general, this procedure will *not* result in the same priority order for projects as the method commonly employed, but it is a better method of evaluating all the alternative uses for funds. This is because it avoids the frequently fatal mistake of betting on whatever venture seems to look most profitable, given only a single most probable forecast.

If desirable projects turn out to be more numerous than company resources can finance, the management must then decide whether it wants to borrow or not. If external financing should be ruled out, the marginal project must be the one with the lowest weighted average return which just exhausts available funds. On the other hand, if all desirable projects do not exhaust available funds, the marginal project is the one whose indifference coefficient for prosperity is just equal to the estimated true prosperity coefficient. The excess funds should be temporarily invested in securities.

ALMOST A GAME

Now, finally, we are ready to have that initial promise redeemed—i.e., that the role of game theory would be explained and be evaluated. Actually, as anyone who has met this theory before will recognize, it has already been introduced! All our matrices have been "games," although, in playing some of them, we have had to construe a few of the rules pretty loosely.

The two players in most of our games have been the businessman and the business cycle. Each has had either two or three "strategies." For the former there have been different types of investment alternatives; for the latter there have been different cycle phases. Indeed, the indifference probabilities calculated by the businessman for depression, recession, and prosperity have an exact parallel in game theory. Those probabilities constitute what would be known as the "business cycle probabilities"—namely, the percentage of the time that the business cycle should provide each of its phases in a random manner to hold the businessman's gains down to a minimum.

Can it be said, then, that our method for deciding on the capital budget marks an extension of game theory concepts to the field of business and economics? In the strictest sense, the answer must be *no*. Ours is not a rigorous game—it does not meet all the conditions requisite for such a game:

In game theory proper, the opposing players are assumed to be completely selfish and intelligent. Charity and stupidity are unknown to either. Clearly the business cycle, however malevolent it may sometimes seem, does not meet these requirements. It is as impersonal as nature. In fact, what we really are doing in problems like ours is playing games with nature. Thus the indifference probabilities in our last matrix are actually *nature's* probabilities. They tell us that, if nature were malevolent, it could minimize its "losses" to the businessman by providing depression, recession, and prosperity, in a random manner, 43%, 24%, and 33% of the time, respectively.

If the businessman were confronting an opponent who could maximize gains and minimize losses by a deliberate choice of strategies, then there would be additional calculations to make and prohibitions to observe. For example, in order to keep a selfish and intelligent antagonist from guessing what he might do and benefiting by the knowledge, the businessman might have to figure out several strategies for himself and then use them randomly. Thus, again in our last matrix, the *businessman's* odds are such that he should invest in government bonds, other securities, and the *Y B/D* refinery, in a random manner, 90%, 2%, and 8% of the time, respectively. Otherwise, faced with a malevolent nature, he would fail to maximize his gains.

It takes some stretching to make a choice of strategies out of a range of possibilities, yet a range of possibilities is all we can get out of nature (as contrasted with a willful opponent); and in the case of some business problems we cannot even get that. Moreover, nature, alias the business cycle, may have some strategies on the matrix that no sensible antagonist would use at all because under all conditions other strategies would give him higher gains or lower payoffs.

Consequently, our games with nature are not of the "purer," more rigorous type. Our version represents a departure by virtue of recognizing four additional facts: (1) nature is not malevolent; (2) the odds of a malevolent nature are really the indifference probabilities of the businessman with respect to his alternative courses of action; (3) any time the estimated odds of nature's strategies differ from the businessman's indifference odds, there is a best strategy for the businessman; and (4) this best strategy, as well as the degree of its "bestness," depends on the relationship between the estimated and indifference odds.

However, any readers who are interested in further pursuing the rules of the game theory proper can do so handily by consulting J. D. Williams, *The Compleat Strategyst* (New York, McGraw-Hill Book Company, Inc., 1954). Anyone who can add and subtract can follow this pleasant and often humorous exposition, whereas most other books on the subject call for more advanced mathematical learning.[3]

OTHER ECONOMIC "GAMES"

If capital budgeting can only borrow from game theory but not take it over in its entirety, what about any other business applications? It should be possible to find in the businessman's competitive world a variety of situations that resemble orthodox games—i.e., where the opponents are not noted for their charity toward each other.

The existence of many such parallels is obvious, but unfortunately game theory in its present state of development is not far enough advanced to handle most of them. (Originated by von Neumann, the theory first achieved a wide audience when he and Morgenstern published their book in 1944.[4]) Thus, game theory still does not deal effectively with situations where there are more than two players or where the loser's losses and the winner's gains do not cancel out. For example:

The most common realistic game cited in economic literature is a duopolistic (two-seller) situation in which each of the duopolists has alternative strategies and seeks the strategy that will maximize his profits.[5] This may be a realistic example, but it is certainly one of limited existence. The businessman may not have a large number of competitors but he usually has at least several. However, to consider several competitors plunges us into games involving more than two players, and here the theory as it now stands leaves much to be desired.

Another possible realistic game on the two-person level is where the opponents are the businessmen and the trade union. But this sort of game is likely to be one in which the solution may harm or benefit both players, or harm one player more than it benefits the other. This throws us into games with a non-zero-sum payoff, where the theory again leaves much to be desired.

To say that game theory, in its more rigorous sense, still has no significant business applications does not of course mean that claims for its

[3] John von Neumann and Oscar Morgenstern, *Theory of Games and Economic Behavior* (Princeton, Princeton University Press, 1944); J. C. C. McKinsey, *Introduction to Theory of Games* (New York, McGraw-Hill Book Company, Inc., 1952); David Blackwell and M. A. Girshick, *Theory of Games and Statistical Decisions* (New York, John Wiley & Sons, Inc., 1954).

[4] See footnote 3.

[5] See L. Hurwicz, "The Theory of Economic Behavior," in George J. Stigler and Kenneth E. Boulding (Editors), *A.E.A. Readings in Price Theory* (Chicago, Richard D. Irwin, Inc., 1952), Vol. VI.

potential have been exaggerated. The day of orthodox game theory may well be on its way, just as the day of linear programming has already arrived in some measures.[6] Meanwhile, businessmen may wish to acquaint themselves with the theory and be on the watch for any practical uses it may have.

CONCLUSION

To summarize briefly, we have seen that forecasting can result in a negative contribution to capital budget decisions unless it goes further than merely providing a single most probable prediction. Without an estimated probability coefficient for the forecast, plus knowledge of the payoffs for the company's alternative investments and calculations of indifference probabilities, the best decision on the capital budget cannot be reached.

Even with these aids the best decision cannot be known for certain, but the margin of error may be substantially reduced, and the businessman can tell just how far off his forecast may be before it leads him to the wrong decision. It is in assessing this margin of error, along with the necessarily quantitative statement of alternative payoffs, that some of the concepts of game theory make their particular contribution to the problem.

EDITORS' NOTE

Bennion presents his analysis using three facilities planning alternatives and three economic forecasts. His framework is not generally applicable because it employs specific alternatives and levels of economic activity. We would improve his framework considerably by generalizing it as a problem with m alternatives and n forecasts.

Let $A_1, \ldots, A_m$ describe various facilities plans, there being m such proposals in general. Describe the forecast conditions as $F_1, \ldots, F_n$ where there are n such forecasts. Finally, let ρ_{ij} stand for the time-adjusted (discounted) rate of return for the ith alternative paired with the jth forecast. Each ρ_{ij} would be arrived at by computing the interest rate which equates the earnings stream to the added investment. There would be m times n such computations.

---

[6] See Alexander Henderson and Robert Schlaifer, op. cit. (footnote 1).

In this general formulation, the capital budgeting problem is presented as follows:

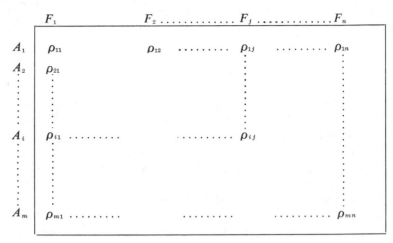

The problem is to select an alternative A_i (where $A_1, \ldots, A_m$ are mutually exclusive). Among others, the following criteria can be used.

1. Select the A_r for which the minimum ρ_{rj} $(j = 1, \ldots, n)$ is greatest. That is, select the alternative for which the worst possible return over-all forecasts $F_1, \ldots, F_n$ is maximized. This strategy is called a MAXIMIN strategy because it will MAXimize the MINimum return or MINIMAX because it will MINImize the MAXimum disadvantage.

2. Select A_r to maximize the maximum return over-all forecasts $F_1, \ldots, F_n$. This strategy is an optimistic or MAXIMAX strategy (which MAXImizes the MAXimum return).

3. If no objective probabilities exist for $F_1, \ldots, F_n$ forecasts, assign an equal probability to each forecast and select the alternative with the greatest payoff. In this case, $p_1 = p_2 \ldots p_n = \dfrac{1.0}{n}$. The payoff is $\sum_{j=1}^{n} p_j \rho_{ij}$. This is an EQUI-PROBABILITY strategy.

There are other game theory strategies which could be used to analyze the uncertainty problem.[7] However, these three criteria illustrate how the facilities planning problem can be formulated in uncertainty terms.

[7] See Luce, R. D. and Raiffa, *Games and Decisions,* John Wiley & Sons, Inc., 1957.

Chapter 17

FACILITIES PLANNING WITH MATHEMATICAL MODELS

XIX.

Mathematical Models in Capital Budgeting*

James C. Hetrick

Some of the major responsibilities of top management are in the fields of long-range planning and capital budgeting. Planning groups are constantly faced with such questions as:

Should we build a new plant?
If so, where is the best place to build it?
And when should it be built?
Or, instead of building, should we expand our existing facilities?
Should we also modernize them?

This broad field of decision making for capital investment is one of the most difficult, one of the most recurrent, and one of the most controversial of management areas. And it is also an area where there are tremendous

---

* From the *Harvard Business Review*, Vol. 39, No. 1, (1961), 49–64. Reprinted by permission of the *Harvard Business Review*.

opportunities for *basic* improvements in operations and policies. Here are just a few of the shortcomings that show up again and again in corporate practice:

> Many companies have never asked themselves such important questions as what the function of capital is in an industry.
>
> Some managements pay only lip service to the idea that decisions should be made to the best advantage of the total enterprise and for the long term. All too frequently, short-term decisions are made that are crippling in the long term.
>
> Capital is often allocated for the good of a department or for a cost center rather than for the company as a whole.
>
> Confusion is likely to result if executives are asked to define the extent to which different investment decisions should be considered as being independent of each other.
>
> It is rarely recognized that the proper rate of return may be different for various parts of the organization. In fact, many managements even fail to discount for differences in useful economic life.

In recent years operations research has been getting much publicity in the solution of the tactical problems associated with day-to-day decision making and immediate operations planning. However, the techniques of operations research can also help management face the issues and arrive at decisions in *strategic* areas such as those involved in planning and budgeting. The shortcomings just mentioned can be overcome, and many important factors in capital investment decisions can be taken into account in a model that truly represents corporate operations and can truly be solved with the computer technology of today.

The approach to capital budgeting that I shall describe in this article is a new one. It has, however, been tested in a variety of situations, and I am convinced that it can be used profitably by a great many companies.

MAKING THE ANALYSIS

In explaining the new technique it will be helpful to refer to a company example:

Let us assume that the company is in one of the process industries. The plant in question is physically adequate but technologically obsolete. Management is faced with the decision whether to invest capital in modernizing the plant or to scrap it for salvage and tax advantages.

If management modernizes the plant, it can take advantage of existing off-site facilities with several possibilities for expansion. If, on the other hand, the plant is scrapped, alternative sources of supply must be utilized. These in turn may involve additional capital investment in modernization, expansion, new transportation, storage facilities, and so on. Alternative possibilities may include purchasing, exchange, and processing agreements with other manufacturers.

In real life there are often thousands of possible combinations of manufacturing, transportation, and marketing investments in a case of this kind. In addition, the *demographic* changes in today's economy present a very real possibility of gross changes in the pattern of demand over as short a period as ten years, so that the operating configuration that is ideal for today's market may, in fact, be highly undesirable just a few years from now. In too many cases the existence of a problem of this complexity leads to total disagreement among members of top management. The disagreement is usually resolved by a compromise solution acceptable in the short term, but without enough regard for long-term corporate interests.

To meet the need, it is often possible to construct a model of the company's activities that permits a *rational decision-making mechanism*. The operations of our process plant, for instance, may be fairly represented as including manufacture, distribution, and sales. Each of these operations has cost components associated with it, which components in turn may be divided into capital costs, fixed operating costs, and variable operating costs. The system may be totally represented by a simple mathematical model, effectively balancing supply and demand on a detailed basis throughout the company's operations. The structure of such an operation might be developed along the lines indicated in the Appendix.

A system of this type is capable of being "optimized"; that is, an operating procedure consisting essentially of an allocation of production and supply can be found to minimize the total cost to the enterprise. This has long been known, and the method has been widely applied to operating problems such as the minimization of transportation costs.[1] It is possible, however, to use the same simple computing method as a guide in making investment decisions.

FUNCTION OF CAPITAL

In order to do this, we must recognize that the first decision to be made involves a definition of the function of capital in the company. What is the capital to do? To an investment banker, the function of capital is to make money, but not necessarily so for the chemical manufacturer. So far as the management is concerned, so far as the mode of operation is concerned,

---

[1] See, for example, Alexander Henderson and Robert Schlaifer, "Mathematical Programming: Better Information for Better Decision Making," reprinted in this book on page 53; C. W. Churchman, R. L. Ackoff, and E. L. Arnoff, *Introduction to Operations Research* (New York, John Wiley & Sons, Inc., 1957).

and so far as the investment policy is concerned, the function of a company is to *get raw material manufactured into a finished product, distribute that product, and sell it to the customer.* These are the operations; these are the objectives, the things to do.

The function of capital, then, is to permit management to meet the manufacturing and marketing objectives more efficiently. A measure of this efficiency is a lowering of the operating cost to the company. This means that the costs used in the model can be stated *without consideration of any capital invested.* They are, in fact, true operating costs for labor, raw materials, utilities, and so on. There are no charges for depreciation, taxes, or return on investment at this stage of manipulation.

PRODUCTION COSTS

We come now to a second important step in the construction of our model, or rather in the philosophy on which the model is based. This has to do with the treatment of production costs.

In many operations the unit cost of production decreases with the volume of the operation, and is generally taken as a variable operating cost. We need not consider it that way. *We can define the true operating cost as the total cost of operating at full capacity, divided by the production at full capacity.* Any cost higher than this is not a cost of production; it is a cost of *non*production.

These two types of costs may be defined by a curve as shown in Exhibit I. (This is a very simple illustration, of course. In many cases the relation-

EXHIBIT I.   PRODUCTION AND NONPRODUCTION COSTS

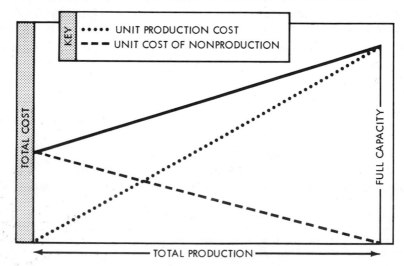

ships might not be nearly so linear as portrayed here.) Note that the unit cost of nonproduction is zero at full capacity and 100% of the production cost when the machines are all stopped.

This treatment of costs is satisfying in that it places a penalty on failure to use a facility, the use of which would increase efficiency. It has a further mathematical advantage: whereas cost as usually defined is a variable, the two costs as now defined are true constants without approximation. This advantage promises an enormous simplification of the computing. The problem may now be solved and the optimal solution found by means of the simple calculation given in the Appendix. The steps are as follows:

(1) Find the cost associated with various modes of operation, taking into account available (or possibly available) manufacturing, transportation, and other facilities.

(2) Compare the differences in the operating costs with the differences in the capital investments required to achieve those costs.

(3) If the relationship is such that the savings in operating costs are at least as much as the *return required* on the capital investment, then the investment should be made. Preferably the return should be calculated on a discounted-cash-flow basis[2] so that the differences in economic life, in extent of obsolescence, and in book value may be fully taken into account.

PRACTICAL ALTERNATIVES

In order to make a sound long-term decision, the problem should be studied at several points in time, the restrictions being assumed for as long a time period as possible. If we are extremely fortunate, we will find that the best modes of operation as calculated for different periods of time are compatible; that is, we will find that the best mode of operation for today can be logically expanded into the best mode of operation for several years from now. Unfortunately, in real cases this may not happen. For example:

In the case described in Exhibit II, it was found that a particular plant should be modernized and operated for three years, should then be placed on a stand-by basis and not enter the distribution system, and should then be re-opened and expanded.

Such a solution, although mathematically valid, is totally impractical. In a case like this, one can define the practical strategies that most nearly fit the ideal. In the example given there are, in fact, three courses of action open to the management:

(1) The management may modernize the plant, keep it open, and adapt the distribution system to its existence in the middle years.

---

[2] For a discussion of the logic, principles, and application of the discounted-cash-flow approach, see Ray I. Reul, "Profitability Index for Investments," HBR July–August 1957, p. 116.

(2) It may modernize and operate the plant in the early term, then close it, and operate without it in the last period of years.

(3) It may shut the plant immediately and operate without it throughout the entire period.

The basic model may be re-solved to meet these practical requirements. The three modes of operation may then be compared by again taking differences in capital and in operating costs over the entire time period and discounting back to present value. The minimum cost alternative can thus be found and accepted.

EXHIBIT II. CASE IN PROGRAMMING A CAPITAL INVESTMENT

A problem arose because of the existence of a manufacturing plant which, although physically adequate, was technologically obsolete and unable to supply the quality of products required in today's market. The plant in question was rather small compared to those then being built. Since it was argued that a plant of this size was at an inherent disadvantage for economic operation, there was considerable managerial controversy over the proper course of action—whether to modernize the operation by construction of better facilities or to scrap the existing plant and supply the area involved from facilities elsewhere, e.g., plants in adjacent states.

POSSIBILITIES CONSIDERED

Investigation of the managerial decisions to be made disclosed that the problem involved the choice of the best combination of facilities shown in Figure A.

The Jonesboro Plant was the one under consideration. It could have been closed, modernized at present capacity, or modernized and expanded in various degrees. The Smithville and Johnstown refineries could also have been modernized at present capacity; other possibilities for them were moderate expansion (enough to remove the bottleneck in existing facilities) or major expansion. Anderson, Boylstown, Charlestown, and Davis represented important market areas each of which, together with Jonesboro, could have acted as a terminal for secondary distribution of the product if transportation facilities were installed (see the dotted-line route) to supplement those existing from Smithville to Anderson and the available barging from Johnstown to Davis. Additional flexibility in operation was provided by the possibility of executing agreements for bulk purchase and sales, product exchange, and raw material processing with other manufacturers in the area.

In all, considering the various combinations of manufacturing and transportation facilities, plus agreements with other manufacturers, there were some hundreds of operating policies to be considered at any given time. Furthermore, the long-term consequences of immediate decisions were of major importance.

Available market forecasts indicated that various means of upgrading product quality would be required. Also, available forecasts of quantity demand, considered to be of acceptable accuracy for the first five years and of lesser accuracy for the next five, indicated that the demand pattern would shift considerably during the period, so that care had to be taken not to penalize operations at some later date so as to make an immediate good showing.

EXPRESSION OF PROBLEM

Analysis disclosed that, for any assumed management decision as to selection of facilities, the operating problem could be expressed as that of optimizing manufacture and distribution of products in a system consisting of approximately 200 destinations and 25 origins (plants, terminals, and points of exchange or purchase). It could

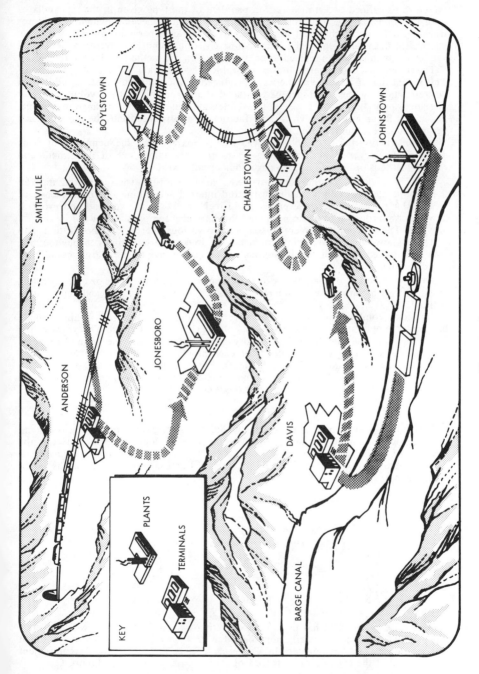

FIGURE A

therefore be defined as a transportation problem of the type given in the Appendix.

In the study of the costs involved, some peculiarities became evident. Rates for trucking, barging, or shipment were linear (i.e., the cost per unit was the same, regardless of the volume shipped). But pipeline costs on a unit basis were nonlinear and varied in a manner which seemed to be dependent on the method of financing.

The major cost component—that of manufacture—was said to be a "step function." This meant that if a basic volume were produced at a certain unit cost, an additional "incremental" volume could then be produced at a lower unit cost per volume *for that increment only,* that a still lower unit cost then applied over a third range of volume, and so on. By appropriate devices these factors were introduced into the model, which became subject to optimization.

In constructing the cost tables, it was early apparent that the definition of costs could easily be varied in such a way as to favor certain types of investment and certain methods of operation. Two particular pitfalls existed:

(1) The divisions of the company—e.g., manufacturing, transportation, marketing—operated virtually autonomously, and internal accounting was on the basis of "transfer prices." Since these prices could include divisional overhead and profit, it was not appropriate to try to minimize them for the company as a whole.

(2) The existing investment was subject to various degrees of amortization, and it was known that new capital would be required at various times throughout the period studied. Accordingly, incautious use of capital investment charges could have led to fallacious answers.

To eliminate these dangers, all costs were constructed on the basis of true operating costs, with such components as interest, insurance, ad valorem taxes, and depreciation omitted.

Particular combinations of facilities were selected on the basis of an approximate balance of supply and demand throughout the period to be studied. The years at the beginning, end, and middle of the period were first studied, and the optimal mode of operation and distribution determined for each practical combination of manufacturing, transportation, and marketing facilities. This resulted in a series of cases for each of the key years. In order to compare these cases, decreases in operating costs were matched against increases in capital requirements.

USE OF MODEL TECHNIQUE

This step is a key point of the model technique. Recognizing that there is not an infinite pool of capital available for investment, we adopt the principal that the *function of capital in industry is not only to earn a return but more specifically to earn the return by decreasing operating expenses.* For example, typical results might be as listed in Figure B.

FIGURE B

Case	Operating cost (millions of dollars)	New investment (millions of dollars)
# 1	$53.0	$10.0
# 2	52.0	12.5
# 3	50.4	16.0
# 4	50.0	18.0
# 5	51.0	20.0

Here Case # 4, which has the lowest operating cost, is the one with which to start comparisons. Case # 5 is clearly not so good as # 4 since both its capital requirement and operating costs are greater. In Cases # 1, # 2, and # 3 capital requirement is decreased at the expense of increased operating cost, as shown in Figure C.

FIGURE C

Case	Increase in cost compared to Case # 4 (millions of dollars)	Decrease in capital compared to Case # 4 (millions of dollars)	Ratio
# 1	$3.0	$8.0	0.375:1
# 2	2.0	5.5	0.364:1
# 3	0.4	2.0	0.200:1

These increases in operating cost may be looked on as the cost of the decreased amount of capital. Obviously the best of these is Case # 3, where $2 million of capital is obtained at an increased operating cost of only $400 thousand per year. That is, Case # 3 is the best of the *alternative* cases.

To determine whether it is *absolutely* preferable requires the establishment of bench marks for comparison. The bench mark is the acceptable return in this type of investment as defined by management. What we want to take into account is the less-than-infinite pool of money available, and the existence within the company of competitive opportunities for investment. The bench mark is properly set by an evaluation on a discounted-cash-flow basis by type of investment. *Thus if a discounted return of 14% over a 25-year economic life is set, the ratio of the decrease in capital divided by the increase in cost is 0.255,* or greater than the 0.200 for Case # 3. Case # 3 is therefore preferable and should be chosen over Case # 4.

Let me put this in a slightly different way. In Case # 3 the company needs to invest $2,000,000 less capital than in Case # 4. At a discounted return of 14%, the company could earn $510,000 on this freed capital ($2,000,000 × 0.255). The price of earning this sum is $400,000, which is the increase in cost of Case # 3. Thus, the company is gaining $110,000 which it would not have if it chose Case # 4.

SOLUTION

Proceeding in this fashion, optimal operating situations in our case example were chosen for the key years at the ends and the middle of the ten-year period. The results showed a curious effect. Because of the shifts in supply and demand during the period, the plant was scheduled to produce at base capacity initially but did not enter the solution (i.e., was closed) at the mid-period; it came in again for production at expanded capacity in the solution for the end period. That is, the computations showed that it would be desirable first to modernize the plant, then to close and "mothball" it, and finally to reopen and expand it. Investigation showed a three-year period over which the plant should be on stand-by.

Such a procedure was, of course, unthinkable from an administrative standpoint. Although a plant may be "mothballed," people cannot be. Therefore, the *practical* alternatives were examined. The company could:

(1) Modernize the plant initially and operate until nonoptimal, then close for good and operate with the next-best arrangement of facilities during the final period.

(2) Modernize initially and operate over the entire period, using the next-best method of operation during the middle period.

(3) Close the plant immediately and operate according to the next-best method during the nonoptimal periods at the beginning and end of the time studied.

To make this choice, the possible investment schedules for each were determined and the model manipulated to find optimal operating costs for each alternative over the entire period of the study. The differences in operating costs and investments were then discounted over the entire period to enable comparison, and a choice was made as before. It appeared that the second alternative was best, and the third alternative next best. The advantage of the second over the third was that total investment was 16% lower, and the return, after discounting, higher.

TREE OF CAPITAL

The basic model gives a "rough cut" solution for a long-term pattern of investment designed to fit the changing conditions envisioned in the plant. The job is not yet finished, however. The model thus far will have considered broad operations without regard to the economic desirability of individual parts. To include this factor we proceed to a second stage of model building. From the results of our computations at this stage we construct a "tree of capital" which diagrams the relation of the various parts of the enterprise in the manufacturing-distribution-selling complex.

The structural relationships in the tree do not depend on company organization. They are, in fact, input-output relations, the facilities at each level being supplied by the facilities at the next level below. The relationships also define two flows: the flow of product from bottom to top (like sap) and the flow of cash from top to bottom (like rain on the leaves).

Initially in the computations, no portion of the enterprise is permitted to earn anything; the cost of supplying the highest level is calculated with the costs that were used in the model. The cash generated is at first assumed to be associated with the highest level of the tree. The various facilities at this level may have very different values for the capital invested and the cash generated. We proceed as follows:

As a first step, we let the cash accrue only to each facility at the highest level and calculate the return on the investment at that point. Some one point will have the lowest rate of return. We now assume that this is a bench-mark rate of return for this type of investment, and we permit every facility at this level to earn at this rate.

All cash *beyond* the amount to be earned is reflected to a pool in a *second-*level facility and associated with that. The same type of analysis is performed at this level for the operations of the system.

The process is repeated at each of the various levels until eventually we come to the bottom of the tree and have a cash pool sufficient to pay off company expenses, overhead, and so on. If there is not enough money to do this, it is evident that some of the bench marks have been set improperly.

If it appears that some of the bench marks are in error, we eliminate the marginally productive facilities at various levels and reallocate our cash until eventually the system *is* in balance. If any major facility is eliminated, the basic model must be changed to reflect this fact and a new solution found to correct the structure of the tree.

FLEXIBILITY ADDED

The model thus gives us flexibility in a most important respect, viz., a balanced amount of parasitic capital is allowed to appear in the company.

The value of this can be readily appreciated if we recall that many companies have a flat rule that a new facility costing, say, a million dollars must return at the appropriate rate on that million dollars, plus a certain percentage to go into company overhead. *This rule does not allow for the attractive marginal investment which indirectly contributes to the total company.* Also, in many cases representation in an area is desirable or even necessary for effective company operations.

There is no general rule, nor *should* there be any general rule, as to the extent to which facilities must support the enterprise. If, in fact, the investment is in balance on the tree of capital, we have a healthy enterprise.

APPORTIONING FUNDS

As a further application of the model-building technique, we can devise another tree which represents not flow of goods but flow of decisions. This flow should closely resemble the scheme indicated by the company's organizational chart. We find here various levels of decision making, with a narrower range of activities and interests as we go to the lower levels. Requests for investment originate at all levels and are passed up to higher levels. At the very highest level top management is faced with the problem of budget allocation, and probably for the first time consideration is given to the question of return to the whole company rather than to a division or department.

Since in the usual case requests for funds exceed the funds available, there is a definite need for an optimum allocation. One procedure here is to begin at the lowest level of the enterprise, incorporate the planned facility into the company model, and determine the prospective return on the capital required. This should be done at the lowest level for each investment proposal, with those reporting to a common point on the second level being grouped together.

The return functions may now be compared. For example:

Suppose that management is considering one proposal to build Unit A and another to build Unit B, both in the same area of decision-making responsibility. Suppose further that if Units A and B are given unlimited funds, the estimated rates of return will be as shown in Exhibit III.

Now, the fact that the return for Unit A is higher than that for Unit B at all levels does *not* imply that all available capital should be invested in

EXHIBIT III.   PROJECTED RATES OF RETURN FOR TWO PROJECTS

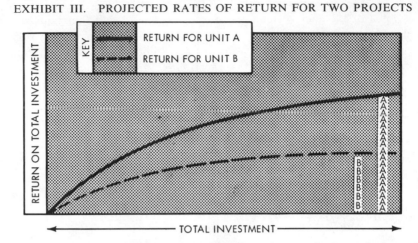

Unit A. Instead, the initial capital should go into Unit A until the point where the *incremental* return falls below the initial rate of return for Unit B (as happens in the last half of the Unit A curve in Exhibit III). At this point some funds should be diverted to Unit B in order to maximize the return to the enterprise as a whole.

In fact, for any given level of investment there is an optimal allocation between the two units. With the necessary data at hand, this result could be expressed in curves as shown in Exhibit IV. We see from this chart that all

EXHIBIT IV.   ALLOCATING FUNDS BETWEEN COMPETING PROJECTS

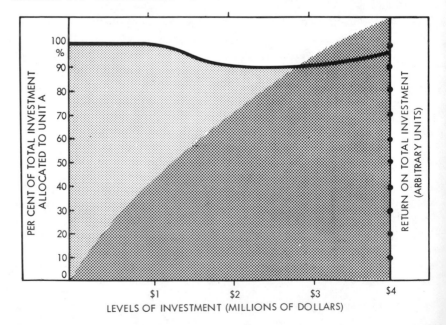

of the first million dollars of investment should go into Unit A; in the case of the second million, however, somewhere around $950,000 should go into A and $50,000 into B; in the case of the third million, about $900,000 should go into A and about $100,000 into B; but after that A's share rises again.

Such a set of curves can be constructed for three or more competing investment opportunities. The result of them all, the output from the analysis of allocation at the lowest level, is the input to a similar analysis for the second level. At the second level, the return-on-investment curves define another set of enterprises competing for capital.

Such an analysis may be carried on step by step to top management, each decision-making level being in turn supplied with a plan for allocation of its funds.

IMPROVING DATA

One caution should be noted. No decision is better than the data available or the assumptions made. This is true for decisions based on a model as well as for those reached by any other means. The model approach, however, has two great virtues:

(1) Assumptions involved in defining a problem are necessarily made explicit when formulated mathematically, although this is not necessarily done in many other approaches.

(2) It is possible in many mathematical models to test the sensitivity of the result to the input data. Such sensitivity analysis may then indicate the areas where additional work in defining economic or operating quantities may be of importance.

APPLICATIONS

How broadly applicable is the kind of analysis I have described? As we have seen, one kind of problem that can be solved is that presented in Exhibit II. But other kinds of problems, too, lend themselves to this type of solution. Let us look at some of them.

CHOICE OF PROCESS

One such problem is that which production executives sometimes face when a company or plant is expanding. To illustrate, here is a situation that has recently come up:

A manufacturer is faced with a sales forecast which makes it necessary for him to expand facilities within a definite period of time. He has a proven process which may be used and which also is used by his competitor. He also has small-scale experimental information on two modifications which make patentable distinctions in the product and affect the economics of production. It is not certain in advance, however, that either of these modifications will apply favorably in large-scale production.

It has been found possible to design plants in various ways. Different designs are affected favorably or unfavorably by the existence in large-scale manufacture of effects observed in small-scale experimentation. A model of the system has been constructed and the theory of games applied to find the solution.

In solving the game, with quantities reflecting the advantage or disadvantage of the proposed process relative to the existent process, it has been found that there are several equally good alternatives. These represent the minimum return to be expected, regardless of what happens in large-scale work. The solution thus shows what is the least to expect in the face of uncertainty, with a high probability that a greater return will be achieved.

MARKETING ANALYSES

Other kinds of problems arise in the distribution system. Here are two illustrations, both from actual experience:

❧ A problem in capital budgeting arose and was solved as a consequence of studying a large geographic area consuming 6% of a company's products but supplying only 3% of its marketing profit. The problem was to—

(a) Find the reasons for the unprofitability.
(b) Determine if the region should be abandoned as a market or, if not, what steps should be taken to make it profitable.

The disproportion of profit to sales was found to be caused partly by the high cost of product and partly by improper marketing. The major sources of supply were plants which were among the company's oldest facilities with a high production cost relative to the company's other plants. This situation was aggravated by high-cost purchases in the area; and, in addition, high transportation costs prevailed.

The direct costs of marketing were comparable with those applying elsewhere, but unallocated expenses were lower. Thus, the region had a problem of inadequate margins.

So a mathematical model of the manufacturing and distribution system was constructed, and optimal operation under a variety of assumptions was studied. The results showed that the region could best be supplied by keeping one plant in its existing state, expanding another plant by approximately 25% of its capacity, and upgrading the product at the remaining plants while maintaining their then-current capacity. At the projected level for unallocated marketing expense, the over-all return to the system was less than the company's target but compared favorably with the company's achievement. Management saw that if these expenses could be reduced below the projected level, a very favorable over-all return could be achieved.

❧ A major manufacturer of consumer goods is faced with the problem of deciding what to do about his distribution system. He currently distributes through a system of franchised distributorships, each of which independently controls field warehouse inventory levels, the intensity of marketing effort at the retail level, and to some extent the intensity of advertising in its locality. In the face of the projected expansion of sales during the foreseeable future, it is apparent that the existing facilities of the distributors will be inadequate.

A study of this problem has incorporated the factors of plant and field inventory, the freight costs required, distributor and dealer markups, and an elaborate forecast of the economic parameters or variables which affect sales. The data produced enable the company to make a decision between (a) systems based on distributorships, regional warehouses, and freight forwarding and (b) direct-to-dealer systems.

SPREADING INVESTMENTS

Still another kind of problem that lends itself to the analytical approach which I have described has to do with the composition of an investment portfolio. For instance:

A large investment company has used the model-building technique to study the problem of constructing a portfolio of investments. At the same time that it has considered the factors of relative return and relative risk in various investment opportunities, it has incorporated not only management's desire for diversification but also the competitive necessity of producing both income in the form of dividends and capital gains in the form of appreciation.

The foregoing cases indicate something of the breadth of applicability of the model manipulation concept. The solutions found have already, in some cases, been applied for a sufficient period of time to show that the results predicted by the model can be achieved.

CONCLUSION

It must be emphasized that use of the model or of any of the mathematical techniques of the operations researcher does not imply management by computer. The mathematical model itself is a tool of management rather than a replacement for management. The factors to be considered in construction of the model are those which are and must be taken into account in *any* thorough decision-making process. These would include, for example:

A description of the potential market over a given period of time in terms of the probable demand pattern for the entire area.

The possible points for production distribution both already in existence and to be contemplated in planning.

Typical production restrictions—for instance, whether or not a given plant may be considered as being tailor-made to produce one product or to be capable of flexible output.

An estimate of the operation and distribution costs, classified as capital and/or noncapital charges and described preferably as a function of the volume of production. (These costs should include actual records as well as expenses projected and studies for new plants.)

Any appropriate managerial restrictions such as a policy of constancy of employment; a decision on whether or not overtime or layoff dollars may be used; a decision on whether or not plant capacity must be fully or almost fully utilized at all times; a rule on whether or not labor productivity or capital investment is to be considered a prime objective; a preference for stating return in absolute dollars rather than as a rate on investment, or vice versa; a decision on whether or not control of a market is considered to have an economic value; or a policy committing the company to uniform exploitation of a broad area.

These quantities constitute the body of facts and assumptions on which the decision must be made.

MORE THOROUGH ANALYSIS

The concept of model building outlined in this article has important advantages for modern business. For one thing, it enables the executive to probe more deeply and more thoroughly into the factors that affect a decision. Characteristically, managerial problems contain many more variables than restrictions, so that in a real case thousands of solutions may exist. The function of management lies in defining realistic assumptions and practical operating conditions. The computer can then perform its function of taking these restrictions and performing the detailed labor of investigating their consequences for the solution.

The output from the manipulation of the model is then a detailed plan of action which is only tentative over the period of study. Indeed, the solution itself may suggest to management introduction of modifications to recognize the effects of additional factors, changes in estimates, possibilities of diversification, and so on. In fact, the existence of the model, and of computers capable of dealing with the model, enables management to make an exhaustive study of possibilities rather than a comparison of some of the more obvious cases.

Of course, construction and manipulation of a model are not to be undertaken lightly, or in the expectation of achieving results overnight. Cost-wise, much depends on the excellence of existing data and the magnitude and complexity of the job to be done; but it is fair to say that data collection and refinement, the incorporation of economic analyses and forecasts, and mathematical analysis and computer operation may be a long and costly process, with costs running from $30,000 to $100,000 in some cases. It should be noted, however, that this figure is largely a "setup cost" and that the model, once constructed, may be kept current at a comparatively low expense so that successive applications can be made relatively cheaply.

To sum up, the use of mathematical models can supply management with a tool for decision making at virtually all levels, from daily operations to budget allocation and long-term capital investment programs. The full potential of the method has not yet been explored, but it is apparent that this technique can be of great aid in managerial decisions.

•   •   •

Appendix

CONSTRUCTION AND USE OF A MODEL

In this article, and in the literature of mathematical programming generally, the terms "model" and "mathematical model" are used rather frequently. *The usual meaning is that of a group of equations which purport to describe the problem under study in such fashion that all proper considerations are explicitly stated, so that the solution of the system of equations is in fact the solution of the real problem.*

By way of illustration, let us construct a model for a relatively simple problem in distribution.

MATHEMATICAL STATEMENTS

Consider the problem of distributing a commodity in a system having balanced supply and demand, in which ten customers, 1 to 10, are supplied from four points, A, B, C, and D. In the broadest form of the case, any customer can be supplied from any one of the four points, and the problem is to determine that policy of distribution which minimizes the cost of transportation for the entire system. Data typical of such a situation might be as given in TABLE A. Here customer demands and warehouse supplies are shown under the columns and to the right of the rows respectively. The numbers in the body of the table represent the unit cost of supplying each customer from each warehouse.

Objectives & Restrictions. The table is itself, in a sense, a model of the problem. a better and more generally expressive model can be constructed by a mathematical statement of objectives and restrictions—the objectives being statements of what is to be accomplished, and the restrictions being statements of all considerations which enter into the policy decision. To express these in equation form, the variable in the solution is defined as being the units of the commodity being supplied from each warehouse to each customer.

TABLE A. THE PROBLEM

	Customer										Warehouse supply
Warehouse	1	2	3	4	5	6	7	8	9	10	
A	4.41	4.60	1.50	2.85	3.82	3.75	3.10	3.97	2.95	3.19	4,443
B	5.56	5.41	2.38	3.31	5.36	4.96	4.36	4.83	3.87	3.25	5,271
C	4.28	5.00	2.10	2.50	3.59	3.65	3.03	4.64	2.91	2.86	2,983
D	6.87	6.63	3.21	4.51	5.98	6.11	5.75	6.53	4.60	6.55	3,651
Customer demand	2,114	1,797	802	2,032	2,760	2,580	923	840	953	1,547	16,348

In TABLE B, x_1 indicates the (unknown) number of units to be supplied to Customer 1 from Warehouse A; x_{36} the number of units from Warehouse D to

TABLE B. THE VARIABLES

Warehouse	Customer									
	1	2	3	4	5	6	7	8	9	10
A	x_1	x_2	x_3	x_4	x_5	x_6	x_7	x_8	x_9	x_{10}
B	x_{11}	x_{12}	x_{13}	x_{14}	x_{15}	x_{16}	x_{17}	x_{18}	x_{19}	x_{20}
C	x_{21}	x_{22}	x_{23}	x_{24}	x_{25}	x_{26}	x_{27}	x_{28}	x_{29}	x_{30}
D	x_{31}	x_{32}	x_{33}	x_{34}	x_{35}	x_{36}	x_{37}	x_{38}	x_{39}	x_{40}

Customer 6; and so forth. This being so, any shipping schedule may be expressed by giving the numerical values associated with each of the x's. One such schedule might be:

$$x_1 = 2,114$$
$$x_2 = 1,797$$
$$x_3 = 532$$
$$x_{13} = 270$$
$$x_{14} = 2,032$$
$$x_{15} = 2,760$$
$$x_{16} = 209$$

$$x_{26} = 2,371$$
$$x_{27} = 612$$
$$x_{37} = 311$$
$$x_{38} = 840$$
$$x_{39} = 953$$
$$x_{10} = 1,547$$

All other x's would be zero, representing shipping combinations not used.

Similarly, the cost associated with any shipping schedule is given by the sum of all products of the values of the variables and the unit costs given in TABLE A. In equation form:

$$\text{Cost} = 4.41\ x_1 + 4.60\ x_2 + 1.50\ x_3 + \cdots + 6.55\ x_{10}$$

This equation is the *objective function,* and the *objective* is to minimize this cost, while meeting all restrictions. The restriction in this simple problem are easily stated: at all points supply and demand must balance. We write one group of equations stating that, for each warehouse, the sum of the variables associated with it (shipments out) must equal the amount available at that warehouse; another group of equations will similarly state that the sum of variables associated with each destination (shipments in) must equal the demand at that point. These restrictions are shown in TABLE C.

All of these equations together represent the model, and the problem as given is that of minimizing the objective function subject to the restrictions. The supply and demand restrictions are the only ones having meaning in the simple problem stated here. In real problems conditions of policy, legal requirements, capacity, physical or chemical properties of materials, and so on may be incorporated.

SOLUTION

At first glance the technique of model construction may seem unnecessarily complicated, but it is not really so. The characteristic of management problems is that, when so stated, the number of variables involved is much greater than the number of equations required to express the restrictions. This is equivalent to the statement— certainly no news to most executives—that there are, in general, many ways to operate in a real system. Thus, even in the simple problem posed, there are many million of shipping schedules that could conceivably be devised. And in any real case the least-cost solution may be by no means obvious. For the data as presented above, the optimum solution and the costs of departure therefrom are shown in TABLE D.

TABLE C. RESTRICTIONS TO BE MET

1. Supply restrictions

$$x_1 + x_2 + x_3 + x_4 + x_5 + x_6 + x_7 + x_8 + x_9 + x_{10} = 4{,}443 \text{ (supply at Warehouse A)}$$
$$x_{11} + x_{12} + x_{13} + x_{14} + x_{15} + x_{16} + x_{17} + x_{18} + x_{19} + x_{20} = 5{,}271 \text{ (supply at Warehouse B)}$$
$$x_{21} + x_{22} + x_{23} + x_{24} + x_{25} + x_{26} + x_{27} + x_{28} + x_{29} + x_{30} = 2{,}983 \text{ (supply at Warehouse C)}$$
$$x_{31} + x_{32} + x_{33} + x_{34} + x_{35} + x_{36} + x_{37} + x_{38} + x_{39} + x_{40} = 3{,}651 \text{ (supply at Warehouse D)}$$

2. Demand restrictions

$$x_1 + x_{11} + x_{21} + x_{31} = 2{,}114 \text{ (demand by Customer 1)}$$
$$x_2 + x_{12} + x_{22} + x_{32} = 1{,}797 \text{ (demand by Customer 2)}$$
$$x_3 + x_{13} + x_{23} + x_{33} = 802 \text{ (demand by Customer 3)}$$
$$x_4 + x_{14} + x_{24} + x_{34} = 2{,}032 \text{ (demand by Customer 4)}$$
$$x_5 + x_{15} + x_{25} + x_{35} = 2{,}760 \text{ (demand by Customer 5)}$$
$$x_6 + x_{16} + x_{26} + x_{36} = 2{,}580 \text{ (demand by Customer 6)}$$
$$x_7 + x_{17} + x_{27} + x_{37} = 923 \text{ (demand by Customer 7)}$$
$$x_8 + x_{18} + x_{28} + x_{38} = 840 \text{ (demand by Customer 8)}$$
$$x_9 + x_{19} + x_{29} + x_{39} = 953 \text{ (demand by Customer 9)}$$
$$x_{10} + x_{20} + x_{30} + x_{40} = 1{,}547 \text{ (demand by Customer 10)}$$

TABLE D. THE SOLUTION

Warehouse	Customer									
	1	2	3	4	5	6	7	8	9	10
A	**940**	0.21	0.55	0.61	0.10	**2,580**	**923**	0.20	0.61	1.00
B	0.18	**1,797**	0.37	**1,087**	0.56	0.15	0.20	**840**	0.42	**1,547**
C	**1,174**	0.78	1.28	0.38	**1,809**	0.03	0.06	1.00	0.68	0.80
D	0.20	0.02	**802**	**945**	**951**	0.10	0.39	0.50	**953**	3.10

In this table, the numbers in bold face represent quantities to be shipped from the indicated warehouse to the indicated customer. Thus Warehouse A is to supply 940 units to Customer 1; 2,580 to Customer 6; and 923 to Customer 7. The remaining table entries in all the warehouse-customer combinations not called for in the optimal solution represent penalty costs. Thus the 0.21 associated with A-2 indicates that the total cost of shipment will be increased by a minimum of 0.21 for each unit shipped from Warehouse A to Customer 2. The fact that all routes other than those called for in the solution have positive costs associated with them indicates that this is a least-cost, or optimal, solution.

There are several surprising features to this solution. It will be noted, for example, that no one of the nine lowest-cost routes (A-3, A-4, A-9, B-3, C-3, C-4, C-7, C-9, and C-10) is actually used. Furthermore, of the 10 customers, only Customer 1 is totally supplied by the least-cost route available to him. Thus Customer 3 is totally supplied from Warehouse D, although the unit costs are lower from any one of the other warehouses; the apparent saving of 1.71 to be achieved by supplying Customer 3 from Warehouse A rather than from Warehouse D becomes an over-all loss of 0.55 for the system. Yet it is to be emphasized that the solution as given is, over-all, that of minimum cost, as may be seen by computing the cost of alternative solutions.

OPTIMIZATION PROCEDURE

The construction of a mathematical model for such a simple problem as that presented by the assignment of a shipping schedule to the four warehouses and ten customers seems like an elaborate and formal procedure of little real value. However, if in large systems there is something to be gained by such an approach, the formal procedure may become more appealing. It will be readily seen that, even for the small problem earlier described, many shipping schedules may be devised; and in a real industrial situation, the magnitude may be such that literally billions of solutions to the problem may exist. Mathematical programming makes the claim that out of these billions of solutions the optimal solution can be found—the solution which is not only a good or even very good method of operation, but which is the best of all possible solutions. This claim may be verified with mathematics no more advanced than addition and subtraction.

Feasible Solution. The first step in optimizing the system is to obtain a "feasible" solution—one that meets the restraints of the problem without regard to cost. In the case of the problem of TABLE A, this may be done systematically in simple fashion. Let the first customer have his demand filled as fully as possible from the first warehouse. If there is more at the warehouse than is needed to supply this first demand, the excess is supplied to the second customer; and so on until the warehouse supply is exhausted.

Generally the customer exhausting the warehouse will not have his demand fully met, in which case the difference is filled from the next warehouse; then the next customer is supplied. The process is continued until all demands are met and all supplies exhausted. For the illustrative problem this gives the shipping schedule shown in TABLE E.

TABLE E.   SHIPPING SCHEDULE

					Customer					
Warehouse	1	2	3	4	5	6	7	8	9	10
A	2,114	1,797	532							
B			270	2,032	2,760	209				
C						2,371	612			
D							311	840	953	1,547

This schedule represents a managerial policy employing 13 of the 40 warehouse-customer combinations possible. Any simple departure from this policy involves use of one of the 27 unused warehouse-customer combinations. Whether or not such departures are good depends on the cost difference resulting from such a departure.

Departures. To evaluate a departure from this policy, we reason as follows. The designated solution represents a balance in supply and demand not only over-all but in each row or column separately and independently. A change in the value of any quantity must be compensated for by an equal and opposite change in another quantity in the same row and another in the same column. These two changes demand in turn two new changes, in a column and a row respectively; and so on.

The process terminates only when it is possible to satisfy both a row change and a column change simultaneously by finding a quantity which can be altered at the intersection of the row and the column. Further, since negative quantities cannot be introduced into the solution, the changes to compensate for introduction of a new variable —that is, employment of a hitherto unused warehouse-customer combination—can be made only by decreasing quantities in the solution.

For example, to depart from the policy defined by the solution given in TABLE E by supplying Customer 1 from Warehouse B demands that the supply to Customer 1 from Warehouse A be decreased by a corresponding amount, since otherwise Customer 1 will be oversupplied. At the same time, the supply to one of Customers 3, 4, 5, or 6 must be depleted to avoid demanding more than the total supply from Warehouse B. Of these, it is seen that if Customer 3 is the one whose supply from Warehouse B is lowered, then increasing the supply to Customer 3 from Warehouse A compensates for both changes so that the solution need not be further disturbed.

Similarly, it may be seen that to depart from the indicated policy by supplying Customer 2 from Warehouse D (combination D-2) involves compensating decreases in A-2, B-3, C-6, and D-7, and equal increases in A-3, B-6, and C-7. In general, the compensating changes involved in utilizing a new route will be traced out by such a series of moves, and there will be only one such series of changes possible.

The economic consequences of such a departure from the assumed policy, in terms of the total change in cost of the shipping schedule, can be found by adding the unit cost associated with any route where the assignment is increased, and subtracting the unit cost if the assignment is decreased. Thus the effect on the first feasible solution of use of the combination B-1 (supplying Customer 1 from Warehouse B) is given by the figures:

$$5.56 - 4.41 + 1.50 - 2.38 = 0.27$$

and use of the combination D-2 (supplying Customer 2 from Warehouse D) changes the solution value by the following amount:

$$6.63 - 4.60 + 1.50 - 2.38 + 4.96 - 3.65 + 3.03 - 5.75 = -0.26$$

Thus the first change increases the total cost, and is therefore unattractive; the second decreases the cost and might be incorporated into the solution. In this manner every possible change may be evaluated by calculating the associated change in cost for unit utilization The solution may then be improved by incorporating the route having the largest associated saving, and doing this to the fullest possible extent.

The extent of incorporation (that is, the number of units to be assigned to this route) may in turn be judged from the compensating changes made in evaluating the cost of unit utilization. Those changes which increase in magnitude need not be considered, since there is no upper limit on their magnitudes. Those which decrease in magnitude, however, may not go below zero, so that the largest change that may be made is equal to the smallest value of the group. When this value is determined, all the routes affected may be changed by the appropriate amount. This constitutes a new solution, corresponding to another policy of operation.

All possible departures from this policy may now be evaluated and the process repeated until a solution is obtained from which all changes are unprofitable. Such a solution is, of course, the optimum one.

Recapitulation. This process of evaluating departures from the first feasible solution has been reviewed in perhaps tedious detail in order to demonstrate two facts:

(1) The manipulation of the model is logical at an elementary level.

(2) The result of the manipulation is truly optimal; it is the best possible solution for the problem as stated.

Summarizing, it may be stated that the optimization procedure consists of certain definite steps:

(1) A model is constructed, consisting of a group of equations which explicitly describe all restrictive relations in the system.

(2) A feasible solution, or possible operational policy, is found without regard to value.

(3) All possible departures from the policy are identified and evaluated for their effects on the value of the policy.

(4) The departure with the greatest unit value is incorporated to the fullest possible extent, making a new feasible solution.

(5) Steps 2, 3, and 4 are repeated until a solution is found which cannot be improved on.

MORE COMPLICATED QUESTIONS

The illustrative examples just presented have been simple in conception and represent what may be felt to be an idealized state. However, various degrees of complexity may be introduced.

Supply Bottleneck. For example, consider another problem of four sources and ten destinations, with the appropriate quantities as given in TABLE F, and the solution as shown in TABLE G.

TABLE F. TRANSPORTATION COST PER UNIT TO DESTINATION

Source	D_1	D_2	D_3	D_4	D_5	D_6	D_7	D_8	D_9	D_{10}	Available from source
					Destination						
R_1	1.45	1.15	0.21	2.54	1.98	0.49	1.00	0.36	2.35	3.00	6,500
R_2	1.67	1.45	0.50	2.80	2.15	0.80	1.26	0.75	2.75	3.25	2,000
R_3	1.48	1.20	0.30	2.59	2.00	0.60	1.10	0.55	2.40	3.00	4,800
R_4	0.85	0.65	0.10	2.00	1.25	0.38	0.89	0.25	1.75	2.25	4,800
Demand at destination	2,000	2,400	1,500	1,300	1,300	2,100	1,800	1,700	2,200	1,800	

TABLE G. SOLUTION TO SECOND PROBLEM

Source	D_1	D_2	D_3	D_4	D_5	D_6	D_7	D_8	D_9	D_{10}
					Destination					
R_1	0.04	0.02	1,500	0.98	0.15	2,100	1,200	1,700	0.02	0.17
R_2	1,400	0.06	0.03	0.02	0.06	0.05	600	0.13	0.16	0.16
R_3	600	2,400	0.02	1,300	0.10	0.04	0.05	0.12	500	0.10
R_4	0.02	0.10	0.47	0.06	1,300	0.47	0.47	0.47	1,700	1,800

It will be noted that the solution calls for destination D_6 to be totally supplied from source R_1. Now, if in fact the capacity of the channel from R_1 to D_6 were limited to, say, 1,000 units, that fact could be reflected by constructing the original problem in the manner shown in TABLE H. Here the destination D_6 has been artificially split into

TABLE H. REVISED TRANSPORTATION COST SCHEDULE

Source	Destination											Available from source
	D_1	D_2	D_3	D_4	D_5	D_6	D'_6	D_7	D_8	D_9	D_{10}	
R_1	1.45	1.15	0.21	2.54	1.98	0.49	M	1.00	0.36	2.35	3.00	6,500
R_2	1.67	1.45	0.50	2.80	2.15	0.80	0.80	1.26	0.75	2.75	3.25	2,000
R_3	1.48	1.20	0.30	2.59	2.00	0.60	0.60	1.10	0.55	2.40	3.00	4,800
R_4	0.85	0.65	0.10	2.00	1.25	0.38	0.38	0.89	0.25	1.75	2.25	4,800
Demand at destination	2,000	2,400	1,500	1,300	1,300	1,000	1,100	1,800	1,700	2,200	1,800	

two synthetic destinations, one of which can be supplied from R_1 and the other of which cannot be so supplied. The symbol "M" simply means a prohibitively large cost associated with the source-destination combination, and might have been carried, for example, as 9.99. Individual variable limitations, whether of fact or of policy, might be indicated in this fashion.

Supply-Demand Imbalance. Other costs may also be readily entered into the model. Thus assume that in the previous problem to the given transportation costs are added manufacturing costs of:

10.0 at R_1	10.2 at R_3
9.9 at R_2	11.1 at R_4

Then the total cost problem becomes as stated in TABLE I. This looks to be quite different. In the original problem, the transportation costs were such that the order of preference of sources for individual destinations was mixed, but with R_4 being first choice in all cases. In the combined cost problem, R_4 is *least* preferable, and the costs have been so chosen that in all cases the order of preference is R_1 over R_2, R_2 over R_3, and R_3 over R_4. Yet this is the same problem and has the same solution. Reflection will show this to be true in general, since in any situation of balanced supply and demand the transportation costs are the only quantities subject to optimization, for the total output of all plants is required, regardless of the cost level involved.

In a situation of unbalanced supply and demand, however, the model based on combined manufacture and transportation costs may give an optimal solution which is quite different from that based on transportation costs alone. Then the model technique may be used to assign the proper level of production at each of the plants, when not all the production of all plants is required. It is especially interesting to note that, when the "incremental" production at different plants is at quite different price levels, it is not necessarily true that the lowest-cost production is to be used in the optimal solution.

Assume, for example, that in the previous illustration an imbalance of supply and demand is created by expanding demand by 10% at all destinations, and expanding supply by 20%. Further assume that the additional, "incremental" supply is available at a cost which is 80% of the cost of the basic supply at the same plant. The resulting distribution problem is represented by the schedule shown in TABLE J.

To represent the imbalance of supply and demand, a fictitious destination, D_{11}, can be introduced, with a fictitious demand equal to the difference between total supply and true demand. At the same time, the difference between production costs of the basic and incremental productions can be reflected by the difference in the cost entries for R_1 and for the increments for R_1, R_2, R_3, and R_4. Finally, the entry "M," having its previous meaning of a very large cost, associated with the fictitious destination for basic production and the zero entry for fictitious demand and incremental production, can be used to ensure that all basic production is employed before the incremental production, dependent on the basic production, enters the solution.

One solution to this problem (there are numerous solutions with equal costs, although none with lower cost) is shown in TABLE K. The numbers in bold face represent costs to the destination.

Unexpected Findings. Surprising things may transpire in investigating optimum costs with a model. For instance, under the particular cost conditions assumed in the preceding illustration, all the additional production required came from the least costly incremental production available. But such action is not always desirable. To demonstrate this, let us vary incremental unit costs only slightly, while keeping them in the same relative order. Let unit production costs of the additional 20% be as follows:

8.00 at R_1	(Base capacity cost 10.0)
7.95 at R_2	(Base capacity cost 9.9)
8.10 at R_3	(Base capacity cost 10.2)
8.55 at R_4	(Base capacity cost 11.1)

The problem thus becomes that of optimizing the possibilities shown in TABLE L.

TABLE I. LAID DOWN COST PER UNIT TO DESTINATION

Source	Destination										Available from source
	D_1	D_2	D_3	D_4	D_5	D_6	D_7	D_8	D_9	D_{10}	
R_1	11.45	11.15	10.21	12.54	11.98	10.49	11.00	10.36	12.35	13.00	6,500
R_2	11.57	11.35	10.40	12.70	12.05	10.70	11.16	10.65	12.60	13.15	2,000
R_3	11.68	11.40	10.50	12.79	12.20	10.80	11.30	10.75	12.65	13.20	4,800
R_4	11.95	11.75	11.20	13.10	12.35	11.48	11.99	11.35	12.85	13.25	4,800
Demand at destination	2,000	2,400	1,500	1,300	1,300	2,100	1,800	1,700	2,200	1,800	

TABLE J. LAID DOWN COST PER UNIT TO DESTINATION WITH SUPPLY AND DEMAND UNBALANCED

Source	Destination											Available from source
	D_1	D_2	D_3	D_4	D_5	D_6	D_7	D_8	D_9	D_{10}	D_{11}	
R_1	11.45	11.15	10.21	12.54	11.98	10.49	11.00	10.36	12.35	13.00	M	6,500
R_2	11.57	11.35	10.40	12.70	12.05	10.70	11.16	10.65	12.65	13.15	M	2,000
R_3	11.68	11.40	10.50	12.79	12.20	10.80	11.30	10.75	12.60	13.20	M	4,800
R_4	11.95	11.75	11.20	13.10	12.35	11.48	11.99	11.35	12.85	13.35	M	4,800
Incremental supply at:												
R_1	9.45	9.15	8.21	10.54	9.98	8.49	9.00	8.36	10.35	11.00	0	1,300
R_2	9.59	9.37	8.42	10.72	10.07	8.72	9.18	8.67	10.67	11.17	0	400
R_3	9.64	9.36	8.46	10.75	10.16	8.76	9.26	8.71	10.56	11.16	0	960
R_4	9.73	9.53	8.98	10.88	10.13	9.26	9.77	9.13	10.63	11.13	0	960
Demand at destination	2,200	2,640	1,650	1,430	1,430	2,310	1,980	1,870	2,420	1,980	1,810	

TABLE K.   SOLUTION TO DISTRIBUTION PROBLEM

Source	Destination										
	D_1	D_2	D_3	D_4	D_5	D_6	D_7	D_8	D_9	D_{10}	D_{11}
R_1	0.04	190	1,650	0	0.13	2,310	1,780	570	0	0.15	M
R_2	2,000	0.04	0.03	0	0.04	0.05	0	0.13	0.14	0.14	M
R_3	0.02	2,450	0.04	1,430	0.10	0.06	0.05	0.14	920	0.10	M
R_4	0.04	0.10	0.49	0.06	1,430	0.49	0.49	0.49	1,390	1,980	M
Incremental supply at:											
R_1	0.04	0	0	0	0.13	0	0	1,300	0	0.15	0.21
R_2	200	0.04	0.03	0	0.04	0.05	200	0.13	0.14	0.14	0.13
R_3	0.02	0	0.04		0.10	0.06	0.05	0.14	110	0.10	850
R_4	0.11	0.07	0.56	0.13	0.07	0.56	0.56	2.06	0.07	0.07	960

TABLE L. LAID DOWN COST PER UNIT TO DESTINATION

Source	Destination											Available from source
	D_1	D_2	D_3	D_4	D_5	D_6	D_7	D_8	D_9	D_{10}	D_{11}	
R_1	11.45	11.15	10.21	12.54	11.98	10.49	11.00	10.36	12.35	13.00	M	6,500
R_2	11.57	11.35	10.40	12.70	12.05	10.50	11.16	10.65	12.65	13.15	M	2,000
R_3	11.68	11.40	10.50	12.79	12.20	10.80	11.30	10.75	12.60	13.20	M	4,800
R_4	11.95	11.75	11.20	13.10	12.35	11.48	11.99	11.35	12.85	13.35	M	4,800
Incremental supply at:												
R_1	9.45	9.15	8.21	10.54	9.98	8.49	9.00	8.36	10.35	11.00	0	1,300
R_2	9.62	9.40	8.45	10.75	10.10	8.75	9.21	8.70	10.70	11.20	0	400
R_3	9.58	9.30	8.40	10.69	10.10	8.70	9.20	8.65	10.50	11.10	0	960
R_4	9.40	9.20	8.65	10.55	9.80	8.93	9.44	8.80	10.30	10.80	0	960
Demand at destination	2,200	2,640	1,650	1,430	1,430	2,310	1,980	1,870	2,420	1,980	1,810	

TABLE M. SOLUTION TO SECOND DISTRIBUTION PROBLEM

Source		D_1	D_2	D_3	D_4	D_5	D_6	D_7	D_8	D_9	D_{10}	D_{11}
						Destination						
R_1		0.04	0.02	**1,650**	0.02	0.15	**2,310**	**1,520**	**1,020**	0.02	0.17	M
R_2		**1,540**	0.06	0.03	0.02	0.06	0.05	**460**	0.13	0.16	0.16	M
R_3		**660**	**2,640**	0.02	**1,430**	0.10	0.04	0.03	0.12	**70**	0.10	M
R_4		0.02	0.10	0.47	0.06	**1,430**	0.47	0.47	0.47	**2,350**	**1,020**	M

Incremental supply at:

	D_1	D_2	D_3	D_4	D_5	D_6	D_7	D_8	D_9	D_{10}	D_{11}
R_1	0.04	0.02	0	0	0.15	0	0	**850**	0.02	0.07	**450**
R_2	0.21	0.27	0.24	0.21	0.27	0.26	0.21	0.34	0.37	0.27	**400**
R_3	0.17	0.17	0.19	0.15	0.27	0.21	0.20	0.29	0.17	0.17	**960**
R_4	0.02	0.10	0.47	0.06	0	0.47	0.47	0.47	0	**960**	0.03

One solution (again there are numerous alternates) is shown in TABLE M.

Note that this solution calls for using fully the incremental output of R_1 although this is *most* expensive, while using none of the incremental output of R_2, which is seemingly the cheapest. Such a result may seem contrary to "common sense," but only because in the "common-sense approach" costs are separately defined and examined, without respect to the entire system.

This result, unexpected as it is, makes one wonder if it might not be desirable to reduce the "base" production at one plant while expanding the "incremental" capacity at another. This possibility can be examined in the model by discarding the concept of incremental capacity, recognizing only used and unused capacities, and assigning a cost to each. The cost of production becomes a fixed quantity, equal to the average unit cost at full production, regardless of the level of production actually used. The unit cost of unused capacity is also fixed and can be shown to be equal to:

(Unit cost of "base" capacity — unit cost at total capacity) × ("base" capacity) ÷ ("incremental" capacity)

It will then be noted that unused capacity appears in the solution with a cost associated. Conceptually, this is important and intuitively satisfying. Failure to use an available facility, the employment of which will increase efficiency, is a neglect of opportunity which should be penalized. Under this concept, the costs of the various plants become those shown in TABLE N.

TABLE N. COSTS OF USED AND UNUSED CAPACITY

Source	R_1	R_2	R_3	R_4
Unit cost, base capacity	10.0	9.9	10.2	11.1
Base capacity	6,500	2,000	4,800	4,800
Unit cost, additional capacity	8.0	7.95	8.10	8.55
Additional capacity	1,300	400	960	960
Average cost	9.666	9.575	9.860	10.675
Unit cost, unused capacity	1.666	1.625	1.750	2.125

And the problem becomes that of optimizing production and distribution in the system. TABLE O shows the laid down cost per unit to destination.

TABLE P shows that not only should the cheap "incremental" production of R_2 not be used, but the base production should also be cut back, as should the base production of R_3, while the apparently expensive base and incremental productions of R_1 should be fully utilized.

The simple model and optimization technique are thus seen to be capable of formulating reasonably complicated managerial questions—and of demonstrating rather surprising answers.

TABLE O. LAID DOWN COST PER UNIT TO DESTINATION

Source	Destination											Available from source
	D_1	D_2	D_3	D_4	D_5	D_6	D_7	D_8	D_9	D_{10}	D_{11}	
R_1	11.12	10.82	9.88	12.21	11.65	10.16	11.57	10.93	12.43	12.93	2.13	7,800
R_2	11.25	11.03	10.08	12.38	11.73	10.38	10.67	10.03	12.02	12.67	1.67	2,400
R_3	11.33	11.05	10.15	12.44	11.85	10.45	10.84	10.33	12.33	12.83	1.63	5,760
R_4	11.53	11.33	10.78	12.68	11.93	11.06	10.95	10.40	12.25	12.85	1.75	5,760
Demand at destination	2,200	2,640	1,650	1,430	1,430	2,310	1,980	1,870	2,420	1,980	1,810	

TABLE P. SOLUTION TO REVISED DISTRIBUTION PROBLEM

Source	Destination										
	D_1	D_2	D_3	D_4	D_5	D_6	D_7	D_8	D_9	D_{10}	D_{11}
R_1	0.04	0.02	**1,650**	0.02	0.15	**2,310**	**1,970**	**1,870**	0.02	0.17	0.21
R_2	**1,940**	0.06	0.03	0.02	0.06	0.05	10	0.13	0.16	0.16	**450**
R_3	**260**	**2,640**	0.02	**1,430**	0.10	0.04	0.03	0.12	**70**	0.10	**1,360**
R_4	0.02	0.10	0.47	0.06	**1,430**	0.47	0.47	0.47	**2,350**	**1,980**	0.20

XX.

A Model for Scale of Operations*

Edward H. Bowman and John B. Stewart†

IMPLICATIONS OF SCALE OF OPERATIONS

The president of a well-established New England company recently asked one of those infrequent but important questions—"Should we add some warehouses to our existing distribution system?" The answer proved to be a dual one: a *no* to the specific problem he had in mind; and a *yes* to one not suspected. Fortunately, the method of solution employed helped provide answers for both problems. Anticipated savings from the first problem alone were 10 percent of net annual profits.

The usefulness of this method is significant in two respects. First, companies with similar problems may find some of the ideas directly applicable to their situations. Second, the general method employed is illustrative of a way of thinking that has broad potential application to business problems. Some similar methods have been receiving increasing management interest under the name of "operations research."

For instance, the same general procedure could be used to determine the best size for salesmen's territories, the best number of branch production facilities, or other issues which are fundamentally problems in the scale of operations.

THE PROBLEM

OPTIMUM WAREHOUSE TERRITORY

This New England company had acquired more than a dozen warehouses in the five states served from its manufacturing plant. Warehouses had been added in some areas and discontinued in others as changing conditions seemed to dictate. These decisions had been made on a "common sense basis," and often had proved advantageous to warehouse operations in one area but at too great a cost in reduced operating efficiency in adjoining areas. The problem was further complicated by the fact that two basic

---

* From the *Journal of Marketing,* national quarterly publication of the American Marketing Association, Vol. 20, No. 3, 242–247. Reprinted by permission of the *Journal of Marketing.*
† The authors are indebted to The Harvey N. Shycon Company, Management Consultants of Boston, for the opportunity to work on this and other interesting problems.

delivery methods are used. One type of distribution involves semi-trailer delivery from plant to warehouse, unload and storage, and then individual deliveries to market, while in the manufacturing plant area, individual or direct delivery to market is the rule.

The general manager recently raised the question of what was the optimum size of a warehouse territory. Some executives believed drivers making deliveries directly from the plant warehouse were spending too much time getting to and from cities located about an hour's drive from the plant.

The problem as restated by the analysts was, "How large a territory should be served by a warehouse to result in a minimum total cost for warehousing, trucking between plant and warehouses, and delivery from warehouse to customers?" It was imperative that this question be answered from an over-all standpoint—covering the company's complete physical distribution system—rather than on an individual territory basis.

CRITERIA FOR OPTIMUM TERRITORY

The real and useful objective of the whole project first had to be determined. Profits would be a good place to start. However, sales for this particular problem were fixed, so to maximize profits was equivalent in this case to seeking minimum costs. The "measure of effectiveness" chosen, after examination of warehouse operations, was cost (within the warehouse district) per dollar's worth of goods distributed. It was this cost which should be minimized. Initially, minimum cost per warehouse sounds good. However, this would yield a legion of very small warehouses which when totaled would give an inefficient total operation.

DETERMINANTS OF COST

Available data were obtained from the company's records. Examination of these data revealed that the cost of material handled in each warehouse district appeared to be primarily dependent upon two opposing factors: the volume of business passing through the warehouse and the area served by the warehouse. The greater the volume handled, the smaller would be the cost per dollar's worth of goods distributed. However, the greater the area served, the greater would be the cost per dollar's worth of goods distributed.

Finding this relationship was, of course, no surprise. The crucial job was to establish the precise relationship between these factors; that is, their relative importance and the rate at which their variation affected the over-all economy of the system. To be satisfactory, the analysis would have to handle both factors simultaneously. This done, it would be possible to predict the cost of distributing goods as the area served by and the volume handled in each warehouse changed. More importantly, the systems could be so arranged that total cost would be minimized.

The analysts recognized that many other variables in this situation could affect the measure of effectiveness. For instance, the price paid for gasoline in each warehouse area would affect the cost of operations in the area and undoubtedly varies throughout the New England states. The particular design of the warehouse, for example, whether the loading platform was at tailgate level of trucks or on the ground, might also affect these costs. However, it was desirable to keep the analysis fairly simple and so only the two factors considered most important were included.

THE WAREHOUSE DISTRICT MODEL

OBJECTIVES AND LIMITATIONS

Because of the great complexity of the "real world," models of aspects of situations are often built as aids to analysis and understanding. These models may be physical replicas, electrical analogues, blue prints, charts and graphs, and so forth. The most abstract and probably the most universal type of model is the mathematical one. It has been widely used in the physical sciences, in some of the social sciences, and in engineering. It is well to keep in mind that none of these models *are* the real world. They are at best *useful* simplified representations or abstractions of it. Mathematical models were chosen for this particular real world because of the precision with which they could portray the relationships involved and with which they could reveal minimum-cost solutions.

ELEMENTS OF THE WAREHOUSE DISTRICT MODEL

To build the mathematical model, it was necessary to understand the economics of the problem. Warehousing costs per dollar of goods handled tend to decrease with increasing volume: costs of supervision and other overhead are spread over more units, labor can usually be used with a lower proportion of idle time, etc. Since distance traveled would be the main factor determining costs associated with area, it followed that this cost would tend to vary approximately with the square root of the area. (Radius and diameter vary with the square root of the area of a circle.) As concentric rings of equal area are added, rings rapidly become narrower, that is, *additional* distance traveled becomes smaller.

MATHEMATICAL EXPRESSION

To summarize, it had been determined that for the problem at issue here, the cost per dollar's worth of goods distributed (the warehouse efficiency) was equal to certain costs which vary inversely with the volume plus certain costs which vary directly with the square root of the area plus certain costs which were affected by neither of these variables. Putting this last factor first, these same variables arranged as a mathematical expression are as follows:

(1) $$C = a + \frac{b}{V} + c\sqrt{A}$$

Notation:
C = cost (within the warehouse district) per dollar's worth of goods distributed—the measure of effectiveness.

V = volume of goods in dollars handled by the warehouse per unit of time.

A = area in square miles served by the warehouse.

a = cost per dollar's worth of goods distributed independent of either the warehouse's volume handled or area served.

b = "fixed" costs for the warehouse per unit of time, which divided by the volume will yield the appropriate cost per dollar's worth distributed.

c = the cost of the distribution which varies with the square root of the area; that is, costs associated with miles covered within the warehouse district such as gasoline, truck repairs, driver hours, etc.

METHOD FOR SOLUTION

The company had over a dozen warehouses and it was possible to determine for each the cost per dollar's worth of goods distributed (C), the volume of goods handled by the warehouse (V), and the area served by the warehouse (A). Then, *by the statistical method of least-squares multiple regression, it was possible to use this warehousing experience and to determine mathematically the values of the coefficients or parameters* a, b, *and* c, *which will make the model the closest predictor of the actual cost for all present warehouses using the individual volume and area figures.*[1]

---

[1] This method minimizes the sum of the squares of the differences between the actual cost and the predicted cost. An expression for this is as follows:
Minimize:

$$\sum_{i=1}^{i=N} \left[C_i - \left(a + \frac{b}{V_i} + c\sqrt{A_i} \right) \right]^2$$

where C_i, V_i, and A_i indicate actual values in a given (the *ith*) branch warehouse operation and the Σ indicates a sum total of all (N) warehouses. Actually a set of three simultaneous equations are solved for a, b, and c.

HOW GOOD WAS THE WAREHOUSE DISTRICT MODEL?

In order to confirm the accuracy of this model, a Cost (C) was computed for each warehouse using the determined values of a, b, and c from the multiple regression calculation and the warehouse's specific figures for V and A. By comparing these computed costs with the actual warehousing costs, the correlation coefficient was found to be .89, indicating a fairly high degree of correlation.

MINIMIZATION WITH THE WAREHOUSE DISTRICT MODEL

CONVERSION OF THE MODEL

Developing this model is only the first step making it possible to predict costs. What is desired is cost minimization. However, in this case, it was necessary to convert a part of the model mathematically in order to minimize it. The object was to express cost as a function of only one unknown (area). A relationship was found between volume and area for each section of New England. This sales density (K), expressed in dollar volume per square mile of area, is

(2)
$$K = \frac{V}{A}$$

Therefore, $V = KA$, and it is possible to substitute this expression for V in the original model, giving

(3)
$$C = a + \frac{b}{KA} + c\sqrt{A}$$

$$\frac{\partial \sum\limits_{1}^{N} \left[C_1 - \left(a + \frac{b}{V_1} - c\sqrt{A_1} \right) \right]^2}{\partial a} = 0$$

$$\frac{\partial \sum\limits_{1}^{N} \left[C_1 - \left(a + \frac{b}{V_1} + c\sqrt{A_1} \right) \right]^2}{\partial b} = 0$$

$$\frac{\partial \sum\limits_{1}^{N} \left[C_1 - \left(a + \frac{b}{V_1} + c\sqrt{A_1} \right) \right]^2}{\partial c} = 0$$

These equations establish what the statistician calls the normal equations.

where *a, b,* and *c* are now specific figures determined from the multiple regression calculation.

COST MINIMIZATION WITH RESPECT TO AREA

What is desired now is an expression for *A* which will make this cost model a minimum. It is possible to do this by differentiation which gives[2]

$$(4) \qquad A = \left(\frac{2b}{cK}\right)^{2/3}$$

This expression for the area *A* indicates that area which would yield a minimum cost and is a function of *b* and *c* (costs calculated from the empirical data) and *K* (the sales density of the area in question).

The cost which is minimized is the explicit cost within the warehouse district. The implicit cost, interest on investment in inventory and equipment, was analyzed and demonstrated to be insignificant for the purposes of this study. The costs also did not include the cost of loading semi-trailer trucks at the plant and transporting them to the branch warehouses, since— as long as goods are handled from a branch warehouse—these costs will be incurred and will not be affected by volume handled or area served by each branch warehouse.

BRANCH WAREHOUSE FINDINGS

The company's actual branch warehouse areas ranged from about 95 to 150 percent of the individually computed optimum areas. This disclosed an answer to a question not originally framed, namely, that most of the branch warehouse areas were too large and that, therefore, there were not enough warehouses in outlying districts.

THE PLANT DISTRICT MODEL

COST RELATIONSHIPS

The problem of the area to be served from the plant warehouse was distinct from the branch warehouse problem since goods which are distributed directly from the plant do not have to be loaded into semi-trailer trucks and transported to the branch warehouses and then unloaded, supervised, and stored in that warehouse. Therefore, as this area served from the plant is increased, these costs are saved. However, increasing this area makes it more expensive to serve the increasingly distant perimeter areas

[2] The expression for differentiation is

$$\frac{dC}{dA} = -\frac{b}{kA^2} + \frac{c}{2\sqrt{A}} = 0$$

from the plant because more of the delivery driver's time and the truck's miles are spent in unproductive time driving to and from the delivery area.

MARGINAL MODEL

The type of model set up for this problem was a marginal model. The plant warehouse area should be expanded out to the point where the cost of serving the marginal area (the last addition) from the plant is equal to the cost of serving it from an optimally placed branch warehouse. Reducing the plant warehouse area from this line would mean that intervening customers served by a branch could be served more cheaply from the plant. Expanding the plant warehouse area beyond these points of marginal equality would mean that the additional customers then served from the plant could be served more cheaply from branch warehouses.

ELEMENTS OF THE MARGINAL MODEL

This model of marginal equality, the cost of handling one piece of goods for the marginal area, follows:

Plant direct delivery cost per piece = branch delivery cost per piece (that is, plant to branch plus branch to customer).

$$\frac{2T_oP_d + T_f + T_dH_d}{P_h(H_d - 2P_dH_m - F_t)} = \frac{S_t + B_e + 2S_oD_p + S_f + 2S_dH_mD_p + I_w}{P_s}$$

$$+ \frac{2T_oD_b + T_f + T_dH_d}{P_h(H_d - 2D_bH_m - F_t)}$$

Notation: T_o = Truck operation cost per mile
P_d = Plant delivery miles
T_f = Truck fixed costs per day (amortization type charge)
T_d = Truck driver costs per hour
F_t = Fixed driver time per day (check in, check out, coffee break, etc.)
D_b = Miles from branch to delivery
S_t = Semi load and unload costs
B_e = Branch expense per semi
S_o = Semi operating costs per mile
D_p = Miles from plant to the branch
S_f = Semi fixed costs per day (amortization type charge)
S_a = Semi driver costs per hour
I_w = Inventory costs per semi per week
H_d = Hours per day
H_m = Hours per mile
P_h = Pieces per hour
P_s = Pieces per semi

Both sides of the equation ultimately resolve to expressions of cost per piece. The distance D_b to the marginal district from the optimally placed branch warehouse is determined from the general model, that is:

$$A = \left(\frac{2b}{cK}\right)^{2/3}$$

From this expression for optimum area may be computed an approximation of the optimum radius $(A = \pi r^2)$ which is the figure used in the model for D_b. The fixed branch expense per semi, B_c, was determined from the value for b in the general model. The figure 2 in each case represents a round trip.

PLANT DELIVERY FINDINGS

Most of the cost expressions in the plant district model could be determined directly from the company's internal records. Several of the costs such as a truck fixed cost per day or cost per mile were checked also from outside sources. After all the specific values were inserted in the model, it could be solved for P_d, the distance from the plant to the farthest district within the plant warehouse area.[3]

Solving the model above for the problem posed indicates that the marginal boundary of the plant warehouse area should be extended out to approximately two and one fourth times the present area radius and that the area to be served from the plant warehouse is thereby increased to five times the original size. Thus, the initial question is answered with an emphatic *no;* that, far from decreasing the plant delivery radius, the company can best be served by increasing that radius.

SUMMARY

GENERALIZATION OF THE METHOD

As many business problems will yield to similar methods of analysis, the particular approach found useful here may be generalized as a sequence of steps as follows:

(1) Following a study to determine the economics of the problem, a measure of effectiveness was selected.

(2) A mathematical model of the problem was built around this measure of effectiveness and included those variables which most appeared to influence the measure of effectiveness.

---

[3] The equation was an implicit expression for P_d. This resulted in a quadratic form, which was then solved for P_d.

(3) The coefficients in the model were chosen by mathematical manipulation (multiple regression) to make it as accurate a symbolic description as possible.

(4) The model was "tested" by statistical means (correlation coefficient).

(5) Again by a mathematical manipulation (differentiation), the model was minimized with respect to the factor to be used in the decision rule. That is, an expression for area was determined, which should give the minimum warehousing cost per dollar's worth of goods distributed in each particular area.

(6) In the special case of the plant warehouse area, an equation of marginal analysis was employed to establish the optimum radius to be served directly from the plant.

VARIATIONS WITHIN THE METHOD

Some variations within the same general framework of analysis might be considered:

(a) The measure of effectiveness might have been cost per pound of goods distributed or some other similar criterion.

(b) The model might have included more variables such as warehouse design, etc.

(c) The coefficients in the model might have been determined from an engineering or cost accounting type of approach. From a chart of accounts and past records and budgets, *a, b, c,* etc., might have been determined. This type of approach is more common in business today. However, by definition (the statistician's), these values could have been no better and might have been poorer.

(d) A tabular or graphical comparison of costs "predicted" by the model to actual warehouse costs might have been used rather than the correlation coefficient.

(e) A tabular, graphical, or trial and error method might have been used to determine the A (area) which minimized the cost expression. However, this would vary with K—the sales density—and, therefore, it would have been necessary to repeat this procedure for selected values of K.

(f) Rather than set up an equation for marginal analysis in the special case of the plant warehouse, it would again have been possible to tabulate, graph, or try many radius distances with their associated costs to determine the best one.

IMPLICATIONS OF THE METHOD

The length of time necessary and the accuracy of results for these different methods of analysis would probably vary with the person using them. It is suspected that the more conventional approach would have been substantially more time consuming and probably less precise. Possibly the best advice is: if the more elegant shoe fits, wear it.

Appendix A: An Introduction to Linear Programming

Linear programming is a reasoning device which systematically evaluates plans, determines whether improvement is possible, and if so, suggests changes to increase the value of the original plan. Thus, linear programming lays a path leading toward optimization where optimization is defined by a maximal or minimal value. Although originally conceived by applied mathematicians, it is essentially a trial-and-error reasoning device. Its use, therefore, is not restricted to mathematicians. Linear programming is limited only in the ability to express relationships in linear mathematical terms and to conceive problems in a programmed fashion.

Specifically, linear programming provides a method to determine the best combination of a series of unknown variables where the solution must lie within certain stated bounds. The bounds (or constraints) may be financial (budgetary), or may involve time (equipment capacity), or quantity (amount shipped). The most straightforward example of linear programming occurs in determining how much of what products to produce when production is limited (constrained) by capacity. For example, consider the Nix Company which produces a deluxe and a standard model Vostok.[1] The deluxe model contributes $3.00 per unit to overhead and profit, and the standard model, one dollar.

The standard model requires 2 fabricating hours per unit to produce, occupies 4 square feet per unit in the warehouse, and does not require any painting. The same figures for the deluxe model are: 3 hours, 3 square feet, and 1 hour to paint. Available fabrication time is limited to no more than 24,000 hours; warehousing space is limited to no more than 36,000 square feet; and time in the painting shop is limited to no more than 6,000 hours. An optimum solution requires the determination of the

[1] This example is based on a problem from R. Stansbury Stockton, *An Introduction to Linear Programming*, Allyn and Bacon, 1960.

number of standard and/or deluxe models to produce in order to maximize the total contribution to overhead without violating the fabricating, ware-housing, and painting constraints.

In the Nix Company problem, the constraints are in terms of fabricating hours, warehouse space, and painting hours. Let S stand for the number of standard models to be produced and D for the number of deluxe:

Fabrication hours:	$2S + 3D \leq 24{,}000$	(A.1)
Warehouse space:	$4S + 3D \leq 36{,}000$	(A.2)
Painting:	$1D \leq 6{,}000$	(A.3)

(A.1) says (in quantitative terms), 2 hours per standard unit times the number of standard units produced plus 3 hours per deluxe unit times the number of deluxe units produced must be less than (or at most equal to) the 24,000 hours of fabricating capacity available. (A.2) says that the amount of warehouse space used to store the standard model (4 square feet per unit times the number of units) plus the space required for the deluxe model (3 square feet times the number of deluxe units produced) cannot exceed the 36,000 square feet available. Finally, since the standard model does not require any painting time, the number of deluxe models times 1 hour cannot exceed the 6,000 painting hours available—(A.3).

The problem is to maximize the total contribution which can also be expressed as a linear function. Each standard unit produced contributes $1; while each deluxe model contributes $3. Any solution, therefore, which maximizes $Z = 1S + 3D$ and is subject to the constraints, will provide an optimal solution. Z is the total contribution consisting of $1 times the number of standard models produced plus $3 times the number of deluxe models produced. (Z is indefinite because S and D are as yet undetermined.)

The problem can be expressed concisely in mathematical terms as follows:

Maximize:	$1S + 3D = Z$	
Subject to:	$2S + 3D \leq 24{,}000$	
	$4S + 3D \leq 36{,}000$	
	$1D \leq 6{,}000$	(A.4)

One additional constraint must be explicitly stated. The amount of either S or D produced must be positive or zero. Negative production (mean-ing that units are de-produced or dismantled) is nonsensical. This con-straint is stated as follows:

$$S \geq 0 \text{ and } D \geq 0$$
or $\qquad S, D \geq 0$ $\qquad\qquad\qquad$ (A.5)

A graphical model provides the easiest way to see the solution to this problem. Consider a two dimensional graph measured in units of S and units of D. The fabricating constraint appears as line (1) in Figure A–1. Line (1) is located as follows:

If $D = 0$, that is, if no deluxe models are produced, $S = \dfrac{24,000}{2}$ $= 12,000$ standard units. In other words, if all of the 24,000 available fabricating hours are allocated to the standard model, then 12,000 standard models can be produced because the standard model requires 2 fabricating hours per unit. By the same reasoning, if $S = 0$, that is, if no standard units are produced, $D = \dfrac{24,000}{3} = 8,000$. The D intercept of 8,000 units and the S intercept of 12,000 units are connected with a straight line because the constraint is linear. Similarly, line (2) is positioned in Figure A–1 with intercepts of 9,000 for S ($D = 0$; and $S = \dfrac{36,000}{4}$) and 12,000 for D ($S = 0$; $D = \dfrac{36,000}{3}$).

Finally, the painting constraint does not affect the amount of the standard model produced, because zero hours of painting capacity are required to produce the standard model. Hence, the maximum amount of

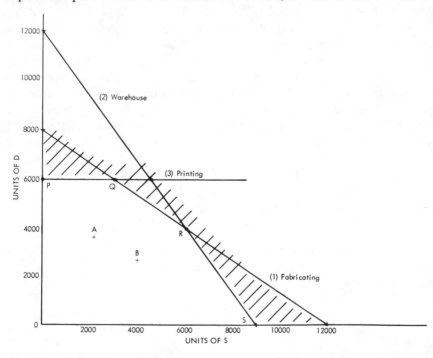

FIGURE A–1. NIX CO.

the deluxe model which can be produced is limited to no more than 6,000 units (6,000 hours divided by 1 hour per deluxe unit). In linear programming language, the painting constraint is "not binding" on production of the standard model.

The solution to the Nix Company problem lies in the area bounded by the vertical axis, the horizontal axis and the shaded area in Figure A–1. A point in this area has coordinates which represent values of S and D. For instance, point A represents $D = 4,000$ and $S = 2,000$. Point B represents $D = 3,000$ and $S = 4,000$. Since a value of less than zero is precluded by (A.5), $S \geq 0$, the solution cannot lie to the left of the vertical axis where S would be negative. Similarly, any point below the horizontal axis would have a negative value for D and would be prohibited by constraint (A.5).

Any point beyond the inner-most set of lines would likewise violate constraint (A.4). For instance, any point beyond line (3), $D \leq 6,000$, would call for more production of D than the paint shop could provide. Therefore, any point outside the polygon 0PQRS is not feasible because of the capacity and non-negativity constraints. The search for an optimal program can, therefore, be limited to points lying within or on the polygon 0PQRS.

Actually, an even stronger statement can be made. The optimal solution, which maximizes the contribution function $1S + 3D = Z$ must lie *on the polygon PQRS*. Any point closer to the origin than the perimeter of PQRS does not provide for the maximum feasible production and, therefore, represents a less than optimal plan. As an example, a point between 0 and P on the vertical axis cannot be an optimum program since more deluxe units could be produced without violating any constraints. These extra units would yield additional contribution and thereby would increase Z.

The same analysis holds for any point lying between 0 and S. Therefore, the optimum program must lie on PQRS because a program lying within 0PQRS will not yield the maximum amount and, hence, will not optimize Z. Because PQRS prescribes the location of a feasible program, it is called a *feasibility polygon*.

Let us solve for the values of S and D at point R where line (1) intersects line (2). We can obtain values for S and D at this point by solving the equations for lines (1) and (2).

$$2S + 3D = 24,000$$
$$4S + 3D = 36,000 \qquad \text{(A.6)}$$

The applicable inequalities in (A.4) have been changed to equalities in (A.6). As discussed previously, any optimum feasible solution will lie on the polygon *PQRS;* or in other words, any optimal solution will utilize all of the available production capacity. If all of the capacity is utilized, the equation which represents the programming of that capacity will not leave any excess capacity (as indicated by the "less than" sign), but will call for the elimination of any excess, usable capacity. The total programmed usage, therefore, will equal that available, and the $\leqq$ in (A.4) becomes an = in (A.6).

The solution can be obtained by multiplying the first equation in (A.6) by -2 and adding to the second:

$$
\begin{array}{r}
4S + 3D = 36{,}000 \\
-4S - 6D = -48{,}000 \\
\hline
-3D = -12{,}000 \\
D = 4{,}000
\end{array}
$$

Substituting $D = 4{,}000$ in (A.4),

$$
\begin{aligned}
4S + 3(4{,}000) &= 36{,}000 \\
4S &= 36{,}000 - 12{,}000 \\
4S &= 24{,}000 \\
S &= 6{,}000
\end{aligned}
$$

Therefore, at point R in Figure A–1, $D = 4{,}000$ and $S = 6{,}000$ units. The Z value at point R is \$18,000, determined as follows:

$$
\begin{array}{lr}
6{,}000 \text{ of } S \text{ @ \$1 ea.} = & \$\ 6{,}000 \\
4{,}000 \text{ of } D \text{ @ \$3 ea.} = & 12{,}000 \\
\hline
Z = & \$18{,}000
\end{array}
$$

The student should verify that at point Q, the total contribution is \$21,000; at point P, \$18,000; and at point S, \$9,000. These values can be determined either graphically or algebraically as above.

Thus, point Q represents the optimal program because the Z value at that point is \$21,000. The Z value or contribution function can be shown as a line passing through point Q. To completely describe the line, another point, preferably an intercept on one of the axes, is needed. This point can be determined as follows:

At point Q the value of Z is \$21,000. The point on the vertical axis which is also on the $Z = \$21{,}000$ line is found by substituting a value of $S = 0$ (indicating an $S = 0$ point on the *vertical* axis) into the contribution function.

$$
Z = 21{,}000 = 3D + 1S = 3D + 1\ (0)
$$
$$
D = \frac{21{,}000}{3} = 7{,}000 \text{ deluxe units}
$$

The horizontal intercept of the Z line can be determined in a similar fashion:

$$Z = 21{,}000 = 3(0) + 1(S)$$
$$Z = 21{,}000 \text{ standard units}$$

This line is called an iso-profit line for $Z = \$21{,}000$. Any point on this line, representing a combination of S and D, will yield a contribution of $\$21{,}000$. Similar lines can be drawn for any other value of Z, all of which will be parallel to the original line. If the slope of the contribution line is exactly equal to the slope of any line forming the feasibility polygon, $PQRS$, then a range of optimum programs can exist. For instance, if the slope of the contribution line for $Z = \$21{,}000$ is exactly equal to the slope of line QR, then any point on QR represents an optimum feasible solution to the problem.

This analysis essentially completes the logic of linear programming. Unfortunately, very few linear programming problems can be expressed in only two dimensions as in the Nix Company problem. Therefore, let us move directly from the two dimensional problem involving two products to the n dimensional problem where there are any finite number of products.

THE SIMPLEX METHOD

The simplex method can be used to solve any linear programming problem. Unfortunately, the simplex method involves some unsophisticated, but complex, mathematics; therefore, we must now digress briefly to examine the mathematics behind the general linear programming problem.

In general, the linear programming problem exists because there are more unknowns than equations. If we had one equation per unknown, the unknowns could be determined by solving the equations simultaneously. But in the general linear programming problem, there are m equations (m is a positive, finite number) and n unknowns. Furthermore $n > m$ (n is greater than m); that is, there are more unknowns than equations.

We can operate on such an equation system by invoking the following theorem:

If there exist any non-negative solutions to a system of m equations (with n unknowns) then at most m unknowns in the solution are positive and the rest are equal to zero.[2]

For instance, consider the following equation system:

$$2X_1 + 4X_2 + 3X_3 + 5X_4 = 26$$
$$X_1 + X_2 + 2X_3 + 4X_4 = 10 \tag{A.7}$$

---

[2] A rigorous proof of this theorem stated in somewhat different terms can be found in Dorfman, Samuelson and Solow, *Linear Programming and Economic Analysis*, McGraw-Hill, 1958, p. 75.

In this equation system, there are four unknowns, X_1, X_2, X_3, and X_4, and only two equations. According to our theorem, only two of the four variables can be positive, and the rest must be equal to zero. Assume that X_1 and X_2 are positive and, therefore, that X_3 and X_4 are zero. Simply removing both X_3 and X_4 from (A.7):

$$2X_1 + 4X_2 = 26$$
$$X_1 + X_2 = 10 \qquad \text{(A.8)}$$

Solving these equations simultaneously by subtracting 2 times the second from the first,

$$2X_1 + 4X_2 = 26$$
$$\underline{-2X_1 - 2X_2 = -20}$$
$$2X_2 = 6$$

Therefore, $X_2 = 3$. Substituting $X_2 = 3$ in (A.8)

$$2X_1 + 4(3) = 26$$
$$2X_1 \qquad = 26 - 12$$
$$2X_1 \qquad = 14$$
$$X_1 \qquad = 7$$

(It makes no difference into which equation of (A.8) $X_2 = 3$ is substituted.) In other words, if X_3 and X_4 equal zero, then $X_1 = 7$ and $X_2 = 3$. A solution to (A.7) is, therefore,

$$X_4 = 0$$
$$X_3 = 0$$
$$X_2 = 3$$
$$X_1 = 7$$

The variables X_1 and X_2 which *are not set equal to zero* are termed *basic variables*. Together they comprise *a basis* for equation system (A.7).

We can use this basis to evaluate the Z value for (A.7). Assume $4X_1 + 2X_2 + 5X_3 + X_4 = Z$

Therefore,

$$Z = 4(7) + 2(3) + 5(0) + 0$$
$$Z = 28 + 6$$
$$Z = 34$$

The selection of X_1 and X_2 as a basis was somewhat arbitrary. Now we know that the X_1, X_2 basis yields a Z value of 34. If we wished, we could try a basis of X_1 and X_3 and compare its Z value to 34. Similarly, we could evaluate bases of X_1 and X_4, X_2 and X_3, X_2 and X_4, and finally X_3 and X_4. In this equation system the number of combinations of pairs of variables is fairly limited; however, in a system of five equations with fifty unknowns, there are 2,118,760 possible bases! Thus we require a systematic procedure to select the basis.

Let us refer to the original equation system.

$$4X_1 + 2X_2 + 5X_3 + X_4 = Z$$
$$2X_1 + 4X_2 + 3X_3 + 5X_4 = 26 \quad \text{(A.8.1)}$$
$$X_1 + X_2 + 2X_3 + 4X_4 = 10 \quad \text{(A.8.2)}$$

Step 1: Subtract (A.7.2) from (A.7.1) to create a coefficient of 1 for X_1 in (A.7.1). Preserve all equations intact *except* (A.7.1).

$$4X_1 + 2X_2 + 5X_3 + X_4 = Z$$
$$X_1 + 3X_2 + X_3 + X_4 = 16 \quad \text{(A.9.1)}$$
$$X_1 + X_2 + 2X_3 + 4X_4 = 10 \quad \text{(A.9.2)}$$

Step 2: Subtract (A.9.1) from (A.9.2) and subtract 4 times (A.9.2) from the Z equation to create a coefficient of zero for X_1 in all equations except (A.9.1). Preserve (A.9.1) intact.

$$-2X_2 - 3X_3 - 15X_4 = Z - 40$$
$$X_1 + 3X_2 + X_3 + X_4 = 16 \quad \text{(A.10.1)}$$
$$-2X_2 + X_3 + 3X_4 = -6 \quad \text{(A.10.2)}$$

Step 3: Multiply (A.10.2) by $-\frac{1}{2}$.

$$-2X_2 - 3X_3 - 15X_4 = Z - 40$$
$$X_1 + 3X_2 + 1X_3 + X_4 = 16 \quad \text{(A.11.1)}$$
$$X_2 - \frac{1}{2}X_3 - \frac{3}{2}X_4 = 3 \quad \text{(A.11.2)}$$

Step 4: Add 2 times (A.11.2) to the Z equation. Subtract 3 times (A.11.2) from (A.11.1).

$$-4X_3 - 18X_4 = Z - 34$$
$$X_1 + \frac{5}{2}X_2 + 5\frac{1}{2}X_4 = 7$$
$$X_2 + 2\frac{1}{2}X_3 + 5\frac{1}{2}X_4 = 3 \quad \text{(A.12)}$$

By virtue of our theorem, $X_3 = X_4 = 0$. Therefore, the revised equation system is

$$0 = Z - 34$$
$$X_1 = 7$$
$$X_2 = 3 \quad \text{(A.13)}$$

Note that the solution, $X_1 = 7$ and $X_2 = 3$ appears explicitly in the equation system. Moreover, since

$$0 = Z^* - 34$$
$$Z = 34$$

The system in the form of (A.12) is a canonical or reduced form of the original system. The coefficients of the canonical form are relative to the coefficients of the original form. Moreover, the solutions of the canonical system are identical to the solutions of the original system. This useful property has already been demonstrated. The variables which appear with a coefficient of $+1$ in the canonical system are the basic variables.

Let us apply this concept to a soap scheduling problem:

A soap factory makes four detergents, Multi, Certo, Fluffi and Permi. It has four process centers, 101, 201, 301, and 401. The time in hours per ton required for each product in each center is:

	M	C	F	P
101	5			10
201		4		
301	8		2	
401	4		1	

The production planning department informs you that the available capacity in the process centers is 6,000 hours in 101, 9,600 in 201, 8,800 in 301, and 4,400 in 401. Multi sells for $12 per ton, Certo for $8, Fluffi for $6, and Permi for $2 per ton. How much of what products should be produced?

The problem is framed as follows. The variables $X_1 \ldots X_4$, (that is X_1 through X_4) are called slack variables. They take up the slack in each process center (row). Thus, the "less than or equal to" in the original problem becomes an "equal to."

M	C	F	P	X_1	X_2	X_3	X_4	
5			10	1				= 6,000
	4				1			= 9,600
8		2				1		= 8,800
4		1					1	= 4,400

For example, the constraint in the case of process center 101 is:

$$5M + 10P \leqq 6000$$

whereas in the format above,

$$5M + 10P + 1X_1 = 6000$$

Variable X_1 represents any time on process 101 which is not utilized by the programmed amount of M and P. The same kind of analysis holds for 201, 301 and 401. Note that the dimension (units) of $X_1 \ldots X_4$ are *hours of time* on the respective process center. In contrast, M, C, F, and P, the real products, are programmed in tons.

The slack variables comprise a basis, because their coefficients are 1 in one equation and zero in all others. Thus, a feasible program is:

$$X = 6,000 \text{ hours}$$
$$X = 9,600 \text{ hours}$$
$$X = 8,800 \text{ hours}$$
$$X = 4,400 \text{ hours}$$

Clearly, we can improve profit-wise on this solution by programming a real product, that is, by *bringing in* a real product to utilize (replace) the slack product (unused capacity).

Step 1: Which product should be produced?

Real product M is worth \$12 per ton. Let us, therefore, bring M into the program.

Step 2: How much of M can be programmed?

The amount of M which can be programmed is limited by centers 301 and 401 (rows 3 and 4) which can produce no more than 1100 tons. Therefore, row 4 governs the amount of M to bring in. Let us bring M into the basis by creating a coefficient of 1 for M in row 4, and zero for M in rows 1 through 3. Refer to the original equation system.

M	C	F	P	X_1	X_2	X_3	X_4		
5			10	1				6000	(A.14.1)
	4				1			9600	(A.14.2)
8		2				1		8800	(A.14.3)
4		1					1	4400	(A.14.4)

Step 2A: Multiply (A.14.4) by 2 and subtract from (A.14.3).

M	C	F	P	X_1	X_2	X_3	X_4		
5			10	1				6000	(A.15.1)
	4				1			9600	(A.15.2)
					1	−2		0	(A.15.3)
4		1					1	4400	(A.15.4)

Step 2B: Multiply (A.15.4) by $\frac{5}{4}$ and subtract from (A.15.1).

M	C	F	P	X_1	X_2	X_3	X_4		
		$\dfrac{-5}{4}$	10	1			$\dfrac{-5}{4}$	500	(A.16.1)
	4				1			9600	(A.16.2)
						1	-2	0	(A.16.3)
	4	1					1	4400	(A.16.4)

Step 2C: Divide (A.16.4) through by 4.

M	C	F	P	X_1	X_2	X_3	X_4		
		$\dfrac{-5}{4}$	10	1			$\dfrac{-5}{4}$	500	
	4				1			9600	
						1	-2	0	
1		$\frac{1}{4}$					$\frac{1}{4}$	1100	(A.17)

The basis is now X_1, X_2, X_3 and M. M replaced X_4. The solution read from (A.17) is

$$1X_1 = 500 \ hours$$
$$1X_2 = 9600 \ hours$$
$$1X_3 = 0 \ hours$$
$$1M = 1100 \ tons$$

All other variables, according to our theorem, are equal to zero. Notice that the dimensions are hours for the basic slack variables and tons for the real basic variable.

Step 3: What product should be brought into the program at this stage? The answer to this question is product C which is worth $8 per ton. But in order to establish a general procedure, we are going to enlarge the (A.17) system.

	$C_j \rightarrow$	12	8	6	2	0	0	0	0	
$C_i \downarrow$	Basis	M	C	F	P	X_1	X_2	X_3	X_4	
0	X_1			$\dfrac{-5}{4}$	10	1			$\dfrac{-5}{4}$	500
0	X_2		4				1			9600
0	X_3							1	-2	0
12	M	1		$\frac{1}{4}$					$\frac{1}{4}$	1100

The "basis" column is simply a listing of the variables in the basis at the present time. The "C_j" row is a listing of the revenue coefficients, in dollars per ton in this case. These C_j's are the coefficients in the Z equation. Since slack time contributes no profit, the C_j's for columns 5, 6, 7, and 8 are zero. Letting j take on a subscript to denote the column, $C_5 = C_6 = C_7 = C_8 = 0$. Similarly, $C_1 = 12$, $C_2 = 8$, $C_3 = 6$ and $C_4 = 2$.

The "C_i" column lists the C_j for the basic variables. Thus, the C_i in row 1 is the C_j for variable X_1 which equals zero. Letting the subscript i take on the row number, $C_2 = 0$, $C_3 = 0$, and $C_4 = 12$ because the coefficient of product M in the Z equation is 12.

We now define a Z as follows: Z_j is the C_i for a row times the coefficient for that row within the tableau, summed by column. Thus, the Z value in the F column (Z_3 where $j = 3$), is equal to

$$\begin{array}{ccc} & \text{Column} & \\ C_i & F & \\ \hline 0 & \text{(times)} \quad \dfrac{-5}{4} & = 0 \\ 0 & \text{(times)} & = 0 \\ 0 & \text{(times)} & = 0 \\ 12 & \text{(times)} \quad \frac{1}{4} & = 3 \\ \hline & & Z_3 = 3 \end{array}$$

Similarly Z_8 (the Z value for the X_4 column) is equal to

$$\begin{array}{ccc} & \text{Column} & \\ C_i & X_4 & \\ \hline 0 & \text{(times)} \quad \dfrac{-5}{4} & = 0 \\ 0 & \text{(times)} & = 0 \\ 0 & \text{(times)} \quad -2 & = 0 \\ 12 & \text{(times)} \quad \frac{1}{4} & = 3 \\ \hline & & Z_8 = 3 \end{array}$$

Finally, a $C_j - Z_j$ row is defined as follows: $C_j - Z_j$ equals the Z value for the column (Z_j) subtracted from the C value at the head of the column (C_j). Thus $C_3 - Z_3$ (the F or third column) equals $6 - 3 = 3$, and $C_8 - Z_8$ (the eighth or X_4 column) equals $0 - 3 = -3$. The $C_j - Z_j$ value represents the marginal revenue for that column.

Let us examine the C_j and Z_j values in more detail. First consider the values in (A.18). Each X value represents the marginal rate of substitution of the column variable for the row variable. For example, the technical constraints state that producing one ton of M will use up 5 hours of X_1. That is, each unit of M programmed at the stage where $X_1 = 6000$ hours requires 5 hours. Similarly, each unit of M requires 8 hours of X_3 and 4 hours of X_4.

C_j		12	8	6	2	0	0	0	0	
	Basis	M	C	F	P	X_1	X_2	X_3	X_4	
0	X_1	5			10	1				6000 hrs.
0	X_2		4				1			9600 hrs.
0	X_3	8		2				1		8800 hrs.
0	X_4	4		1					1	4400 hrs.

$$\text{(A.18)}$$

The marginal rate of substitution of C (column 2) for X_2 (row 2) is 4. That is, it takes 4 hours of X_2 to produce one ton of C. The reader can also verify that the marginal rate of substitution of F for X_3 is 2 and of F for X_4 is 1. The marginal rate of substitution of P for X_1 is 10.

We defined the Z_j value as the product of C_i times the row X, summed by column. Z_j for column 1 (product M) equals

Basis	C_1		M	
X_1	0	(times)	5	0
X_3	0	(times)	8	0
X_4	0	(times)	4	0
			Z_1 =	0

Since the values in the M column represent the marginal rates of substitution of M for X_1, X_2, X_3, and X_4, the Z value for the M column represents the revenue given up for one unit of M produced. The tableau shows that 5 hours of X_1, 8 hours of X_3, and 4 hours of X_4 are given up to produce one ton of M. Since X_1, X_3 and X_4 bring in zero dollars per hour, no revenue is given up to produce one ton of M.

The C_j represents the revenue per ton for the column variable. For example, the revenue per ton for M is \$12; for C, \$8; for F, \$6; and for P, \$2. If, in the case of M, a marginal ton can be produced for zero dollars given up (the Z_j value), then the marginal revenue for one unit of M is \$12 $-$ \$0, or \$12. In general terms, the marginal revenue is $C_j - Z_j$ (once again, because C_j equals the revenue per ton brought in and Z_j equals the revenue given up to produce one unit of the column variable). Referring to tableau (A.18), the marginal revenue for the M column is zero dollars because it is already in the basis. The marginal revenue for the C column is \$8; for the F column, \$3; and for the P column, \$2. The marginal revenue for the X_4 column is -3, representing a *marginal cost* of $3. (The Z_j value represents the sum of the revenues *given up* to produce one ton of the column variable or the foregone revenue for one ton of the column variable. The C_j value represents the revenue per ton for the column variable. Therefore, the $C_j - Z_j$ value represents the revenue per ton minus the foregone revenue per ton or the marginal revenue per ton of the column variable. Thus, if $C_j - Z_j$ is negative, the revenue given up (Z_j) is greater than the revenue obtained (C_j), and $C_j - Z_j$ is a marginal cost.) The reader may find it necessary at this stage to reread and study tableaus (A.14) through (A.18) in order to master the reasoning associated with the simplex method.

As augmented, the tableau representing a first-trial solution is

C_j		12	8	6	2	0	0	0	0	
C_i	Basis	M	C	F	P	X_1	X_2	X_3	X_4	
0	X_1			$-\dfrac{5}{4}$	10	1			$-\dfrac{5}{4}$	500
0	X_2		4				1			9600
0	X_3							1	-2	0
0	M	1		$\frac{1}{4}$					$\frac{1}{4}$	1100
	Z_j	12	0	3	0	0	0	0	3	
	$C_j - Z_j$	0	8	3	2	0	0	0	-3	

$$(A.19)$$

The marginal revenue for product C ($C_2 - Z_2$ where $j = 2$) is $8. Therefore, C is the next product to bring into the program. No more than 2400 tons (9600 divided by 4) can be produced. Product C is brought in by creating a zero in rows one, three and four of column two and by making the 4 in row two a 1. Fortunately, the zeros are already there. Therefore, we need only divide row two by 4.

C_j		12	8	6	2	0	0	0	0	
C_i	Basis	M	C	F	P	X_1	X_2	X_3	X_4	
0	X_1			$-\dfrac{5}{4}$	10	1			$-\dfrac{5}{4}$	500 hours
8	C		1				$\frac{1}{4}$			2400 tons
0	X_3							1	-2	0 hours
12	M	1		$\frac{1}{4}$					$\frac{1}{4}$	1100 tons
	Z_j	12	8	3	0	0	2	0	3	
	$C_j - Z_j$	0	0	3	2	0	-2	0	-3	

$$(A.20)$$

Thus,
$$X_1 = 500 \text{ hours}$$
$$C = 2400 \text{ tons}$$
$$X_3 = 0 \text{ hours}$$
$$M = 1100 \text{ tons}$$

The marginal revenue for F is \$3. (See the "3" in $C_3 - Z_3$.) Since $C_4 - Z_4$ (product P) equals \$2, product F should be brought into the program. Multiply row four by 5 and add to row one to create a zero in row one, column three.

C_i	C_j Basis	12 M	8 C	6 F	2 P	0 X_1	0 X_2	0 X_3	0 X_4	
	X_1	5			10	1				6000 hours
	C		1				¼			2400 tons
	X_3							1	−2	0 hours
	M	1		¼					¼	1100 tons

Multiply row four by 4.

C_i	Basis	C_j 12 M	8 C	6 F	2 P	0 X_1	0 X_2	0 X_3	0 X_4	
0	X_1	5			10	1				6000 hours
8	C		1				¼			2400 tons
0	X_3							1	−2	0 hours
6	F	4		1					1	4400 tons
	Z_j	24	8	6	0	0	2	0	6	
	$C_j - Z_j$	−12	0	0	2	0	−2	0	−6	

Notice that F has replaced M in the previous basis. That is, a real product replaced a real product.

What product next? Product F should be brought in because it has a positive marginal revenue of \$2. (See $C_4 - Z_4 = 2$.) Divide row one by 10 to bring P into the basis. No other reduction is necessary.

C_i	Basis	C_j 12 M	8 C	6 F	2 P	0 X_1	0 X_2	0 X_3	0 X_4	
2	P	½			1	$-\dfrac{1}{10}$				600 tons
8	C		1				¼			2400 tons
0	X_3							1	−2	0 hours
6	F	4		1					1	4400 tons
	Z_j	25	8	6	2	$\dfrac{2}{10}$	2	0	6	
	$C_j - Z_j$	−13	0	0	0	$\dfrac{-2}{10}$	−2	0	−6	

This tableau presents an optimal program because all $C_j - Z_j$ values are negative. No product can increase the present Z value because none has a positive marginal revenue. The basis at this stage is composed of P, C, X_3 and F.

$$1P = \quad 600 \text{ tons}$$
$$1C = 2400 \text{ tons}$$
$$1X_3 = \quad\quad 0 \text{ hours}$$
$$1F = 4400 \text{ tons}$$

In summary, let us describe the simplex method in a flow diagram form:

1. State the problem as a system of linear equations and a linear functional to be maximized or minimized.

2. Determine a basic feasible solution (usually consists of the slack variables).

3. Determine Z_j, the marginal foregone revenue, for each column.

4. Subtract each column Z_j from its coefficient in the linear functional, C_j.

IF MAXIMIZING		IF MINIMIZING

5a. Is there a $(C_j - Z_j)$ which is positive (greater than zero)?

5b. Is there a $(C_j - Z_j)$ which is negative (less than zero)?

6a. If *no*, STOP. (Basic feasible solution is optimal program.)

6b. If *yes,* select most positive $C_j - Z_j$ and bring that variable into the basic solution.

6c. If *no*, STOP. (Basic feasible solution is optimal program.)

6d. If *yes,* select most negative $(C_j - Z_j)$ and bring that variable into the basic solution.

7a. Re-cycle to block 3 above.

7b. Re-cycle to block 3 above.

Why bother with the simplex method? First, it is more methodical, especially in the exchange steps, than the initial method. Second, the simplex method is the general method in use at the present time. Third, the simplex method displays more information. For example, as noted previously, the $C_j - Z_j$ value is equal to the marginal revenue for the product represented by that column. Thus, the cost of producing product M is $13 per ton because its marginal revenue is $$-13$ (the equivalent of a marginal cost). Similarly, the marginal cost of X_1 is $.20 because its marginal revenue is $$-\frac{2}{10}$. Since X_1 represents slack time on process center 101 (row 1), the marginal cost of not having one hour on process center 101 is $0.20. In other words, the *opportunity cost* of process center 101 is $.20 per hour. Similarly, the opportunity cost of center 201 (product X_2) is $2 per hour, and the opportunity cost of center 401 is $6 per hour. Thus the simplex method provides much more than the basic program information.

GENERALIZING THE LINEAR PROGRAMMING PROBLEM

Thus far the discussion has centered around the solution of specific, relatively elementary problems. Much of the existing literature in linear programming consists of discussions of methods of solution and short cut techniques for the *general* LP problem rather than a *specific* problem. We can round out the discussion of the Simplex Method by introducing a general problem and the accompanying notation enabling us to think of linear programming in terms other than the conditions of a specific example.

The general problem may be stated as follows: maximize (or minimize) the function:

$$Z = c_1 x_1 + c_2 x_2 + \ldots + c_n x_n$$

Z is a dependent variable which is a function of (depends upon) the independent variables $x_1 \ldots x_n$ (read x_1 through x_n). The independent variables are subject to constraints:

$$a_{11} x_1 + a_{12} x_2 + \ldots + a_{1n} x_n \leqq b_1$$
$$a_{21} x_1 + a_{22} x_2 + \ldots + a_{2n} x_n \leqq b_2$$
$$\cdot \quad \cdot \qquad \cdot \quad \cdot \qquad \cdot \quad \cdot \qquad \cdot \quad \cdot \qquad \cdot$$
$$a_{m1} x_1 + a_{m2} x_2 + \ldots + a_{mn} x_n \leqq b_m$$
$$x_1, x_2, \ldots, x_n \geqq 0$$

In this notation system, the first subscript refers to the row of the term and the second subscript, to the column. Thus, a_{12} is the a for row one, column two. a_{mn} is the a for the mth row, n^{th} column. Consequently, $a_{mn} x_n$ is the product of a for the mth row, n^{th} column times x for the nth column. The Z value is, therefore, equal to $c_1 x_1 + c_2 x_2 + \ldots + c_n x_n$ where the dots refer to columns between column two and column n, the last column.

In short form, the subscripts i and j are used to refer to a column and a row. Thus $a_{ij}x_j$ $(i = 1, j = 2)$ means $a_{12}x_2$ or the AX product for the first row, second column. By use of this short form notation, the general linear programming problem can be expressed as follows:

$$\text{Optimize:} \qquad Z = c_{ij}x_j$$
$$\text{Subject to:} \qquad a_{ij}x_j \leq b_i \qquad (i = 1, \ldots, m)$$
$$x_j \geq 0 \qquad (j = 1, \ldots, n) \qquad \text{(A.21)}$$

The $(i = 1, \ldots, m)$ $(j = 1, \ldots, n)$ notation means "with i running from 1 through m and j running from 1 through n."

Referring to (A.21) and following the general Simplex rules, we can indicate the general method of solution as follows:

Convert the m constraint inequalities to m equations by inserting m slack variables, $x_{n+1} \ldots x_{n+m}$

$$a_{11}x_1 + a_{12}x_2 + \ldots x_{n+1} = b_1$$
$$a_{21}x_1 + a_{22}x_2 + \ldots x_{n+2} = b_2$$

$$a_{m1}x_1 + a_{m2}x_2 + \ldots x_{n+m} = b_m$$

or in tableau form:

x_1	x_2	...	x_n	x_{n+1}	x_{n+2}	...	x_{n+m}	
a_{11}	a_{12}	...	a_{1n}	1	0	...	0	b_1
a_{21}	a_{22}	...	a_{2n}	0	1	...	0	b_2
.	.	...	.			...		.
a_{m1}	a_{m2}	...	a_{mn}	0	0	...	1	b_m

Recalling the important theorem on which the Simplex Method is based, we know that the optimal solution of the general problem will involve no more than m non-zero unknowns (or x's). Stated in another manner, we know that the optimal solution will involve at least n unknowns with a value of zero. At this point it must not be forgotten that there are a total of $n + m$ unknowns—n original unknowns plus the m slack variables, one for each constraint equation.

The Simplex Method of solution consists of choosing an initial feasible solution with m non-zero unknowns (as mentioned previously the typical first solution is to consider the slack variables as non-zero and all real variables, $x_1 \ldots x_n$, as zero valued) and proceeding in step-wise fashion to test the existing solution for optimality, moving to a new feasible solution with an improved Z when the solution is not optimal. By this method, an optimal solution will always be reached in a finite, although sometimes very large, number of steps.

The two example problems we have discussed have both been maximizing problems in which we have been attempting to maximize some profit or contribution function. Minimizing problems, to minimize a cost function for example, can also be solved by the Simplex Method. The technique for minimizing an objective function (the Z function) is very similar to that used for maximizing. In fact, the techniques developed for problems requiring Z to be maximized can be used directly for minimizing problems by simply maximizing $-Z$ (which is equivalent to minimizing Z) and re-writing the constraints so that the inequality sign is in the same direction as in maximizing problems. For example:

re-write   Minimize: $Z = c_1 x_1 + c_2 x_2 + \ldots + c_n x_n$
                  Subject to: $a_{11} x_1 + a_{12} x_2 \ldots a_{1n} x_n \leqq b_1$
as: Maximize: $-Z = -c_1 x_1 - c_2 x_2 - \ldots - c_n x_n$
                  Subject to: $-a_{11} x_1 - a_{12} x_2 - \ldots - a_{1n} x_n \geqq b_1$

In tableau form, the minimizing problem can be written:

$c_j \rightarrow -c_1$	$-c_2$	$\ldots$	$-c_n$	0	0	$\ldots$	0	
x_1	x_2	$\ldots$	x_n	x_{n+1}	x_{n+2}	$\ldots$	x_{n+m}	
$-a_{11}$	$-a_{12}$	$\ldots$	$-a_{1n}$	-1			0	b_1
$-a_{21}$	$-a_{22}$	$\ldots$	$-a_{2n}$		-1		0	b_2
		$\cdot \ \cdot \ \cdot$						$\cdot$
$-a_{m1}$	$-a_{m2}$	$\ldots$	$-a_{mn}$				-1	b_m

Occasionally, linear programming problems will be formulated so that they contain constraints which are redundant, or worse, not compatible. Two examples can be shown graphically. Suppose two constraints of a certain problem are:

(1) $2x_1 \leqq x_2$
(2) $\;\; x_1 \leqq x_2 + 1$

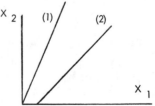

Constraint (1) says the solution must be above line (1). It is clear, however, that if constraint (1) is satisfied, constraint (2) will also be satisfied since a point cannot be above line (1) but below line (2). Constraint (2) in this case is redundant.

An example of conflicting constraints would be:

(1) $x_1 \leqq x_2 + 1$
(2) $x_1 \geqq x_2 + 2$

The first constraint says the solution must be *above* line (1), and the second, that the solution must be *below* line (2). Clearly no point can satisfy both constraints. In this case the constraints conflict. Fortunately, most management problems properly formulated will not result in such situations.

The Dual Problem

Every linear programming problem has an associated dual problem which may be viewed somewhat as a "mirror image." If the original linear programming problem, called the primal, is a maximizing problem, its dual will be a minimizing problem. The constant coefficients in the objective (Z) function of the primal become the constant column of the constraint equations of the dual and vice versa. In addition, rows of coefficients in the constraint equations become columns of coefficients in the constraint equations of the dual.

If the primal problem is one of maximizing a profit function where equipment capacity is constrained, then the dual problem will be one of minimizing the value or "shadow price" which should be assigned to each unit of process capacity. For example, the dual might yield a result saying that the minimum value of one hour of machine A's time is $6. If there is a job which can be done on machine A which will produce at least $6 of profit per hour on the machine, it can be scheduled on machine A. If, however, a job which would produce only $5 profit per hour on machine is the best available, it should not be scheduled.

An excellent discussion of the dual problem can be found in:

R. Dorfman, P. Samuelson, and R. Solow
Linear Programming and Economic Analysis
McGraw-Hill Book Co., Inc., 1958.

A. Charnes, W. Cooper
Management Models and Industrial Applications of
Linear Programming, Vol. I
John Wiley & Sons, Inc., 1961.

A good example of a primal and dual problem similar to the problem discussed in this appendix can be found in:

H. Bierman, L. Fouraker, and R. Jaedicke
Quantitative Analysis for Business Decisions
Richard D. Irwin, Inc.,
Homewood, Illinois, 1961.

Appendix B: The Fundamentals of Calculus

Calculus is a basic branch of mathematics which is extremely useful in solving maximizing and minimizing problems. It determines the rate of change of a dependent variable with respect to an independent variable. For example, calculus can tell us how total cost changes with respect to the volume of goods produced. Calculus can also be used to determine the maximum or minimum value of a dependent variable, for example, cost, with respect to an independent variable, such as the production rate. This discussion will not attempt to develop proficiency in calculus; it will simply describe necessary calculus concepts so that the reader can appreciate the application of calculus to production problems.

THE CONCEPT OF A FUNCTION

The first fundamental of calculus is the concept of dependency. The phrase "is a *function* of" simply means "depends upon." For instance, we can say *"y depends upon x"* and connote exactly the same meaning as *"y* is a function of *x."* Thus, the mathematical terminology "is a function of" is the same as the layman's terminology "depends upon." The mathematical notation used to denote *"y* is a function of *x"* is $y = f(x)$, which reads *"y* equals f of *x."*

By convention, x is assigned to the independent variable and y to the

392

dependent variable. That is, the value of y is a function of (depends upon) a given value of x. Assume that

$$y = f(x)$$
$$\text{and } f(x) = 8x - x^2$$
$$\text{so that } \quad y = 8x - x^2$$

Given a value for x, the independent variable, we can determine y as the dependent variable. If $x = 1$, for example

$$y = 8x - x^2$$
$$y = 8(1) - (1)^2$$
$$y = 8 - 1$$
$$y = 7$$

If x is 2,

$$y = 8x - x^2$$
$$y = 8(2) - (2)^2$$
$$y = 16 - 4$$
$$y = 12$$

A table of values for x and y is given below:

x	0	1	2	3	4	5	6	7
y	0	7	12	15	16	15	12	7

We can graph these values of x and y as follows:

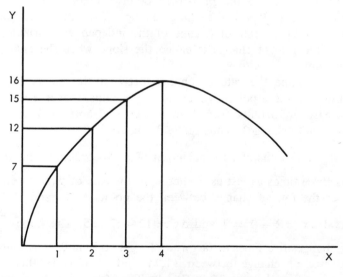

FIGURE B–1

In Figure B-1, the dimension on the horizontal axis equals the value of x and the vertical axis the value of y. Thus, any point on the curve can be located by specifying its x and y values. Any pair of such values belongs to the function if the point representing the coordinates of x and y lies on the curve. For example, the coordinate $x = 4$, $y = 16$—denoted (4,16) (the x value by convention is specified first)—lie on the curve, but the point (4,18) does not. This statement can be verified by examining Figure B-1 and also by substitution in the original function. Substituting $x = 4$ in the function yields:

$$y = 8x - x^2$$
$$y = 8(4) - (4)^2$$
$$y = 32 - 16$$
$$y = 16$$

Thus, the point (4,16) belongs to the function. However, the point (4,18), when substituted in the function, yields:

$$y = 8x - x^2$$
$$y = 8(4) - (4)^2$$
$$18 = 32 - 16$$
$$18 \neq 16$$
$$(\neq \text{ means "does not equal")}$$

Therefore, (4,18) does not belong to the function. Any point can be tested in the same way.

In addition to having the properties described above, functions also exhibit a slope. The slope is the rate of change of the dependent variable, y, with respect to the rate of change of the independent variable, x. By convention, the rate of change is called the slope when the change in x equals one unit.

Let us determine the rate of change between the points (1,7) and (4,16). Between those points, y increases by 9 units, that is from 7 to 16, and x increases by 3 units, from 1 to 4. Let us denote the increase by a Δ sign (to signify change). Thus $\Delta x = 3$ and $\Delta y = 9$. The slope is, therefore, $\frac{\Delta y}{\Delta x} = \frac{9}{3} = 3$ units of y for each unit of x. According to this measure, y changes three times as fast as x, that is, at the rate of three to one.

Consider the rate of change between the points (1,7) and (2,12). In this interval $\Delta x = 2 - 1 = 1$ and $\Delta y = 12 - 7 = 5$. The slope $\frac{\Delta y}{\Delta x} = \frac{5}{1}$, that is, y changes five times as fast as x. To get still another measure, consider the rate of change between (1,7) and (3,15). In this interval, $\Delta x = 3 - 1 = 2$ and $\Delta y = 15 - 7 = 8$. Therefore, the slope equals 4.

Clearly the slope as determined by $\dfrac{\Delta y}{\Delta x}$ depends upon the interval on the function over which the measurements are made. For summary purposes, these results are presented in tabular results below. Clearly, we could form

Point	Point	Δx	Δy	$\dfrac{\Delta y}{\Delta x}$
(1,7)	(2,12)	1	5	5
	(3,15)	2	8	4
	(4,16)	3	9	3
	(5,15)	4	8	2
	(6,12)	5	5	1

as many $\dfrac{\Delta y}{\Delta x}$ ratios as we cared to select intervals. The $\dfrac{\Delta y}{\Delta x}$ ratio is, therefore,

not an exact measure of either the rate of change of the function or the slope.

Let us narrow our attention to the immediate neighborhood of the point (1,7). By reducing the Δx interval, we also reduce Δy, and obtain a more exact measure of the slope at point (1,7). Observe the following table.

Point	Point ($y = 8x - x^2$)	Δx	Δy	$\dfrac{\Delta y}{\Delta x}$
(1,7)	(1.5, 9.75)	.5	2.75	5.50
	(1.4, 9.24)	.4	2.24	5.60
	(1.3, 8.71)	.3	1.71	5.70
	(1.2, 8.16)	.2	1.16	5.80
	(1.1, 7.59)	.1	.59	5.90

Apparently we have still not selected a small enough value for Δx to get an exact measurement of the slope, because $\dfrac{\Delta y}{\Delta x}$ is still increasing when $x = 1.1$ and $\Delta x = .1$. Furthermore, as we reduce Δx, the slope, $\dfrac{\Delta y}{\Delta x}$, continues to increase. Clearly some other tack is required to obtain the exact and unique value of the slope at (1,7).

Let (x_0, y_0) denote the point at which we desire to determine the exact slope. Denote the slope by the letter b.

$$b = \frac{\Delta y}{\Delta x}$$
$$y = y - y_0 = f(x) - f(x_0)$$

But $\qquad f(x) = f(x_0 + \Delta x)$

Therefore, $\quad \Delta y = f(x_0 + \Delta x) - f(x_0)$

And $\qquad b = \dfrac{\Delta y}{\Delta x} = \dfrac{f(x_0 + \Delta x) - f(x_0)}{\Delta x}$ $\qquad\qquad$ (B.1)

In the case where $f(x) = 8x - x^2$,

$$f(x_0 + \Delta x) = 8(x_0 + \Delta x) - (x_0 + \Delta x)^2$$
$$= 8x_0 + 8\Delta x - x_0{}^2 - 2x_0\Delta x - (\Delta x)^2$$

Substituting in (B.1)

$$b = \dfrac{8x_0 + 8\Delta x - x_0{}^2 - 2x_0\Delta x - (\Delta x)^2}{\Delta x} - \dfrac{8x_0 - x_0{}^2}{\Delta x}$$

Breaking the complex fraction into a series of fractions,

$$b = \dfrac{8x_0}{\Delta x} + \dfrac{8\Delta x}{\Delta x} - \dfrac{x_0{}^2}{\Delta x} - \dfrac{2x_0\Delta x}{\Delta x} - \dfrac{(\Delta x)^2}{\Delta x} - \dfrac{8x_0}{\Delta x} + \dfrac{x_0{}^2}{\Delta x}$$

Finally, dividing as appropriate by Δx, and cancelling

$$b = 8 - 2x_0 - \Delta x$$

The slope, b, at point x_0 is dependent upon x_0 and Δx, but not on y or Δy. Thus,

$$b = \dfrac{\Delta y}{\Delta x} = 8 - 2x_0 - \Delta x \qquad\qquad\text{(B.2)}$$

The slope, therefore, depends upon the interval Δx which we more or less arbitrarily chose in the previous examples. The act of choosing a Δx, however small, introduced the approximation which prevented us from reaching a final decision about the slope.

Let us, therefore, use the measure of slope obtained in (B.2), but simply let $\Delta x = 0$. The slope b would, therefore, be measured *exactly* at point (x_0, y_0) without introducing the inaccuracy of selecting an arbitrary Δx. Under those conditions, the slope equals

$$\begin{aligned} b &= 8 - 2x - \Delta x \\ &= 8 - 2x - 0 \\ &= 8 - 2x \end{aligned}$$

At the point where $x_0 = 1$, the slope b equals $8 - 2(1) = 8 - 2 = 6$. We were getting close to the exact measure of slope in our previous example where $\Delta x = .1$ and $\dfrac{\Delta y}{\Delta x} = 5.90$ and was increasing. Since the slope is dependent only upon the value of x_0, we can determine b at any point on the function.

x	$b = 8 - 2x$
1	6
2	4
3	2
4	0
5	−2
6	−4

We notice that the slope decreases to zero and then becomes negative. Moreover, from Figure B-1, we can observe that the slope is zero where the curve is a maximum—at point (4,16). We will use this concept shortly.

Let us review briefly the ideas which have been suggested. The entire analysis was based on the concept of a function. A function indicates dependence—conventionally y depends upon x or $y = f(x)$. The slope of the curve representing this function is denoted b and is equal to $\dfrac{\Delta y}{\Delta x}$. Since $\Delta y = y - y_0 = f(x) - f(x_0)$,

$$b = \frac{f(x) - f(x_0)}{\Delta x}$$

If $y = f(x) = 8x - x^2$ (and $y_0 = 8x_0 - x_0^2$),

$$b = 8 - 2x_0 - \Delta x$$

Precisely at point x_0, $\Delta x = 0$, and

$$b = 8 - 2x_0.$$

The slope at point x_0 (where $\Delta x = 0$) is called the *derivative* of the function. Technically, the derivative is the rate of change, $\dfrac{\Delta y}{\Delta x}$, as Δx *approaches* zero. However, for our purposes, we can define the derivative as the slope at x where $\Delta x = 0$.

The derivative is usually denoted as follows:

1. $\dfrac{dy}{dx}$, or

2. $\dfrac{d}{dx} [f(x)]$, or

3. $f'(x)$

Thus, if $y = f(x) = 8x - x^2$,

$$1.\ \frac{dy}{dx} = 8 - 2x$$

$$2.\ \frac{d}{dx}\ [8x - x^2] = 8 - 2x$$

$$3.\ f'(x) = 8 - 2x$$

Fortunately we need not work out the derivative for each function we face. Someone else has cataloged derivatives determined just as we determined $\frac{d}{dx}\ [8x - x^2] = 8 - 2x$ in (B.1) and (B.2). First, we can catalog four general rules (a is a constant; $g(x)$ is also a function of x).

$$1.\ \frac{d}{dx}\ [a \cdot f(x)] = a \cdot \frac{d}{dx}\ [f(x)]$$

$$2.\ \frac{d}{dx}\ [f(x) + g(x)] = \frac{d}{dx}\ [f(x)] + \frac{d}{dx}\ [g(x)]$$

$$3.\ \frac{d}{dx}\ [f(x) \cdot g(x)] = f(x) \cdot \frac{d}{dx}\ [g(x)] + g(x) \cdot \frac{d}{dx}\ [f(x)]$$

We can also catalog some specific rules.

$$4.\ \text{If } f(x) = a,\ \frac{d}{dx} f(x) = 0$$

$$5.\ \text{If } f(x) = x,\ \frac{d}{dx} f(x) = 1$$

$$6.\ \text{If } f(x) = g^a,\ \frac{d}{dx} f(x) = ag^{a-1}\frac{dg}{dx}$$

$$6'.\ \text{If } f(x) = x^a,\ \frac{d}{dx} f(x) = ax^{a-1}$$

Let us use these rules in some examples.

$$1.\ f(x) = ax^2 + bx + c$$

By rule 2,

$$\frac{d}{dx} f(x) = \frac{d}{dx}\ ax^2 + \frac{d}{dx}\ bx + \frac{d}{dx}\ c$$

By rule 1,

$$\frac{d}{dx}f(x) = a \cdot \frac{d}{dx}x^2 + b\frac{d}{dx}x + c\frac{d}{dx}1$$

By rule 6',

$$\frac{d}{dx}f(x) = a \cdot 2x + b\frac{d}{dx}x + c\frac{d}{dx}1$$

By rule 5,

$$\frac{d}{dx}f(x) = a \cdot 2x + b + c\frac{d}{dx}1$$

By rule 4,

$$\frac{d}{dx}f(x) = a \cdot 2x + b + 0$$

Therefore,

$$\frac{d}{dx}[ax^2 + bx + c] = 2ax + b$$

2. A more meaningful example—

$$A = \text{average (unit) cost}$$

$$q = \text{quantity produced}$$

$$A = \frac{100}{q} + \frac{q}{625}$$

Since $$\frac{100}{q} = 100q^{-1}$$

$$A = 100q^{-1} + \frac{q}{625}$$

By rule 2,

$$\frac{dA}{dq} = \frac{d}{dq}(100q^{-1}) + \frac{d}{dq}\left(\frac{q}{625}\right)$$

By rule 6',

$$\frac{dA}{dq} = -1 \cdot 100q^{-2} + \frac{d}{dq}\left(\frac{q}{625}\right)$$

By rule 5,

$$\frac{dA}{dq} = -100q^{-2} + \frac{1}{625}$$

Therefore,

$$\frac{dA}{dq} = -100q^{-2} + \frac{1}{625}$$

Many different derivatives can be determined with the simple set of rules given here.

FINDING MAXIMA AND MINIMA IN FUNCTIONS OF ONE VARIABLE

Figure B-1 indicates that the curve reaches a maximum value for y, the dependent variable, when $x = 4$. The table of values indicates the same conclusion, although the exact point is not determined in either the table or the graph. We can certainly observe that on either side of point $(4,16)$ the y value is less than 16, but we cannot be certain at what point the curve reaches a maximum for y.

Let us turn to the slope concept of calculus to determine the exact point where y is a maximum. If we adopt the convention of algebra, that values to the right of zero are positive and to the left, negative, we can apply a sign to the slope value. In Figure B-2 [1] line OA has a negative slope, and line OB has a positive slope. Line OC has a larger slope than either OA or OB; in fact, OC has an infinite slope. The slope of both ON and OP is

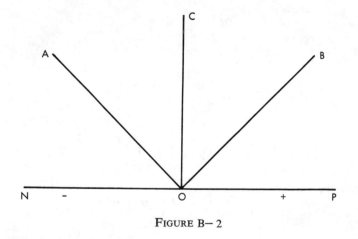

FIGURE B– 2

---

[1] The concept of Figure B-2 was first suggested to the authors in a set of class notes by W. Starbuck of Purdue University, Krannert Graduate School of Industrial Administration.

zero—the sign makes no difference. Beginning with *ON*, the slope increases to a maximum at *OC* and decreases to zero at *OP*. Thus, *OA* has a larger slope than *ON;* and *OC* than *OA*, but the slope of *OB* is smaller than *OC*.

Bringing this concept to the function $y = 8x - x^2$, we observe in Figure B-3 that the slope *decreases* to zero at the maximum point and then goes negative. In other words, the slope of the curve is positive to the left of the

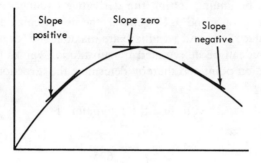

Slope positive   Slope zero   Slope negative

FIGURE B−3

point where the curve changes direction and then becomes negative. One can induce that at the maximum point, called an inflection point, the slope is zero at the instant when it goes from $+$ to $-$. In this function, the inflection point provides a maximum value for *y*.

But the derivative also gives the slope of the curve. In this case, when $y = 8x - x^2$,

$$\frac{dy}{dx} = 8 - 2x$$

At the inflection point, the slope equals zero; so we simply set the derivative equal to zero:

$$\frac{dy}{dx} = 8 - 2x = 0$$

and solve for the value of *x*.

$$8 = 2x$$
$$4 = x$$

Plugging $x = 4$ into the functional expression, we obtain a value for *y*.

$$y = 8x - x^2$$
$$= 8(4) - (4)^2$$
$$= 16$$

Therefore, the calculus indicates that the values of $x = 4$, $y = 16$ (point 4,16) is a maximum value for y. (Since we obtained a value for y from the expression $y = 8x - x^2$, we are guaranteed that the point (4,16) lies on the function.)

To generalize, one can always obtain the value of the variables at any point of inflection by setting the derivative equal to zero. However, the point of inflection could be a maximum or a minimum. If a function has a maximum *and* a minimum, setting the derivative equal to zero will yield two pairs of values for x and y. In general, the use of calculus will yield as many pairs of values for x and y as there are maxima and/or minima. Those which are minima can be determined by substituting values for x to either side of the inflection point and thereby determine the direction in which the slope is changing. [2]

Let us apply this method to find the minimum of

$$A = \frac{100}{q} + \frac{q}{625}$$

where A = average (unit) cost, and q = quantity produced.
Earlier we determined that

$$\frac{dA}{dq} = 100q^{-2} + \frac{1}{625}$$

Setting the derivative equal to zero, we obtain

$$100q^{-2} = \frac{1}{625}$$
$$\frac{100}{q^2} = \frac{1}{625}$$
$$q^2 = 62{,}500$$
$$q = \sqrt{62{,}500}$$
$$q = 252 \text{ (approximately)}$$

Substituting $q = 252$ into the function,

$$A = \frac{100}{252} + \frac{252}{625} = .80 \qquad \text{(approximately)}$$

---

[2] Actually, the test is better accomplished by taking the derivative of the derivative, termed the second derivative, and denoted $\frac{d^2y}{dx^2}$. If $\frac{d^2y}{dx^2} < 0$ at (x_0, y_0), then $f(x_0)$ is a maximum. If $\frac{d^2y}{dx^2} > 0$ at (x_0, y_0), then $f(x_0)$ is a minimum. If $\frac{d^2y}{dx^2} = 0$, then $f(x_0)$ may be a maximum or a minimum and the test suggested above might be tried.

Substituting $q = 200$ into the function, we get

$$A = .82 \qquad\qquad \text{(approximately)}$$

Therefore, since the point $(200,.82)$ lies above the point $(252,.80)$, the derivative found a minimum.

FINDING MAXIMA AND MINIMA IN FUNCTIONS OF SEVERAL VARIABLES

We have been working with functions of one variable, that is, where y depends only upon x. In many cases, y depends upon several independent variables. Assume, for example, that $y = f(x, z)$ (y is a function of x *and* z).

$$y = f(x, z) = x^3 + 5z + 10$$

The slope of y with respect to x considered solely is the *partial derivative* of y with respect to x, denoted $\dfrac{\partial y}{\partial x}$. The rate of change of y with respect to z is denoted $\dfrac{\partial y}{\partial z}$. The rule for partial derivatives is to consider all variables but the particular one under consideration as constants. Where

$$y = f(y, z) = x^3 + 5z + 10$$

consider z a constant when taking $\dfrac{\partial y}{\partial x}$ and consider x a constant when taking $\dfrac{\partial y}{\partial z}$. Since the derivative of a constant is zero,

$$\frac{\partial y}{\partial x} = 3x^2 + 0 = 3x^2$$

Similarly,

$$\frac{\partial y}{\partial z} = 0 + 5 = 5$$

(The reader should verify these partial derivatives by using the rules for simple derivatives.)

Partial derivatives are in a sense a special case of simple derivatives. If there is more than one independent variable, there will generally be one equation for each derivative (or as many equations as independent variables). Examples:

1. $f(x, y, z) = yx^2 + zx + c$

$$\frac{\partial}{\partial x} = 2yx + z$$

$$\frac{\partial}{\partial y} = x^2$$

$$\frac{\partial}{\partial z} = x$$

2. $f(x, y) = (x - a)^2 \cdot (y - b)^2$

$$\frac{\partial}{\partial x} = 2(x - a) \cdot (y - b)^2$$

$$\frac{\partial}{\partial y} = 2(y - b) \cdot (x - a)^2$$

3. We can also illustrate partial derivatives in a simple inventory model. Consider an item in inventory with the following properties:

$A =$ the reorder cost for the item including order processing and manufacturing setup cost

$s =$ the annual rate of usage in units

$i =$ the inventory carrying cost in $ per unit per year

$q =$ the size of the ordered lot

Since the inventory level varies between zero and q, the average inventory level is $\frac{q}{2}$. With an inventory carrying cost of i, the annual cost is

$$\text{Annual carrying cost} = i\frac{q}{2} \tag{B.3}$$

The annual usage is s units and the number ordered per lot is q; therefore, the number of times per year that the item will be ordered is $\frac{s}{q}$. Since the cost per order is A, the annual ordering cost is

$$\text{Annual ordering cost} = A\frac{s}{q} \tag{B.4}$$

The total cost, C, is therefore the summation of the ordering cost and the carrying cost, or (B.3) plus (B.4).

$$C = i\frac{q}{2} + A\frac{s}{q} \tag{B.5}$$

To minimize the total cost, take the partial derivative of C with respect to each independent variable. First with respect to i (employing the rule that the derivative of a product is the sum of the derivatives of each term times the others)

$$\frac{\partial C}{\partial i} = \frac{q}{2} \tag{B.6}$$

The partial derivative of i with respect to itself is 1. Therefore, since all other variables are considered constant and the derivative of a constant is zero, all the terms but one "wash out" and leave only

$$\frac{\partial C}{\partial i} = \frac{q}{2} \qquad \text{for (B.6)}.$$

Taking the partial derivative of C with respect to q in (B.5),

$$C = i\frac{q}{2} + A\frac{s}{q}$$

$$\frac{\partial C}{\partial q} = \frac{i}{2} - Asq^{-2} \tag{B.7}$$

(B.7) is significant because it gives the rate of change of C with respect to q. To minimize C, set (B.6) equal to zero and solve.

$$\frac{\partial C}{\partial q} = \frac{i}{2} - Asq^{-2} = 0$$

$$\frac{i}{2} = Asq^{-2}$$

$$\frac{i}{2} = \frac{As}{q^2}$$

$$q^2 = \frac{2As}{i}$$

$$q = \sqrt{\frac{2As}{i}} \tag{B.8}$$

The reader would do well to verify (B.6, B.7 and B.8) using the derivative rules and the concept of a partial derivative. (B.8) is the traditional economic lot size formula. Using this formula to determine the lot size q will minimize the total cost of storing and ordering the item of inventory.

SUMMARY

1. The derivative is a mathematical expression which gives the exact slope at a point on the function.
2. Since the slope at either a maximum or minimum is zero, the maxima and minima can be obtained by setting the derivative equal to zero and solving for the undetermined variables.

INTEGRATION

Integration is the reverse of differentiation. Whereas in differentiation, we determine the mathematical expression for the slope of a function, in integration we determine the function given the slope of the function.

For example, can we infer $f(x)$ if we know that $\dfrac{dy}{dx} = 8 - 2x$? Let us try $f(x) = 8x - x^3$

$$\frac{d}{dx}[8x - x^3] = 8 - 3x^2$$

Therefore, $f(x) = 8x - x^3$ *is not* the function. Next, try $f(x) = 8x - x^2$

$$\frac{d}{dx}[8x - x^2] = 8 - 2x$$

Therefore, it appears that the function $f(x) = 8x - x^2$ goes with the derivative $8 - 2x$. But the derivative of $f_1(x) = 20 + 8x - x^2$ is the same as the derivative of $f(x) = 8x - x^2$

$$f(x) = 8x - x^2 \qquad\qquad f_1(x) = 20 + 8x - x^2$$

$$\frac{d}{dx}[8x - x^2] = 8 - 2x \qquad \frac{d}{dx}[20 + 8x - x^2] = 8 - 2x$$

Thus, the inference process of finding an $f(x)$ which yields $\dfrac{d}{dx}f(x) = 8 - 2x$ is not entirely the answer, because the derivative of any constant is 0. Therefore, the derivative of $f(x) = A + 8x + x^2$ is the same as the derivative of $f(x) = 8x - x^2$ where $A = $ any constant.

Sometimes we can solve for A. For example, if we know that the point (4,16) lies on the function, then A must equal zero.

$$\frac{d}{dx}[A + 8x - x^2] = 8 - 2x$$
$$16 = A + 8(4) - (4)^2$$
$$16 = A + 32 - 16$$
$$A = 0$$

In general, however, in finding the function by inference from the derivative, we must always beware that an unknown constant may be part of the function.

The process of finding the function when the derivative is known is called integrating. Integration is denoted by

$$\int (. \ . \ . \ . \ .) dx$$

1. $\int (2ax + b) dx = ax^2 + bx + A$

    consequently, $\dfrac{d}{dx} (ax^2 + bx + A) = 2ax + b)$

The A cannot be determined in this case.

2. $\int (bx^{-2} + cx^{-3}) dx = -bx^{-1} - \dfrac{1}{2} cx^{-2} + A$

    because $\dfrac{d}{dx} (bx^{-1} - \dfrac{1}{2} cx^{-2} + A) = -bx^{-2} + cx^{-3}$

The A cannot be determined.

3. $\int \left(-100q^{-2} + \dfrac{1}{625} \right) dq = 100q^{-1} + \dfrac{q}{625} + A$

    because $\dfrac{d}{dq} (100q^{-1} + \dfrac{q}{625} + A) = -100q^{-2} + \dfrac{1}{625}$

Fortunately, we need not go through the inference process each time an integral is required. Just as there are elaborate derivative tables available, there are also detailed integral tables. We need only remember that $\dfrac{dA}{dx} = 0$, and, therefore, that each integral may have an unknown constant.

Index

Index

[Numbers in italics refer to footnotes in the text.]

411

ROBERT H. BOCK, Assistant Professor in Production at Northwestern University, is a graduate of Purdue University, receiving his B.S., M.S., and Ph.D. from that institution, with majors in Mechanical Engineering, Industrial Engineering and Industrial Management, respectively. Professor Bock attended the Ford Foundation Summer Program on the application of mathematics to business held at the University of Michigan.

WILLIAM K. HOLSTEIN earned his B.S. degree at Rensselaer Polytechnic Institute, majoring in Chemical Engineering. He received his M.S. degree from Purdue University in Industrial Management. He served on the staff at Purdue in the Graduate School of Industrial Administration, where he also received his Ph.D. degree in Industrial Economics and acted as Graduate Admissions Coordinator for the Graduate School of Industrial Administration. He is presently Assistant Professor of Business Administration at Harvard University.

This book is printed in Times Roman type, a highly legible and versatile masculine face, simple in design and medium in weight. It was created in 1932 by Stanley Morison, typographic consultant, for *The Times* of London. The text body is complemented by the use of Bodoni Bold in the part and chapter openings and reading titles, making a fine contrast in lights and darks in the total book design.